CW00401148

REVISE AQA GCSE (9–1)
Combined Science: Trilogy
REVISION WORKBOOK
Foundation

Series Consultant: Harry Smith

Authors: Nora Henry, Nigel Saunders and Catherine Wilson

Also available to support your revision:

Revise GCSE Study Skills Guide   9781447967071

The **Revise GCSE Study Skills Guide** is full of tried-and-trusted hints and tips for how to learn more effectively. It gives you techniques to help you achieve your best – throughout your GCSE studies and beyond!

Revise GCSE Revision Planner   9781447967828

The **Revise GCSE Revision Planner** helps you to plan and organise your time, step-by-step, throughout your GCSE revision. Use this book and wall chart to mastermind your revision.

REVISE GCSE
Study Skills
GUIDE

REVISE GCSE
REVISION PLANNER

For the full range of Pearson revision titles across KS2, KS3, GCSE, Functional Skills, AS/A Level and BTEC visit:
www.pearsonschools.co.uk/revise

Question difficulty
Look at this scale next to each exam-style question. It tells you how difficult the question is.

Contents

- - - - - - - - - - - - - - -

A small bit of small print:
AQA publishes Sample Assessment Material and the Specification on its website. This is the official content and this book should be used in conjunction with it. The questions have been written to help you practise every topic in the book. Remember: the real exam questions may not look like this.

Microscopes and magnification

1 A student uses a light microscope. The eyepiece lens has a magnification of ×10 and the objective lens has a magnification of ×5. What is the total magnification? Tick **one** box.

> Always answer multiple-choice questions, even if you don't actually know the answer or can't work it out.

×2 ☐   ×5 ☐   ×15 ☐   ×50 ☐   **(1 mark)**

2 Scientists use light microscopes and electron microscopes to study cells. Describe how these two types of microscope differ in their magnification and resolution.

> **Guided**

The magnification of a light microscope is usually ....

than the magnification of an electron microscope. The level of detail seen with a

light microscope is .... than that with an electron

microscope because its resolution is .... **(2 marks)**

3 The photo is an electron micrograph of part of a human liver cell.

> **Maths skills** An answer to 1 significant figure is sufficient.

mitochondrion ——

nucleus ——

2 µm

(a) Estimate the length of the mitochondrion.

.... **(1 mark)**

(b) Estimate the diameter of the nucleus.

.... **(1 mark)**

4 A bacterial cell is viewed through a microscope. The size of the image of the cell is 1.5 mm. The magnification is ×750.

(a) Calculate the size of the real cell in mm. Use this equation:

$$\text{size of real object} = \frac{\text{size of image}}{\text{magnification}}$$

....

....mm **(1 mark)**

(b) Give your answer to part (a) in µm.

> **Maths skills** 1 µm = 0.001 mm (multiply by 1000 to convert from mm to µm)

....

....µm **(1 mark)**

5 Explain how electron microscopy has increased scientists' understanding of subcellular structures.

....

....

....

.... **(2 marks)**

Had a go ☐   Nearly there ☐   Nailed it! ☐

Animal and plant cells

1 Which of the following structures is the site of protein synthesis in a cell? Tick **one** box.

cell membrane ☐   mitochondrion ☐   ribosome ☐   nucleus ☐   **(1 mark)**

2 The diagram shows a type of cell.

nucleus   cell wall

Y   X

> Look at the labelled features of the cell. Are these found in animal cells, plant cells or both types of cell?

(a) Name the type of organism that has cells like this.

.... **(1 mark)**

(b) Identify the structures labelled **X** and **Y**.

X ....

Y .... **(2 marks)**

(c) Describe the function of the nucleus.

....

.... **(2 marks)**

3 Compare the functions of the cell membrane and the cell wall.

> **Compare** means that you need to describe the similarities and/or differences of both structures, not just one structure.

> **Guided**

The cell membrane controls ....

....

However, the cell wall is made of cellulose which...

.... **(2 marks)**

4 Algal cells contain subcellular structures called chloroplasts. Describe the function of these subcellular structures.

> Chloroplasts in algal cells have the same function as chloroplasts in plant cells.

....

....

....

.... **(2 marks)**

Eukaryotes and prokaryotes

1　Animal cells are examples of eukaryotic cells. Bacterial cells are examples of prokaryotic cells. Complete the table to show which features are present in these cells. Place a tick (✓) in each correct box to show where a feature is present.

	Animal cells	Bacterial cells
Cytoplasm		
Cell membrane		
Cell wall		
Nucleus		

(4 marks)

2　Describe how the genetic material is arranged in prokaryotic cells, such as bacterial cells.

> Guided

The chromosomal DNA is arranged to form a ....

Some bacterial cells also contain .... **(2 marks)**

3　Write the following measurements in order of increasing size.

1 cm	50 μm	100 mm	200 nm

(smallest) .... (largest)　**(1 mark)**

4　Convert the following measurements to metres in standard form.

Maths skills Numbers in standard form are written as: $A \times 10^n$

- A is a number greater than or equal to 1, and less than 10
- n is a power of 10

(a)　0.0022 m

.... **(1 mark)**

(b)　0.45 mm

.... **(1 mark)**

(c)　97 μm

.... **(1 mark)**

5　The diameter of a liver cell is 2.5×10^{-5} m. The diameter of a bacterial cell is 2.0×10^{-7} m.

> Guided

(a)　Calculate how many times larger the liver cell is than the bacterial cell.

$$\frac{2.5 \times 10^{-5}}{2.0 \times 10^{-7}} =$$

.... **(2 marks)**

(b)　Give the order of magnitude of the diameter of the bacterial cell.

> The order of magnitude of the diameter of the liver cell is –5.

.... **(1 mark)**

(c)　Determine how many orders of magnitude larger the liver cell is than the bacterial cell.

.... **(1 mark)**

Specialised animal cells

1 The diagram shows a sperm cell.

Draw **one** line from each structure to the correct function.

acrosome — nucleus — mitochondrion — tail

Structure	Function
acrosome	releases energy for the cell
nucleus	allows cell to move
mitochondrion	carries genetic information
tail	releases enzymes to aid entry to an egg cell

(4 marks)

2 The diagram shows a human red blood cell.

Red blood cells contain haemoglobin. This protein binds to oxygen so it can be carried in the bloodstream.

Suggest a reason why the red blood cell does not contain a nucleus.

.... **(1 mark)**

3 The diagram shows a nerve cell.

Nerve cells connect with other cells, and carry electrical impulses between distant parts of the body.

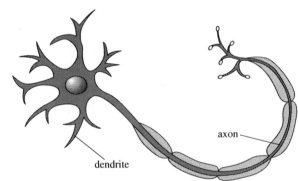

axon

dendrite

(a) Complete the table by placing a tick (✓) to show the correct function of each part.

	Part	
Function	axon	dendrite
makes a connection with another nerve cell		
carries impulses from one end of the cell to the other		

(2 marks)

(b) Explain one way in which the nerve cell is adapted to its function.

> Describe one labelled part and then say how it allows the cell to do its job.

....

.... **(2 marks)**

4 Describe what happens as cells differentiate in animals.

> **Guided**

Most types of animal cells differentiate at an .... stage.

As a cell differentiates, it acquires different ....

that allow it to ....

Cell division in mature animals is mainly restricted to .... **(4 marks)**

Specialised plant cells

1 The diagram shows a longitudinal section through phloem tissue. It consists of sieve cells and companion cells. Phloem is a transport tissue that carries dissolved sugars through a plant.

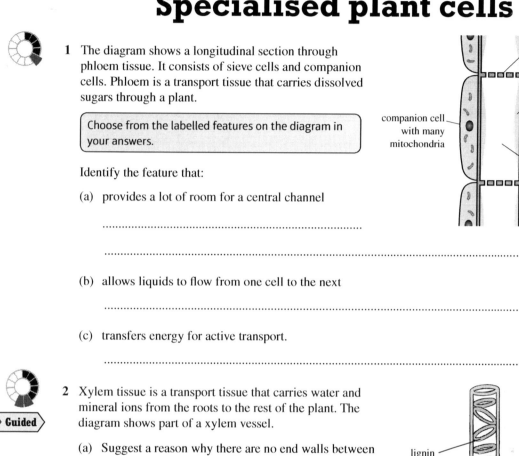

Choose from the labelled features on the diagram in your answers.

Identify the feature that:

(a) provides a lot of room for a central channel

....

.... **(1 mark)**

(b) allows liquids to flow from one cell to the next

.... **(1 mark)**

(c) transfers energy for active transport.

.... **(1 mark)**

Guided

2 Xylem tissue is a transport tissue that carries water and mineral ions from the roots to the rest of the plant. The diagram shows part of a xylem vessel.

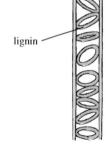

(a) Suggest a reason why there are no end walls between individual xylem cells.

Xylem tissue consists of hollow tubes formed by dead xylem cells. There are no end walls so that

....

.... **(2 marks)**

(b) Lignin is a tough substance that builds up in xylem cells.

Give a reason why lignin is important to the function of xylem tissue.

....

.... **(1 mark)**

3 Describe how, during the life of the organism, the ability of plant cells to differentiate differs from the ability of animal cells to differentiate.

What is different about when the cells can differentiate?

....

....

....

.... **(2 marks)**

Required practical – Using a light microscope

 1 Describe the function of the following parts of a light microscope:

> Some designs of microscope use a mirror instead of a lamp.

(a) the lamp

.... **(1 mark)**

(b) the stage with clips

.... **(1 mark)**

(c) the coarse focusing wheel.

.... **(1 mark)**

2 A student viewed plant cells using a light microscope. He made a biological drawing of some of the cells.

> Guided

Figure 1 shows the image seen through the microscope. **Figure 2** shows the student's drawing.

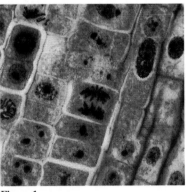

Figure 1

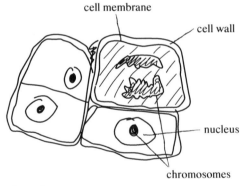

Figure 2

Identify **three** faults with the student's drawing.

1 The drawing is made with a pen rather than with a ....

2 ....

3 .... **(3 marks)**

3 The highest magnification of a microscope allows smaller details to be observed. Give **two** drawbacks of using the highest magnification rather than the lowest magnification.

....

.... **(2 marks)**

 4 A student is observing a slide under high power. She cannot find the part she wants to study. Describe how the student should bring this part into view.

> Think about the steps needed to use the microscope safely to make the necessary adjustments.

....

....

.... **(3 marks)**

Mitosis

1 Which of the following are produced when a cell divides by mitosis? Tick **one** box.

   two genetically different diploid daughter cells ☐

   two genetically identical diploid daughter cells ☐

   four genetically identical haploid daughter cells ☐

   four genetically different haploid cells ☐   **(1 mark)**

2 Give **three** reasons why mitosis takes place.

   > Guided

   1 to produce new individuals by .... reproduction

   2 ....

   3 .... **(3 marks)**

3 The graph shows the mass of DNA in the nucleus of a cell over a 24-hour period.

   > You need to understand the three overall stages of the cell cycle, but do not need to know the different phases of mitosis.

   Relative mass of DNA in the nucleus

   Time in hours

   (a) The cell is in interphase at part **A**. Identify one other labelled part of the graph (**B**, **C** or **D**) where the cell is in interphase.

   .... **(1 mark)**

   (b) Draw one line from each part (**B**, **C** and **D**) to what is happening in the cell cycle.

Part	What is happening
B ●	● mitosis
C ●	● cell division
D ●	● chromosomes are being copied

   (3 marks)

4 The photograph shows onion root tip cells viewed through a microscope.

   (a) Describe what is happening in the cell labelled **X**.

   ....

   ....

   ....

   ....

   .... **(2 marks)**

   (b) Describe what would happen next to the cell labelled **X** so it would form daughter cells.

   > Think about the cytoplasm and cell membrane of the cell.

   ....

   .... **(2 marks)**

Stem cells

1 What is a stem cell? Tick **one** box.

an undifferentiated cell ☐

a specialised cell of an organism ☐

a cell found only in embryos ☐

a cell that causes diabetes and paralysis ☐

> The last option cannot be correct because stem cells may be able to help conditions such as these.

(1 mark)

2 Some plant tissues contain stem cells.

(a) Give the name of the tissue where plant stem cells are found.

.... **(1 mark)**

(b) The tissue named in part (a) is found at the tip of roots.

   (i) Give **one** other place in a plant where this tissue is found.

   .... **(1 mark)**

   (ii) What is the function of stem cells in the tip of roots?

> Include the name of at least one other tissue in your answer.

   ....

   .... **(2 marks)**

(c) Plant stem cells can be used to produce clones of plants quickly and economically. Describe **two** reasons why people may want to produce such clones.

Rare species can be cloned so they ....

....

.... **(2 marks)**

3 Leukaemia is a disorder in which white blood cells do not function normally. Adult stem cells from the bone marrow of a donor can be transplanted to the patient, where they differentiate to produce normal white blood cells.

(a) What is the meaning of the term 'differentiate'?

....

.... **(2 marks)**

(b) Give **two** risks of using adult stem cells for medical treatments.

1 ....

2 .... **(2 marks)**

(c) In therapeutic cloning, an embryo is produced with the same genes as the patient. Suggest **one** disadvantage of using stem cells from an embryo like this.

....

.... **(1 mark)**

Diffusion

1 Describe what is meant by the term 'diffusion'.

> **Guided**

Diffusion is the .... of particles, so that there is a

net movement of particles from an area of ....

to an area of .... **(2 marks)**

2 Substances can diffuse when they are in the gas state or in solution. The temperature of the gas or solution is one of the factors that affects the rate of diffusion.

(a) Give **two** other factors that can affect the rate of diffusion.

> Remember that diffusion can happen across cell membranes.

1 ....

2 .... **(2 marks)**

(b) Why does the rate of diffusion increase as the temperature increases?

> Think about what happens to the movement of particles in gases and solutions as the temperature increases.

....

.... **(1 mark)**

3 Urea is a waste substance that diffuses from the cytoplasm of cells into the blood plasma. Which part (cell cytoplasm or blood plasma) contains the higher concentration of urea? Give a reason to explain your answer.

....

....

.... **(2 marks)**

4 The diagram shows two dissolved substances in neighbouring cells, separated by a cell membrane.

(a) Give the direction in which substance A diffuses across the membrane.

> Count the number of particles of substance A on each side.

....

.... **(1 mark)**

(b) There is no overall diffusion of substance B. Use information from the diagram to explain why.

....

....

.... **(2 marks)**

Exchange surfaces

1 A student investigated how quickly diffusion happens in agar gel. The gel contained dilute sodium hydroxide solution and phenolphthalein indicator, which made it pink. He cut the gel into cubes of different side lengths and placed all the cubes in dilute hydrochloric acid. The student timed how long the cubes took to become completely colourless. Which of the following took the longest time for this change? Tick **one** box.

> Hydrochloric acid diffuses into the cubes and neutralises the sodium hydroxide inside, causing a colour change.

one 5-mm cube ☐   two 10-mm cubes ☐

four 5-mm cubes ☐   one 20-mm cube ☐   **(1 mark)**

2 The small intestine is adapted for the efficient absorption of digested food molecules.

(a) Name the finger-like structures that cover the lining of the small intestine.

.... **(1 mark)**

Guided (b) Describe **three** ways in which the structures named in part (a) are adapted to provide an effective exchange surface.

Their shape gives them a large ....

They provide a short diffusion path because ....

.... A network of blood capillaries inside them

ensures that .... **(3 marks)**

3 A cube-shaped cell has a side length of 10 μm.

(a) Calculate the surface area of the cell. Give your answer in μm².

> Remember that a cube has six equal square sides.

.... **(1 mark)**

(b) Calculate the volume of the cell. Give your answer in μm³.

.... **(1 mark)**

(c) Use your answers to parts (a) and (b) to calculate the surface area to volume ratio of the cell.

.... **(1 mark)**

4 The diagrams show two types of worm, a flatworm and an earthworm. They are similar in size.

(a) Name the type of worm that is likely to have the larger surface area to volume ratio. Give a reason for your answer.

Flatworm   Earthworm

....

.... **(1 mark)**

(b) Suggest why the earthworm has a transport system (a heart and blood vessels) but the flatworm does not.

....

.... **(2 marks)**

Osmosis

1 Describe what is meant by osmosis.

> Osmosis is the diffusion of .... from a ....
>
> solution to a .... solution through a
>
> .... **(4 marks)**

2 A student cut two pieces of the same size from a potato. She put one piece of potato into some distilled water. She put the other piece of potato into a strong solution of glucose. She left the potato pieces for 5 hours and then looked to see if they had become longer.

(a) Why is it important that the two pieces of potato are the same size at the start?

....

....

....

.... **(2 marks)**

(b) Describe what she would notice about the size of each piece of potato at the end of the experiment.

Potato in distilled water: ....

Potato in strong glucose solution: .... **(2 marks)**

3 This apparatus can be used to model osmosis in cells.

(a) The Visking tubing is partially permeable. Describe what 'partially permeable' means.

....

....

....

.... **(2 marks)**

(b) The level of liquid in the glass tube gradually rises when the apparatus is left for a few hours. Explain why this happens.

> Water passes through the Visking tubing. Which way does it move overall, and which process is involved?

....

....

....

.... **(2 marks)**

glass tube, water, sugar solution, Visking tubing

Required practical – Investigating osmosis

1 A student investigated the effect of solutions with different concentrations of sucrose on the mass of potato tissue. He used a cork borer to cut equal-sized cylinders of potato, then weighed each one. The student placed the cylinders in the different solutions. He removed them

Concentration in g/dm³	Initial mass in g	Final mass in g	Change in mass in g	Percentage change in mass
0	2.60	2.85		9.6
70	2.51	2.67	0.16	6.4
140	2.65	2.72	0.07	2.6
210	2.52	2.45	−0.07	−2.8
280	2.58	2.43	−0.15	

after a few hours, dried them with a paper towel and weighed them again. The table shows his results.

(a) Calculate the **two** missing values in the table. Use these values to complete the table.

Change in mass = 2.85 − 2.60 = ... g

Percentage change in mass = $\dfrac{-0.15}{2.58} \times 100$ = ...% **(2 marks)**

(b) Complete the graph to show the percentage change in mass against concentration in g/dm³. **(2 marks)**

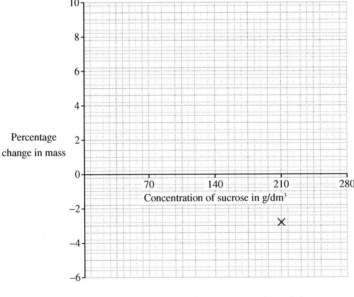

Percentage change in mass

Concentration of sucrose in g/dm³

 Maths skills Plot the remaining points carefully, at least to within half a square.

Draw a line of best fit. This can be curved or straight, depending on the data, but should ignore points that are clearly anomalies.

(c) Use the completed graph to estimate the concentration of the potato tissue.

.... **(1 mark)**

(d) The student used a balance with a resolution of ±0.01 g. Explain, using the readings at 70 g/dm³ as an example, why the student did not use a balance with a resolution of ±0.1 g instead.

The **resolution** of an instrument is the smallest change in the quantity being measured that gives a perceptible change in the reading. What readings would a ±0.1 g balance give?

....

....

.... **(3 marks)**

Active transport

1   Cells move sodium ions from a low concentration inside the cell to a high concentration outside the cell. What process do cells use to do this? Tick **one** box.

diffusion ☐   osmosis ☐   active transport ☐   dissolving ☐   **(1 mark)**

2   The table shows some features of two transport processes. Complete the table by placing a tick (✓) in each correct box to show the features of diffusion and of active transport.

> **Guided**

Feature	Diffusion	Active transport
involves the movement of particles	✓	✓
requires energy		
can happen across a partially permeable membrane		
net movement down a concentration gradient		

(4 marks)

3   Plants require nitrate ions for healthy growth. Plants move nitrate ions from very dilute solutions in the soil to higher concentrations in the root hair cells.

(a)   Give a reason why nitrate ions cannot be moved by osmosis.

....

.... **(1 mark)**

(b)   Use the information given to explain why diffusion is not responsible for moving these ions.

> Think about what happens during diffusion.

....

....

.... **(2 marks)**

> **Guided**

(c)   Explain why the rate of respiration may increase in root hair cells during the uptake of nitrate ions.

The nitrate ions are being moved by ....

This process requires .... from .... **(3 marks)**

4   Active transport is used to move dissolved glucose from the gut to the blood plasma.

Some toxins prevent the release of energy by mitochondria. Predict the effect of these toxins on the absorption of glucose into the plasma. Explain your answer.

....

....

....

.... **(3 marks)**

13

Extended response – Cell biology

 The diagrams show a bacterial cell and a plant cell. The diagrams are not drawn to scale.

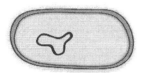

Bacterial cell

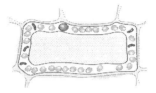

Plant cell

Compare the structures of these two cells, including subcellular structures and their functions.

> You will be more successful in extended response questions if you plan your answer before you start writing.
>
> In your answer to this question, you need to think about:
>
> - the similarities between the cells
>
> - the differences between the cells.
>
> For each structure that you identify, remember to describe its function.
>
> You should try to use the information given in the question.

....

....

....

....

....

....

....

....

....

....

....

....

....

....

....

....

.... **(6 marks)**

The digestive system

1   The diagram shows part of the human digestive system. Identify the organs labelled A to E.

> Organs in the digestive system include the liver, large intestine, pancreas, small intestine and stomach.

A ....

B ....

C ....

D ....

E .... **(5 marks)**

2   The stomach is an organ in the digestive system. It is composed of several types of tissue.

Guided

(a) Describe what is meant by a tissue.

A tissue is a group of cells with a similar .... and

.... **(2 marks)**

(b) Describe what is meant by an organ.

....

.... **(2 marks)**

(c) The digestive system is an organ system. Name **two** other organ systems in the human body.

1 ....

2 .... **(2 marks)**

3   Digestive enzymes in the digestive system convert large, insoluble molecules in food into small soluble molecules.

(a) Complete the table to show the features of carbohydrase, protease and lipase enzymes.

> The **substrate** is the substance changed by an enzyme.

Type of enzyme	Substrate	Product(s)
carbohydrase		simple sugars
protease	proteins	
lipase		

(4 marks)

(b) Amylase is an example of a carbohydrase. Name the substance broken down by amylase.

.... **(1 mark)**

15

Required practical – Food testing

1 A student carried out a test to detect lipids in a food sample. This is the method she used.

Detecting lipids
A Grind up a small sample of dry food and transfer it to a beaker.
B Add distilled water and stir to disperse the food.
C Half fill a test tube with this mixture and add three drops of Sudan III stain.
D Shake gently to mix, and record your observations.

(a) Name suitable laboratory apparatus that can be used to grind up dry food samples.

.... **(1 mark)**

(b) What will the student observe if the food sample contains lipids? Tick **one** box.

a blue-stained layer floating on a layer of water ☐

a blue-stained layer underneath a layer of water ☐

a red-stained layer floating on a layer of water ☐

a red-stained layer underneath a layer of water ☐   **(1 mark)**

2 Describe the test you would use to find out if protein is present in egg white.

> Guided

Put some egg white in a test tube. Add an equal volume of ....

.... and shake to mix. If protein is present, the mixture turns

.... **(2 marks)**

3 A student carried out a test on samples of two different foods. He dissolved each sample in water and added Benedict's solution. The student heated the mixtures in test tubes for about 5 minutes, and then recorded his observations.

(a) Describe how the student can heat the mixtures safely.

> A Bunsen burner is not necessary to carry out these tests.

....

.... **(2 marks)**

(b) One mixture turns green and the other turns red. Explain what these observations show.

....

....

....

.... **(2 marks)**

4 Flour is a powdery dry food.

Describe the test you would use to find out if starch is present in a sample of flour.

> Say what you would do and what you would see.

....

.... **(2 marks)**

Enzymes

1   Bile is released into the small intestine. It emulsifies fat there. What is the effect of this process? Tick **one** box.

Stomach acid is neutralised.   ☐

Fat is digested to form fatty acids and glycerol.   ☐

The surface area of the fat is increased.   ☐   **(1 mark)**

Guided

2   'Biological' washing powders contain enzymes including proteases and lipases. These break down food stains on clothes. Explain why proteases can break down proteins in food stains but lipases cannot.

The active site in proteases matches the shape of .... but

....   **(2 marks)**

3   Certain bacteria are adapted to live in hot water springs. The graph shows how the activity of an enzyme found in these bacteria is affected by temperature.

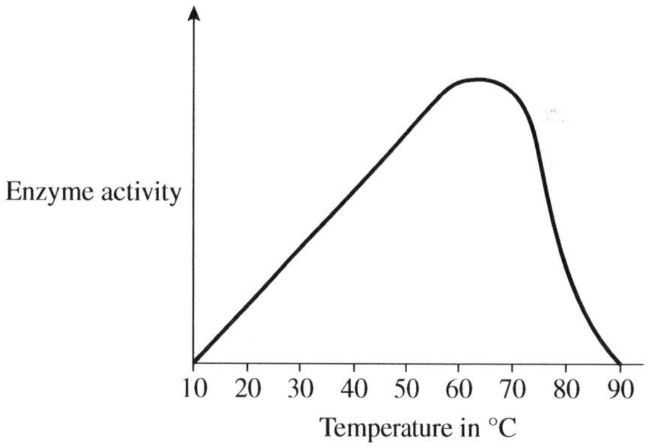

Enzyme activity

(a) Give the optimum temperature for this enzyme.

.... **(1 mark)**

Temperature in °C

(b) Why is there no enzyme activity at 90 °C?

....

Use your knowledge of the effect of high temperatures on the structure of proteins such as enzymes.

....

....

....   **(2 marks)**

4   The graph shows the effect of pH on the activity of three digestive enzymes.

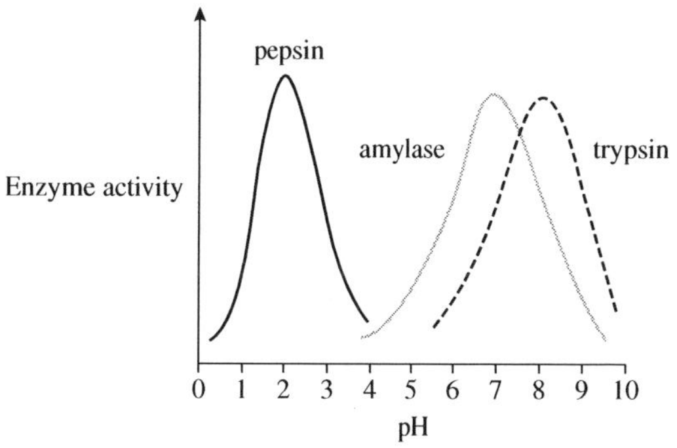

(a) Amylase is a carbohydrase. Give its optimum pH.

.... **(1 mark)**

pepsin

amylase   trypsin

Enzyme activity

(b) The pH inside the stomach is about 2, but inside the small intestine the pH is about 7.

Which protease (pepsin or trypsin) is best suited to work in the stomach? Give a reason for your answer.

pH

....

....   **(1 mark)**

Required practical – Investigating enzymes

Guided

1 A student investigated the effect of pH on the activity of trypsin. Trypsin digests the proteins in photographic film, turning it clear. The student used the apparatus shown in the diagram. She measured the time taken for trypsin solution to turn pieces of film clear at different pH values.

The table shows her results.

pH	2	4	6	8	10
Time in min	>10	7.5	3.6	1.2	8.3
Rate in /min	0	0.13			

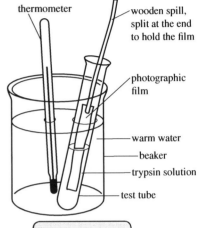

(a) Complete the table by calculating the rate at each pH.

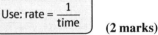

Use: rate = $\dfrac{1}{\text{time}}$

(2 marks)

(b) Plot a graph using the completed results in the table. Choose a suitable scale and label for the *x*-axis.

> Your *x*-axis scale should allow the plotted points to cover at least half the area of the graph. Remember to draw a line of best fit.

(3 marks)

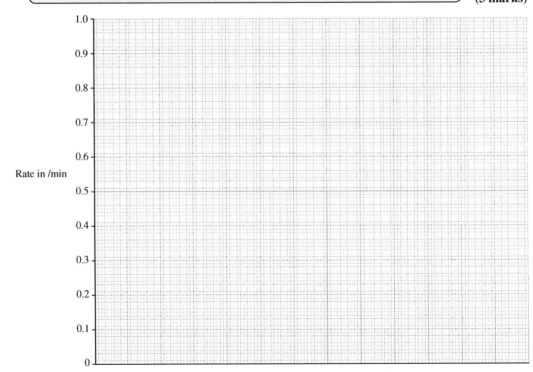

Rate in /min

(c) Describe **two** improvements the student could make to her method.

1 ....

2 .... **(2 marks)**

The blood

1 Draw **one** line from each blood component to the correct function.

Blood component	**Function**
plasma	carries other blood components
platelet	part of the body's immune system
red blood cell	involved in forming blood clots
white blood cell	carries oxygen

(4 marks)

2 Blood contains red blood cells.

(a) Name the cell structure, normally found in cells, that is missing in human red blood cells.

.... **(1 mark)**

(b) Name the compound in red blood cells that gives them their colour.

.... **(1 mark)**

Guided

(c) The diagram shows some red blood cells.

Describe **two** ways in which red blood cells are adapted to carry out their function.

Their biconcave shape gives them a large ....

for diffusion to happen efficiently. They are also flexible, which lets them ....

.... **(2 marks)**

3 The plasma transports soluble products of digestion, including glucose and amino acids. Name **two** waste substances transported by the plasma.

1 ....

2 .... **(2 marks)**

4 There are different types of white blood cells, phagocytes and lymphocytes. Describe a function of each type of cell.

> Phagocytes are named after the Greek word 'phagein', which means 'to eat', but do not write that phagocytes *eat* pathogens (disease-causing organisms).

Phagocyte: ....

.... **(1 mark)**

Lymphocyte: ....

....

.... **(2 marks)**

5 How do platelets protect the body from infection?

....

....

.... **(2 marks)**

Blood vessels

1 Which of the following types of blood vessel contains blood at the lowest pressure?
Tick **one** box.

artery ☐   vein ☐   capillary ☐   **(1 mark)**

2 The diagram shows a cross-section through a vein and an artery.

large lumen —————— [vein diagram]   thick wall with muscle
                                                              and elastic fibres —————— [artery diagram]

vein   artery

(a) Give a reason why the vein has a large lumen.

....   **(1 mark)**

(b) Explain why the artery has a thick wall with
muscle and elastic fibres.

> Think about the reason why the
> artery wall is thick, and why it
> contains muscle and elastic fibres.

....

....

....

....

....

....   **(3 marks)**

3 Substances diffuse between blood in the capillaries and the body cells around them.
Explain how the capillaries are adapted to this function.

Guided

The capillaries are about as wide as one red blood cell, so the distance oxygen

must travel to the capillary wall is .... The walls are

only one cell thick, so ....   **(2 marks)**

4 Explain how the structure of veins helps them carry blood back to the heart.

....

....

....

....   **(2 marks)**

The heart

Guided

1 The heart is connected to four major blood vessels. Complete the table below.

Blood vessel	Carries blood from	Carries blood to	Carries oxygenated blood (✓ or ✗)
aorta	heart	body	✓
pulmonary artery			
pulmonary vein			
vena cava			

(4 marks)

2 (a) Why is the heart mainly muscle?

....

.... **(2 marks)**

(b) Give the route taken by blood through the heart from the vena cava to the aorta.

....

....

.... **(3 marks)**

3 The diagram shows a section through the human heart.

> Remember that the heart is drawn and labelled as if you are looking towards the front of someone's chest. So the left side of the heart is shown on the right of the diagram.

(a) The part labelled **A** is a heart valve. What is its function in the heart?

....

....

.... **(2 marks)**

(b) Name the part labelled **B** and describe its function.

....

.... **(2 marks)**

(c) Explain why the muscle at **C** must be thicker than the muscle on the other side of the heart.

....

....

.... **(3 marks)**

21

The lungs

1   The diagram shows parts of the respiratory system.

Identify the structures labelled **A** and **B**.

A   ....

B   ....   **(2 marks)**

2   Gas exchange happens at the surface of the alveoli in the lungs.

(a)   Name the process by which gas exchange happens.

   ....   **(1 mark)**

> **Guided**

(b)   Describe the directions in which gas exchange happens.

   There is a net movement of carbon dioxide from...

   to ...., and a net movement of oxygen from

   ....   **(2 marks)**

(c)   Explain **two** ways in which the structure of the alveoli is adapted for efficient gas exchange.

   ....

   ....

   ....

   ....

   ....   **(4 marks)**

3   Emphysema is a type of lung disease where elastic tissue in the alveoli breaks down. The diagram shows the appearance of an alveolus damaged by lung disease compared with a healthy alveolus.

Symptoms of emphysema include shortness of breath and an increased breathing rate. Explain why.

> Think about how the changes shown in the diagram affect lung function.

Healthy alveolus

Alveolus damaged by lung disease

   ....

   ....

   ....

   ....   **(2 marks)**

Cardiovascular disease

1 In coronary heart disease, layers of fatty material build up inside the coronary arteries.

(a) Explain how this can lead to a heart attack.

> Which organ is supplied with blood by the coronary arteries?

....

....

.... **(3 marks)**

(b) Describe how coronary heart disease may be treated using:

> Say what each treatment is and what it does.

(i) a stent

....

.... **(2 marks)**

(ii) statins.

....

.... **(2 marks)**

2 In some people, the heart valves may become faulty.

(a) Give **two** ways in which a heart valve may not function properly.

1 ....

2 .... **(2 marks)**

(b) Give **two** ways in which faulty heart valves can be replaced.

1 ....

2 .... **(2 marks)**

(c) Give **one** problem caused by faulty heart valves.

....

.... **(1 mark)**

3 The table summarises some of the benefits and drawbacks of the different types of treatment for cardiovascular disease.

> Guided

Type of treatment	Benefits	Drawbacks
lifestyle changes such as dietary change	no side effects, may reduce risk of other health problems	may take a long time to work, may not work effectively
medication with drugs		
surgery, including transplants		

Complete the table to show a benefit and drawback of each type of treatment.   **(6 marks)**

Had a go ☐   Nearly there ☐   Nailed it! ☐

Health and disease

1 Health may be described as the state of physical and mental wellbeing.

   Disease is a factor that can affect health. Give **one** other factor that can affect health.

   > What might affect physical wellbeing or mental wellbeing?

   .... **(1 mark)**

2 Diseases can be communicable or non-communicable.

   (a) Name the type of disease that can be passed from person to person.

   .... **(1 mark)**

   (b) Give **one** example of:

   (i) a communicable disease

   .... **(1 mark)**

   (ii) a non-communicable disease.

   .... **(1 mark)**

   > **Guided**

   (c) Complete the table to show features of these two types of disease.

	Communicable disease	Non-communicable disease
Number of cases	rapid variation over time	
Distribution of cases		

   (2 marks)

3 A student was interested in studying how diseases may interact with each other. This is part of the student's research notes.

   > The scabies mite is a tiny arthropod. Holding hands with an infected person for a lengthy time can transmit it. The mite burrows into the skin and lays its eggs there. Burrow marks usually appear in warm places, such as skinfolds. However, a lumpy red rash can appear anywhere on the body. This allergic immune response causes severe itching, and repeated scratching may break the skin's surface.

   Use this information to help you answer these questions.

   (a) Explain why scabies is a communicable disease.

   ....

   ....

   .... **(2 marks)**

   (b) Explain why itchy skin itself is a non-communicable disease.

   ....

   ....

   .... **(2 marks)**

Lifestyle and disease

1 The chart shows how the body type of a person is related to their mass and height.

A man is 190 cm tall and has a mass of 120 kg. Explain why his doctor might advise him to eat less.

> Use the chart to determine the man's body type.

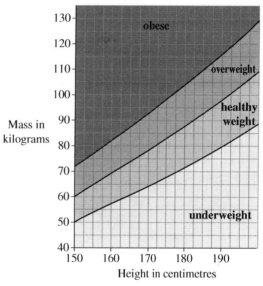

....

....

....

.... **(2 marks)**

2 Ionising radiation is a risk factor for developing cancer.

(a) Give **two** features of a risk factor with a proven causal mechanism.

1 ....

2 .... **(2 marks)**

(b) Describe what is meant by cancer.

....

.... **(2 marks)**

3 The chart shows the results of a survey into the relationship between body mass and the incidence of Type 2 diabetes.

(a) Describe the trend shown by this graph.

....

....

.... **(2 marks)**

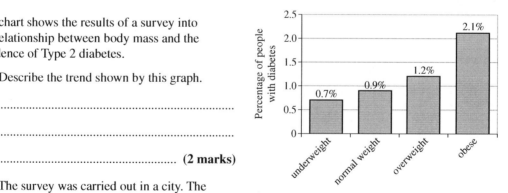

(b) The survey was carried out in a city. The population of the city was 19.5 million people.

(i) Use the graph to calculate the total percentage of people in the city who had Type 2 diabetes.

.... **(1 mark)**

(ii) Use your answer to part (i) to calculate the number of people in the city who had Type 2 diabetes.

$$\text{Number of people with diabetes} = \frac{\text{percentage with diabetes}}{100} \times \text{population}$$

$$= \frac{.................................}{100} \times ....$$

$$= ....$$

(2 marks)

Alcohol and smoking

1 The graph shows how the risk of having a car accident changes at different concentrations of alcohol in the blood. Use this graph when answering the questions.

(a) In England and Wales, the legal limit for drivers is 80 mg per 100 cm³ of blood.

(i) Give the increase in the risk of having a car accident at the legal limit.

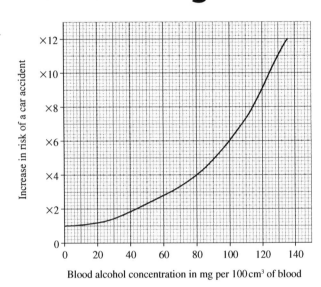

.... **(1 mark)**

(ii) Identify the blood concentration that increases the risk of having a car accident eight times.

.... **(1 mark)**

⟩ **Guided** ⟩ (b) Describe the trend shown by the graph.

As the concentration of alcohol in the blood rises, the risk of having a car

accident .... The change in the risk increases

as the .... **(2 marks)**

(c) Give a reason to explain the trend shown by the graph.

....

.... **(1 mark)**

2 The pie chart shows the number of deaths caused each year in America by smoking-related diseases.

(a) Calculate the percentage of deaths from lung cancer. Give your answer to 3 significant figures.

🔢 **Maths skills** Calculate the total number of deaths shown in the pie chart first.

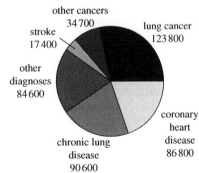

....

Percentage of deaths from lung cancer .... **(2 marks)**

(b) Other than the risk of developing the diseases shown in the pie chart, give **one** reason why pregnant women are advised not to smoke.

....

.... **(1 mark)**

The leaf

1 Which of the following best describes a leaf? Tick **one** box.

cell ☐   tissue ☐   organ ☐   organ system ☐   **(1 mark)**

2 Leaves are supported by the stem, which is connected to the root. Give **two** functions of the root.

1 ....

2 ....   **(2 marks)**

3 The diagram shows a cross-section of part of the leaf of a plant.

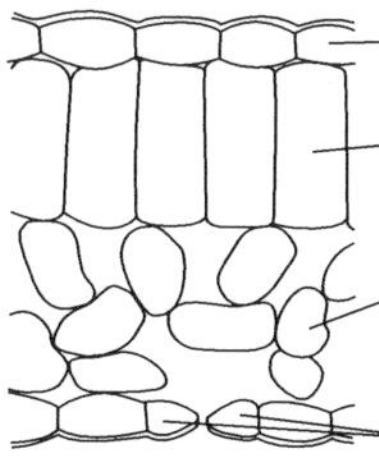

- epidermal cells
- palisade mesophyll cells
- spongy mesophyll cell
- X

(a) About 80% of the photosynthesis in a leaf happens in the palisade mesophyll tissue.

   (i)   Name the subcellular structure in which photosynthesis happens.

   ....   **(1 mark)**

   (ii) Give a reason why the palisade | Think about how well these
         mesophyll cells are box shaped. | cells pack together in the leaf.

   ....   **(1 mark)**

(b) The cells labelled **X** are found mostly on the underside of the leaf.

   (i)   Identify these cells.

   ....   **(1 mark)**

   (ii) Name the structure formed by these cells.

   ....   **(1 mark)**

(c) The upper epidermis is covered by a layer called the cuticle. Suggest a reason why:

> **Guided**

   (i)   the cuticle is thin and transparent

   This is so that light can ....   **(1 mark)**

   (ii) the cuticle is waxy

   ....   **(1 mark)**

(d) Describe how the cells in the spongy mesophyll | Look at the diagram to help you.
    tissue produce air spaces for gas exchange.

   ....

   ....   **(1 mark)**

Transpiration

1 How do mineral ions and water enter root hair cells? Tick **one** box.

Mineral ions and water enter by active transport. ☐

Mineral ions enter by diffusion and water by active transport. ☐

Mineral ions enter by active transport and water by osmosis. ☐

Mineral ions enter by diffusion and water by osmosis. ☐ **(1 mark)**

2 Describe the process of transpiration.

Guided

Water .... from the leaves, mostly through the

.... This causes a pull so that water moves through

the .... and is replaced by water entering the roots. **(3 marks)**

3 A student investigated the number of stomata on the upper and lower surfaces of a leaf. This is the method she used.

> Coat the leaf surface with colourless nail varnish and let it dry.
> Peel off the dry layer of nail varnish with sticky tape and stick it onto a microscope slide.
> Using a microscope, count the stomata in several equal-sized areas.

The table shows the student's results.

Area	Number of stomata	
	Lower surface	Upper surface
A	22	0
B	18	2
C	23	3
D	19	1

> **Maths skills** To find the mean, add all the values together then divide the total by the number of values.

(a) Calculate the mean number of stomata on each surface.

Lower surface: ....

Upper surface: .... **(2 marks)**

(b) Explain why the lower surface should lose most water.

....

.... **(2 marks)**

(c) The size of the opening in a stoma can vary, depending on the external conditions.

(i) Give **one** advantage to a plant of having closed stomata when the soil is dry.

.... **(1 mark)**

(ii) Transpiration helps to keep the leaf cool. Give **one** other reason why a plant's stomata should not remain completely closed.

> What substances, other than water vapour, pass through the opening?

....

.... **(1 mark)**

Investigating transpiration

1 The apparatus in the diagram was used to investigate the movement of water in the shoot of a plant. Circle A shows the position of an air bubble at the start of the experiment. Circle B shows its position at the end.

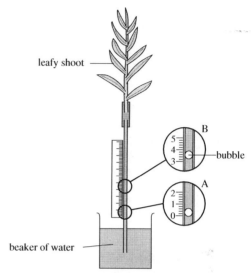

leafy shoot

bubble

B

A

beaker of water

(a) What distance did the air bubble travel? Tick **one** box.

2.6 cm ☐

3.2 cm ☐

3.5 cm ☐

3.9 cm ☐ **(1 mark)**

(b) In a similar experiment, a student investigated the effect of the wind on the rate of transpiration. He used an electric fan to simulate wind blowing. He measured the distance travelled by the bubble in 5 minutes with the fan off or on. The table shows the student's results.

Fan	Distance travelled by bubble in mm
off	90
on	130

Guided

(i) The bubble travelled through a capillary tube with a diameter of 0.5 mm. Calculate the rate of transpiration in mm^3/min when the fan was off. Give your answer to 1 decimal place.

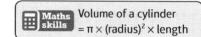
Maths skills Volume of a cylinder $= \pi \times (radius)^2 \times length$

radius of tube $= \dfrac{0.5}{2} = $ .... mm

volume travelled $= \pi \times$ .... $\times\ 90 = $ .... mm^3

rate of transpiration $= \dfrac{\text{.............................}}{5} = $ .... mm^3/min   **(2 marks)**

(ii) Describe what the results show about the rate of transpiration.

....

.... **(1 mark)**

2 (a) Which row in the table shows the changes to temperature and humidity that produce higher rates of transpiration? Tick **one** box.

Temperature	Humidity	
increased	increased	☐
increased	decreased	☐
decreased	decreased	☐
decreased	increased	☐

(1 mark)

(b) Give a reason why increasing the light intensity increases the rate of transpiration.

.... **(1 mark)**

Translocation

1 In which plant tissue does translocation take place? Tick **one** box.

phloem ☐   xylem ☐   meristem ☐   mesophyll ☐   **(1 mark)**

2 Describe what is meant by translocation.

....

....

....

....   **(2 marks)**

Guided

3 Complete the table by placing a tick (✓) in each correct box to compare the features of transpiration and translocation.

Structure or mechanism	Transpiration	Translocation
xylem	✓	
phloem		
pulled by evaporation from the leaf		
energy needed		

(4 marks)

4 The rate of translocation in a growing plant was measured using the method described below.

> Enclose the leaves with a plastic bag and seal the bag against the stem.
> Add carbon dioxide containing radioactive carbon atoms to the plastic bag.
> Extract sucrose solution from two different places in the stem at various times.
> Analyse the sucrose solution for the presence of radioactivity.

Sucrose solution was extracted from two places 0.4 m apart. The time taken for radioactivity to travel between these places was 67 minutes. Calculate the mean rate of translocation in mm/s.

> **Maths skills** Remember that 1 m = 1000 mm, and 1 minute = 60 s.

....

....

Mean rate = ... mm/s   **(2 marks)**

5 Meristem tissue is found at the growing tips of shoots and roots. Describe the function of the stem cells in this tissue.

....

....

....

....   **(2 marks)**

Extended response – Organisation

The diagram shows the main features of the human heart and circulatory system.

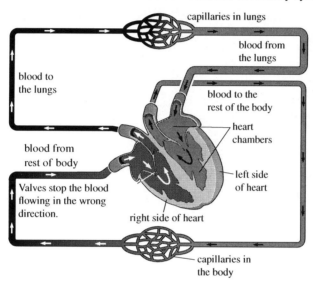

capillaries in lungs

blood from
the lungs

blood to
the lungs

blood to the
rest of the body

heart
chambers

blood from
rest of body

left side
of heart

Valves stop the blood
flowing in the wrong
direction.

right side of heart

capillaries in
the body

Describe the journey taken by blood around the body and through the heart, starting from
when it enters the right side of the heart. In your answer, include the names of major blood
vessels and chambers in the heart.

> You will be more successful in extended response questions if you plan your answer before
> you start writing.
>
> You could follow the blood around the diagram with a finger, writing the name of each blood
> vessel or chamber in order as you go.
>
> When you answer this question:
>
> • **don't** explain how the different components of the heart and circulatory system work and
>
> • **don't** identify any blood vessels in the 'rest of the body' except for the aorta.
>
> You should try to use the information given in the question.

....

....

....

....

....

....

....

....

.... **(6 marks)**

Viral diseases

1 Which of the following is a disease caused by a virus? Tick **one** box.

rose black spot ☐   gonorrhoea ☐   malaria ☐   influenza ☐   **(1 mark)**

2 The table shows some possible features of viruses. Some of these are correct and some are incorrect.

Feature	Incorrect (✗)
Viruses are about the same size as cells.	
Viruses can infect plants or animals.	
Viruses reproduce outside cells.	
Viruses are spread by direct contact, air or water.	

(a) Complete the table by placing a cross (✗) in the box next to each incorrect feature.   **(2 marks)**

(b) For each incorrect feature identified in part (a), write a correct version of that feature.

....

....   **(2 marks)**

3 Tobacco mosaic virus (TMV) is a plant pathogen. It destroys chloroplasts in the leaves.

Guided

(a) Infection with TMV causes a distinctive 'mosaic' pattern of lighter-coloured areas on the leaves. Suggest an explanation for why parts of the leaves become discoloured.

Chloroplasts contain .... Lighter-coloured areas appear

where ....   **(2 marks)**

(b) Explain why infected plants do not grow very well.

....

....

....

....

....   **(3 marks)**

4 Measles is a viral disease that causes a fever.

(a) Give **one** other symptom of measles.

....   **(1 mark)**

(b) Give a reason why most young children are vaccinated against measles.

> What can happen if complications occur during a measles infection?

....

....   **(1 mark)**

(c) Describe **one** way in which the measles virus can be spread from person to person.

....

....   **(1 mark)**

Bacterial diseases

1 Which of the following is a disease caused by a bacterium? Tick **one** box.

TMV   ☐

cold   ☐

cholera   ☐

ringworm   ☐   **(1 mark)**

2 Salmonella food poisoning is spread by bacteria in or on food.

Give **one** symptom of salmonella food poisoning.

....   **(1 mark)**

3 Joseph Lister was a surgeon in the nineteenth century. In those days, surgeons did not wash their hands before operations. Patients often died from bacterial infections after surgery.

(a) Suggest a reason to explain why patients became infected during surgery.

....

....   **(1 mark)**

(b) Lister advised surgeons to use a fine spray of phenol solution during surgery. This substance had been used to clean sewers at the time. The table shows the effect of following Lister's advice.

Number of patients dying from infections per 100 operations	
Without Lister's advice	**With Lister's advice**
45	15

Describe the effect of Lister's advice on the number of patients dying from infections.

> Use information from the table in your answer.

....

....

....   **(2 marks)**

4 Gonorrhoea is a sexually transmitted infection (STI) caused by a bacterium.

(a) Give **one** symptom of gonorrhoea.

....   **(1 mark)**

(b) Penicillin is an antibiotic. In the past, gonorrhoea was easily treated with penicillin. Give a reason why this treatment is much less successful today.

....

....   **(1 mark)**

5 A patient has a sore throat caused by a bacterial infection. Explain how this infection makes the patient ill.

> Guided

Bacteria get into the body, where they ....

The bacteria produce .... which damage ....   **(2 marks)**

Fungal and protist diseases

1 Different pathogens cause different diseases. Which row in the table shows the type of pathogen that causes each disease? Tick **one** box.

Rose black spot	Malaria	
fungus	protist	☐
fungus	fungus	☐
protist	fungus	☐
protist	protist	☐

(1 mark)

2 Athlete's foot is a fungal disease. It commonly affects the skin between the toes, causing itchy, sore and flaky skin.

(a) Name the type of substance that can be used to treat fungal infections.

> You do not need to identify a particular cream or powder in your answer.

.... **(1 mark)**

(b) Why are you more likely to get athlete's foot if you share towels with other people?

....

....

.... **(2 marks)**

3 Rose black spot is a disease of plants. Purple or black spots develop on the leaves. These leaves often turn yellow and drop early. Explain why rose black spot affects the growth of infected plants.

> **Guided**

If the leaves are damaged or there are fewer leaves, ...

is reduced. The plant cannot make enough .... **(2 marks)**

4 A microorganism called *Plasmodium* causes malaria, a disease that can be fatal. *Plasmodium* has a life cycle that includes the mosquito.

(a) Give **one** symptom of malaria.

.... **(1 mark)**

(b) Describe the role of the mosquito in the spread of malaria.

....

....

.... **(2 marks)**

(c) Explain why the use of mosquito nets helps to reduce the risk of infection with *Plasmodium.*

....

....

....

....

.... **(3 marks)**

Human defence systems

1 The human body has some non-specific defence mechanisms against pathogens.

(a) Give **one** way in which the following features defend the body against pathogens.

(i) Hairs in the nose.

.... **(1 mark)**

(ii) Hydrochloric acid in the stomach.

.... **(1 mark)**

(b) Describe the role of the skin in protecting the body from infection.

....

.... **(2 marks)**

(c) Tears contain an enzyme that helps to protect the body from infection.

Describe how this enzyme protects the eyes against infection.

....

....

.... **(2 marks)**

2 The diagram shows a section of epithelium in a human bronchiole, one of the tubes in the lungs.

(a) Name substance **A**.

.... **(1 mark)**

(b) Describe the role of substance **A** in protecting the lungs from infection.

> Give a feature of this substance and say what it does to pathogens.

....

....

.... **(2 marks)**

(c) The structure labelled **B** is a part of the epithelial cells.

(i) Name structure **B**.

.... **(1 mark)**

(ii) Describe how these epithelial cells help to protect the lungs from infection.

The structures on the surface of the cells move in ....,

which move ....

.... **(3 marks)**

Had a go ☐   **Nearly there** ☐   **Nailed it!** ☐

The immune system

1 White blood cells are an important part of the immune system. Some of these cells produce antibodies.

> **Guided**

(a) Describe how antibodies defend the body against pathogens.

> What type of substance are antibodies, and what do they do?

Antibodies are .... They attach to ....

produced by the pathogen, which leads to its destruction.   **(2 marks)**

(b) Describe **two** other ways in which white blood cells help to defend against pathogens.

1 ....

....

2 ....

....

....   **(4 marks)**

2 It is possible to detect antibodies that are effective against the measles virus. The graph shows the concentration of these antibodies in the blood of a young child during two local outbreaks of measles.

Concentration of antibodies in blood

(a) The first time the child was infected by the measles virus is shown by the arrow labelled 1.

Describe what happens to the concentration of antibodies in the child's blood in the first five weeks.

> Look at the shape of the line in weeks 0 to 5. In your answer, include the time taken for the concentration of antibodies to reach a maximum.

....

....

....   **(2 marks)**

(b) The child recovered from her measles infection. She was infected by the measles virus again a few weeks later, at a time shown by the arrow labelled 2.

Give **two** ways in which the increase in the concentration of antibodies differs from the first infection.

....

....

....   **(2 marks)**

(c) Explain why the child showed no symptoms of measles in the second outbreak.

....

....

....   **(2 marks)**

> Look at your answer to part (b) to help you.

Vaccination

1 Vaccination can prevent illness in an individual and reduce the spread of a pathogen in a population.

(a) What does a vaccine contain? Tick **one** box.

a live active pathogen ☐

a dead form of a disease ☐

an inactive form of a pathogen ☐   **(1 mark)**

(b) Give **two** drawbacks of vaccination.

> Include a general side effect that some people may develop temporarily.

....

.... **(2 marks)**

Guided

(c) Vaccination prevents a person from becoming ill from infection with a pathogen. This works even if they are exposed to the pathogen a long time after receiving the vaccine. Explain why.

The vaccine causes white blood cells to make .... against

the pathogen. If the same pathogen enters the body again, white blood cells

respond ....

.... **(3 marks)**

2 The MMR vaccine is effective against measles, mumps and rubella. In 1998, a group of doctors suggested that there was a connection between receiving the MMR vaccine and developing autism. This made some parents afraid of having their babies vaccinated. The graph shows how the percentage of babies in the UK who were given the MMR vaccine changed afterwards.

Percentage of babies vaccinated with MMR

100 ← group of doctors publish their study

90

80

Year

1992 1994 1996 1998 2000 2002 2004 2006 2008 2010 2012

(a) In which year was the rate of MMR vaccination lowest?

.... **(1 mark)**

(b) The number of children suffering from measles increased in the period 1998–2004. Suggest a reason why.

....

.... **(1 mark)**

(c) Vaccinated people are immune and so cannot become infected. Give a reason that explains why it is not necessary for every child in the population to be immunised.

....

.... **(1 mark)**

Antibiotics and painkillers

1 Penicillin is an example of an antibiotic.

(a) Antibiotics do not damage body tissues. Give a reason why antibiotics are used to treat bacterial infections in people.

.... **(1 mark)**

> **Guided**

(b) A man has a very bad cold. Colds are caused by viruses. The man asks a pharmacist if he should take some penicillin to help cure his cold. Explain whether the pharmacist would advise the man to take penicillin.

The pharmacist's advice would be .... penicillin.

This is because antibiotics .... viruses. **(2 marks)**

2 Some hospitals have problems with a bacterium called MRSA. MRSA is resistant to many common antibiotics. The graph shows how many people died from MRSA infection between 2000 and 2008.

(a) Describe the pattern shown by the graph.

....

....

....

.... **(2 marks)**

(b) Suggest a reason why the number of deaths changed:

(i) between 2000 and 2005

....

.... **(1 mark)**

(ii) after 2006.

| Antibiotic-resistant bacteria were still present in the population in these years. |

....

.... **(1 mark)**

3 (a) Where do viruses reproduce? Tick **one** box.

in bodily fluids   ☐

inside living cells   ☐

in water droplets from sneezes   ☐

on door handles and other surfaces   ☐ **(1 mark)**

(b) Why is it difficult to develop safe drugs that destroy viruses?

| Scientists have discovered many substances that damage viruses, but most are not safe to use as drugs. Think about why this is. |

....

.... **(1 mark)**

New medicines

1 Which of the following is a drug that was traditionally extracted from willow?
Tick **one** box.

aspirin ☐   digitalis ☐   insulin ☐   penicillin ☐   **(1 mark)**

2 The development of a new medical drug involves a series of tests. Testing can move to the next stage only if the substance has successfully passed the previous stage.

Guided

(a) Complete the table to show the correct order of stages in developing a new medical drug.

Stage	Order (1 to 5)
substance tested in a small number of healthy people	
discovery of a substance that may be a new medical drug	1
drug given widely by doctors to treat patients	
substance tested in cells and tissues in the lab	
substance tested in a large number of people with the disease it may treat	

(2 marks)

(b) Give **two** functions of a clinical trial in the development of a new medical drug.

....

....

....

.... **(2 marks)**

(c) Describe **one** stage of pre-clinical testing in the development of a new medical drug.

....

.... **(1 mark)**

3 Scientists trialled a new medical drug intended to lower blood pressure. Group A contained 1000 people with normal blood pressure and Group B contained 1000 people with high blood pressure. Half the volunteers in each group were given the new medicine and half were given a placebo. At the end of the trial, the scientists determined the number of volunteers in each group with high blood pressure.

The graph shows the results.

(a) What is a placebo?

....

.... **(1 mark)**

(b) Explain how the results for Group B show that the medicine may reduce high blood pressure.

> Remember that Group B consisted of people with high blood pressure.

....

....

....

.... **(2 marks)**

Extended response – Infection and response

Many infectious diseases can be treated using vaccines and antibiotics. Edward Jenner developed the first vaccine, against smallpox, in 1796. Alexander Fleming discovered the first antibiotic, penicillin, in 1928. Medicine has been transformed since then by the wide availability of these and other vaccines and antibiotics.

Compare the use of vaccines and antibiotics in the treatment of infectious diseases.

> You will be more successful in extended response questions if you plan your answer before you start writing.
>
> Remember that the command word **compare** requires you to describe the similarities and differences of both things given in a question, not just one of them. For example, you could compare:
>
> - how vaccines and antibiotics work
> - when they can be used
> - what type of pathogen they are effective against
> - their benefits and drawbacks.
>
> You should try to use the information given in the question.

....

....

....

....

....

....

....

....

....

....

....

....

....

....

....

....

....

(6 marks)

Photosynthesis

1 What is photosynthesis? Tick **one** box.

an exothermic process in which energy is transferred to the chloroplasts by light ☐

an endothermic process in which energy is transferred to the chloroplasts by light ☐

an exothermic process in which energy is transferred from the chloroplasts by light ☐

an endothermic process in which energy is transferred from the chloroplasts by light ☐

(1 mark)

2 Photosynthesis can be represented by this equation: $6CO_2 + 6H_2O \rightarrow C_6H_{12}O_6 + 6O_2$

Use the symbol equation above to help you write the corresponding word equation.

.... **(1 mark)**

3 Plants have many uses for the carbohydrate produced by photosynthesis.

(a) Some of this carbohydrate is converted into substances for use in energy stores. Name **one** of these storage substances.

.... **(1 mark)**

(b) Some of this carbohydrate is converted into substances that are not used in energy stores. Name **one** of these products and describe what the plant uses it for.

> This question is about a different use of the sugars from the use described in part (a), so make sure that you pick a product that is not used for energy storage!

Product: ....

Use: .... **(2 marks)**

4 The rate of photosynthesis may be affected by the carbon dioxide concentration and temperature.

(a) Give **two** other factors that may affect the rate of photosynthesis.

1 ....

2 .... **(2 marks)**

Guided

(b) Sketch (i) a graph to show how the rate of photosynthesis may be affected by carbon dioxide concentration, and (ii) a graph to show how the rate of photosynthesis may be affected by temperature.

> A sketch is an approximate drawing. You do not need values on your graphs but you should label the axes.

(i)

Rate of photosynthesis

Carbon dioxide concentration

(ii)

(4 marks)

Had a go ☐   Nearly there ☐   Nailed it! ☐

Required practical – Investigating photosynthesis

1 A student investigated how the rate of photosynthesis in pondweed changed with light intensity. She placed a lamp at different distances from pondweed in a test tube. She counted the number of bubbles produced in 1 minute. The table shows her results.

Distance from lamp in cm	5	10	15	20	25	30
Number of bubbles	48	34	24	16	10	6

(a) Complete the graph using the results shown in the table.   **(3 marks)**

> **Maths skills** Plot the points accurately on the grid (to within half a square). Draw a line of best fit. This can be curved or straight, depending on the data, but it should ignore points that are clearly anomalies.

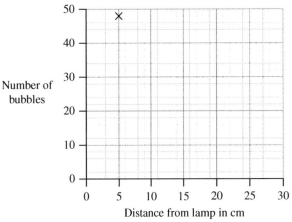

(b) Determine the distance from the lamp that should produce 12 bubbles in a minute.

.... **(1 mark)**

(c) How does the number of bubbles change as the distance from the lamp increases?

....

.... **(1 mark)**

(d) Old-fashioned filament lamps become hot with use, causing the surroundings to heat up. Modern LED lamps warm up very little when in use.

   (i)   The student used a filament lamp in her experiment. Describe a suitable safety precaution needed to reduce the risk of harm. Give a reason for your answer.

   ....

   ....

   .... **(2 marks)**

   (ii) Explain, in terms of photosynthesis, why it is better to use an LED lamp.

   ....

   ....

   .... **(2 marks)**

Respiration

1 Which of these is the word equation for aerobic respiration? Tick **one** box.

glucose → lactic acid ☐

glucose → ethanol + carbon dioxide ☐

glucose + oxygen → lactic acid + water ☐

glucose + oxygen → carbon dioxide + water ☐

(1 mark)

2 Energy is transferred by respiration in cells.

(a) Give **three** uses for this energy in animals.

keeping warm, ...

.... **(3 marks)**

(b) Explain whether respiration is an exothermic reaction or an endothermic reaction.

> Say what type of reaction it is, and why.

....

....

....

.... **(2 marks)**

3 Plants use energy transferred by light for photosynthesis. Suggest an explanation for why plants need to respire continuously.

....

.... **(2 marks)**

4 Anaerobic respiration can take place in yeast cells.

(a) Give another name for this process.

.... **(1 mark)**

(b) Anaerobic respiration in yeast has economic importance. Give **two** uses of this process.

> Think about food and drinks that can be manufactured.

....

.... **(2 marks)**

5 (a) Anaerobic respiration can happen in plant cells and in muscle cells. Use words from the box to complete the sentences.

presence	lactic acid	water
ethanol	oxygen	absence

> You will not need to use all the words to answer the question.

Both processes happen in the .... of oxygen. In plant cells,

anaerobic respiration produces carbon dioxide and .... but in

muscle cells it produces .... instead. **(3 marks)**

(b) Aerobic respiration and anaerobic respiration can happen in muscle cells.

Give **one** way in which these processes are similar.

.... **(1 mark)**

Responding to exercise

1 Which row in the table shows changes that happen during exercise? Tick **one** box.

Breathing rate	Breath volume	
decreased	decreased	☐
decreased	increased	☐
increased	increased	☐
increased	decreased	☐

(1 mark)

2 The graph shows the pulse rate of an athlete at rest, and after 5 minutes of different types of exercise.

(a) Calculate the percentage increase in pulse rate between jogging and running.

100 – 80 = ... beats/min

percentage increase =

$\frac{..........}{80}$ × 100 = ... %

(2 marks)

(b) Explain why the pulse rate increases as the amount of activity increases.

> The pulse rate is the same as the heart rate.

....

....

....

....

....

(3 marks)

3 The graph shows how oxygen consumption changes before, during and after exercise. The intensity of the exercise kept increasing during the period marked 'Exercise'.

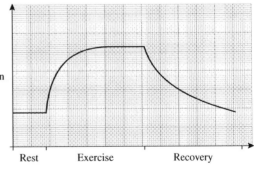

(a) Give a reason why oxygen consumption increases when exercise starts.

....

....

(1 mark)

(b) Give a reason why oxygen consumption reached a maximum, even though the intensity of exercise kept increasing.

....

....

(1 mark)

Metabolism

1 What is metabolism? Tick **one** box.

the rate at which food is digested to soluble molecules ☐

how quickly respiration happens in mitochondria in cells ☐

how efficiently waste substances are removed from a cell or body ☐

the sum of all the reactions in a cell or the body ☐ **(1 mark)**

2 The liver is an important organ in the body. Its cells can carry out many different conversions of one substance to another. Give **two** examples of these conversions.

> Guided

1 excess glucose into .... for storage in the liver

2 excess amino acids into ammonia (then into ....) **(2 marks)**

3 Glucose can be used to synthesise amino acids in living organisms.

(a) Name the ion needed to form amino acids using glucose.

> Remember that glucose and other carbohydrates do not contain nitrogen atoms, but amino acids do.

.... **(1 mark)**

(b) Name the type of complex substance made from many amino acids.

.... **(1 mark)**

(c) Glucose molecules can be combined to form complex carbohydrates. Name **two** of these complex carbohydrates formed by plants.

> One of these compounds is used for storage.

1 ....

2 .... **(2 marks)**

4 Lipids are fats and oils.

(a) Name the **two** different substances that react together to form lipids.

1 ....

2 .... **(2 marks)**

(b) Describe how many molecules of each substance named in part (a) are needed to form **one** lipid molecule.

....

.... **(1 mark)**

5 Name **three** types of digestive enzyme, and their substrates.

> A **substrate** is the substance acted on by an enzyme.

1 ....

2 ....

3 .... **(3 marks)**

Extended response – Bioenergetics

Photosynthesis and aerobic respiration are important processes in plants. They involve different reactants and products, and take place in different parts of the cell.

Compare photosynthesis and aerobic respiration. In your answer, you should include equations, descriptions of energy transfer and relevant subcellular structures.

> You will be more successful in extended response questions if you plan your answer before you start writing.
>
> Remember that the command word **compare** requires you to describe both things given in a question, not just one of them. So take care to describe:
>
> - the similarities between the two processes
>
> - the differences between the two processes.
>
> Give word equations (or correctly balanced chemical equations) as part of your answer.
>
> Make sure that you do **not** include anaerobic respiration in your answer, because this is not required here.
>
> You should try to use the information given in the question.

....

....

....

....

....

....

....

....

....

....

....

....

....

....

....

....

....

(6 marks)

Homeostasis

1 Explain what is meant by homeostasis.

Homeostasis is the regulation of the .... of

a cell or organism to maintain ....

in response to .... changes.   **(3 marks)**

2 Homeostasis uses automatic control systems, which may involve nervous responses or chemical responses. These systems include three main parts.

(a) Describe the function of receptor cells.

....

....

....

....   **(2 marks)**

(b) The pancreas can act as a coordination centre. Name **one** other coordination centre.

....   **(1 mark)**

(c) Homeostatic systems include effectors.

(i) Name **two** types of effectors.

1 ....

2 ....   **(2 marks)**

(ii) Describe what effectors do in a homeostatic control system.

....

....

....

....   **(2 marks)**

3 Human body temperature is controlled so it remains close to 37 °C.

(a) Give **two** other body conditions that are controlled.

1 ....

2 ....   **(2 marks)**

(b) The body responds if its temperature falls. Use words from the box to complete the sentences.

stimulus	receptors	decreases	environment
increases	muscles	glands	coordination

You will not need to use all the words to answer the question.

When the temperature falls, ... detect this change and send

information to the .... centre. Responses happen so that the

temperature ....   **(3 marks)**

Neurones

1 The nervous system contains three main types of neurones. Sensory neurones carry electrical impulses from receptors to the central nervous system or CNS (the brain and spinal cord). Give **one** function of:

(a) relay neurones:

.... **(1 mark)**

(b) motor neurones:

.... **(1 mark)**

2 The table shows the speeds at which nerve impulses are transmitted through different kinds of neurones.

Myelin sheath	Impulse speed in m/s
present	25
absent	3

(a) Descibe the effect of the presence of the myelin sheath.

> Remember to include what the effect is, using information from the table.

....

.... **(1 mark)**

(b) Multiple sclerosis (MS) is a disorder in which the myelin sheath surrounding neurones in the spinal cord is destroyed. Suggest an effect that this would have on the movement of a person with MS.

....

.... **(1 mark)**

3 The diagram shows a sensory neurone connected to receptor cells in the skin.

> Guided

axon terminals

axon

cell body

dendron

myelin sheath

dendrites attached to receptor cells

Explain how the sensory neurone is adapted to its function.

> What do the axon terminals, myelin sheath, dendrites, and axon and dendron do?

The axon and dendron are long so the neurone can ....

....

....

....

.... **(4 marks)**

Reflex actions

1 The diagram shows the synapse between two neurones (**X** and **Y**).

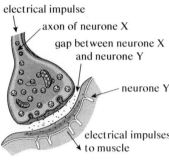

(a) Which neurone (**X** or **Y**) is a motor neurone? Give a reason for your answer.

....

.... **(1 mark)**

Guided

(b) Describe how signals pass across the gap from neurone **X** to neurone **Y**.

Neurone X releases a ....

which ....,

causing .... **(3 marks)**

2 Choose **three** words from the box to complete the sentence about the features of reflex actions.

Guided

innate	slow	automatic	conscious	learned	rapid

Reflex actions are innate , ..., and .... **(3 marks)**

3 The diagram shows components of a reflex arc.

(a) Describe what is meant by a stimulus.

....

.... **(1 mark)**

(b) Describe the pathway taken by a nerve impulse in a reflex arc.

> Begin with a stimulus and end with a response.

....

....

....

....

.... **(4 marks)**

Required practical – Investigating reaction times

1 Two students carried out an investigation into human reaction times. This is the method they used.

> Student A sat with her forearm resting on the bench, with her hand over the edge. Student B held a 30-cm ruler so that Student A's thumb was just touching the ruler, level with the zero mark at the bottom. Student B then dropped the ruler and Student A caught it. The distance the ruler dropped before she managed to catch it was recorded.

The students repeated the experiment several times. The table shows their results.

Drop number	1	2	3	4	5	6
Drop distance in mm	193	186	190	184	181	176

(a) Calculate the mean distance.

> **Maths skills** To calculate the mean, add the values together then divide the total by the number of values.

....

....

....

.... mm   **(1 mark)**

(b) The reaction time can be determined from the drop distance. One way to do this involves the equation:

$$\text{reaction time in s} = \sqrt{\frac{\text{drop distance in cm}}{491}}$$

    (i) Identify the result in the table that corresponds to Student A's quickest reaction time. Give a reason to explain your answer.

        ....

        ....

        ....   **(2 marks)**

Guided

    (ii) Calculate Student A's reaction time for drop 1. Give your answer to 2 significant figures.

> Remember to convert from mm to cm, and to use the equation given to you.

        $\text{distance} = \dfrac{\text{..............}}{10} = $ .... cm

        ....

        .... s   **(3 marks)**

(c) Student B thought that Student A was getting better with practice. Give a reason to explain this thought.

    ....

    ....

    ....   **(2 marks)**

Hormones

1 (a) The endocrine system involves hormones. Use words from the box to complete the sentences.

target	neurones	glands	muscle

> You will not need to use all the words to answer the question.

Hormones are secreted by .... They are then carried by the

blood to a .... organ, where they produce an effect. **(2 marks)**

(b) Which row in the table correctly compares features of the endocrine system with the nervous system? Tick **one** box.

Endocrine system	Nervous system	
slow, short-lasting	fast, long-lasting	☐
fast, long-lasting	slow, short-lasting	☐
slow, long-lasting	fast, short-lasting	☐
slow, long-lasting	fast, long-lasting	☐

(1 mark)

2 Label the diagram to identify the endocrine glands **A** to **F**.

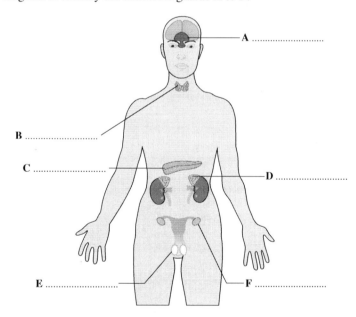

(6 marks)

3 Complete the table to show where each hormone is produced, with **one** example of its target organ.

> Guided

Hormone	Produced in	Target organ
adrenaline	adrenal gland	heart / muscles
FSH and LH		
insulin		
oestrogen		
progesterone		
testosterone		

(6 marks)

Blood glucose regulation

1 (a) Excess glucose is removed from the blood and converted into another substance for storage. Name this storage substance.

.... **(1 mark)**

Guided

(b) The table shows the events that happen after a person eats a meal. Complete the table to show the order in which the events take place.

Event	Order (1 to 5)
Pancreas increases secretion of insulin.	
Blood glucose concentration falls.	
Blood glucose concentration rises.	1
Insulin causes muscle and liver cells to remove glucose from blood.	
Pancreas detects rise in blood glucose concentration.	

(3 marks)

2 The graph shows an example of changes in blood glucose concentration during the day.

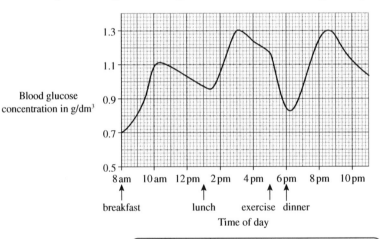

(a) Give the blood glucose concentration at 3 pm.

> Remember that you can draw lines on the graph if this helps you to work out your answer.

.... **(1 mark)**

(b) What happens to the blood glucose concentration between breakfast and lunch?

> Include values taken from the graph to support your answer.

....

....

....

....

.... **(3 marks)**

(c) Explain the effect of exercise on the blood glucose concentration.

> Look at the shape of the graph between 'exercise' and 'dinner'. Say what happens and why.

....

....

.... **(2 marks)**

Diabetes

1 A population of 1 864 035 people was sampled to estimate the occurrence of Type 2 diabetes. The results were divided into groups according to body mass index (BMI). People who have a BMI greater than 30 are obese. The bar chart shows the results.

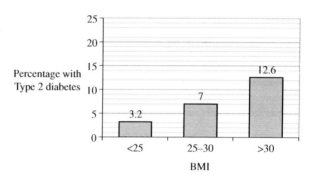

(a) Use the information to calculate the number of people in this population with Type 2 diabetes.

Total percentage with Type 2 diabetes = 3.2 + 7 + 12.6 = ...%

Number of people = ... × $\dfrac{1\,864\,035}{100}$

= ....   **(2 marks)**

(b) Suggest a reason why the number calculated in part (a) may not be accurate.

> Do not suggest an error in your calculation as a reason.

....

.... **(1 mark)**

(c) What do the results in the bar chart show?

> Look for a trend and use the values shown to inform your answer.

....

....

.... **(2 marks)**

2 Diabetes exists as Type 1 and Type 2.

(a) Compare the causes of Type 1 diabetes and Type 2 diabetes.

....

....

....

.... **(2 marks)**

(b) Explain how Type 1 diabetes is treated.

....

....

....

.... **(2 marks)**

(c) Give **one** way in which Type 2 diabetes may be controlled.

.... **(1 mark)**

Reproductive hormones

1 Reproductive hormones cause secondary sex characteristics to develop during puberty.
   Oestrogen is the main female reproductive hormone.

   (a) Name the main male reproductive hormone.

   .... **(1 mark)**

   (b) Give **one** effect the hormone named in part (a) has on the testes.

   .... **(1 mark)**

   (c) Give **two** effects the main reproductive hormones have on both boys and girls at
        puberty.

   1 ....

   2 .... **(2 marks)**

2 The diagram below shows typical timings of some features in the menstrual cycle.

X ⟍ ┌──────────────┐
     │   │
     │ ┌─────────────────────┐
     │ │ lining of uterus   │
     │ │ building up   │
     │ └─────────────────────┘
     │   ┌──┐ ⟍ Y
     │   │ │
     │   ┌────────────────────────────────────┐
     │   │ lining of uterus continues to thicken │
     │   └────────────────────────────────────┘
     1   7   14   21   28
          Day of cycle

   (a) Identify the process happening between days 1 and 5, labelled X in the diagram.

   .... **(1 mark)**

   Guided   (b) Give the name and function of:

   (i) LH

   Name: ....

   Function: stimulates the release of an egg   **(2 marks)**

   (ii) FSH

   Name: ....

   Function: .... **(2 marks)**

   (c) Which process happens around day 14 (labelled **Y** in the diagram)?

   .... **(1 mark)**

   (d) Name the **two** hormones involved in
        maintaining the lining of the uterus.

   ┌─────────────────────────────┐
   │ You will need to name hormones │
   │ not given in part (b).   │
   └─────────────────────────────┘

   ....

   .... **(2 marks)**

Contraception

1 Fertility can be controlled by a variety of hormonal and non-hormonal methods of contraception.

(a) Name the surgical method used to sterilise men.

.... **(1 mark)**

(b) Barrier methods of contraception prevent the sperm reaching an egg.

(i) Name **two** barrier methods of contraception.

1 ....

2 .... **(2 marks)**

(ii) Why may spermicidal agents improve the effectiveness of these methods?

.... **(1 mark)**

2 Similar to any medical drug, oral contraceptives may have side effects. The table shows the results of a study into blood clotting in 100 000 women.

	Non-smoker, not on 'the pill'	Non-smoker, on 'the pill'	Smoker, not on 'the pill'
Number with blood clotting	8	40	100

(a) What is a suitable conclusion from these results? Tick **one** box.

> The first option cannot be correct because 8 in 100 000 is 0.008%, not 8%.

~~8% of women non-smokers who are not on the pill get blood clotting.~~ ☐

The chance of a woman on the pill getting a clot increases 2.5 times if she smokes. ☐

1% of women smokers who are not on the pill get blood clotting. ☐

The chance of a non-smoker getting a clot increases 5 times when on the pill. ☐ **(1 mark)**

(b) Suggest **one** group of women missing from the results table.

.... **(1 mark)**

3 The table shows some information about two oral contraceptives. Both inhibit release of FSH and LH.

	Mini-pill	Combined pill
Contents	progesterone	oestrogen, progesterone
Success rate	96–99%	>99%

(a) The success rates assume that the pills are taken as prescribed. Explain why a woman is more likely to become pregnant if she does not take her pills regularly.

FSH causes an egg to .... and LH causes an egg to

.... A missed pill causes the level of progesterone

to ...., so ....

.... **(4 marks)**

(b) Progesterone may also be delivered by using implants. Suggest an advantage of this method of contraception over the mini-pill, and give a reason for your answer.

....

....

.... **(2 marks)**

Extended response – Homeostasis and response

It is important for the body to control the concentration of glucose in the blood. Diabetes is a condition in which the body cannot properly control blood glucose concentration.

Compare the causes and treatments of Type 1 diabetes and Type 2 diabetes.

> You will be more successful in extended response questions if you plan your answer before you start writing.
>
> You may wish to explain first how insulin controls blood glucose levels. This will make it easier to go on to describe the causes and treatments of the two types of diabetes. There is no need to include detailed symptoms in your answer.
>
> You should try to use the information given in the question.

....

....

....

....

....

....

....

....

....

....

....

....

....

....

....

....

....

....

....

....

.... **(6 marks)**

Sexual and asexual reproduction

1 Complete the table to compare features of sexual and asexual forms of reproduction.

	Sexual reproduction	**Asexual reproduction**
Mixing of genetic information	mixes genetic information from each parent	
Characteristics of offspring		

(2 marks)

2 The diagram shows a cell with two pairs of chromosomes undergoing meiosis.

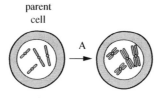

Describe what is happening during the stage labelled **A**.

.... (1 mark)

3 The diagram shows a cell about to divide by meiosis.

In the space below, draw the daughter cells that are produced from this cell.

> Your diagram should show the correct number of cells, with the correct number of chromosomes in each one.

(2 marks)

4 A cell contains 20 chromosomes. It divides by meiosis.

(a) Give the number of chromosomes in each daughter cell.

.... (1 mark)

(b) Explain why the daughter cells are not genetically identical.

....

.... (2 marks)

DNA and the genome

1 What word describes the entire genetic material of an organism? Tick **one** box.

genome ☐   chromosome ☐

genotype ☐   phenotype ☐   **(1 mark)**

2 The genetic material in the nucleus of a cell is a substance called DNA.

(a) Name the structure, found in the nucleus, that contains DNA.

.... **(1 mark)**

(b) Give the number of strands in a single DNA molecule.

.... **(1 mark)**

(c) Describe the shape of the structure formed by the strands in a DNA molecule.

.... **(1 mark)**

⟩ **Guided** ⟩ (d) Describe, in terms of DNA, what is meant by a gene.

A gene is a small section of DNA that ....

.... **(2 marks)**

3 The whole human genome has been studied. This is important because it allows scientists to search for genes linked to different types of disease. Give **two** other ways in which the understanding of the human genome is important.

1 ....

....

2 ....

.... **(2 marks)**

4 Scientists have discovered that a mutation in the human *BRCA1* gene increases a woman's risk of developing breast cancer. Suggest one benefit and one drawback to a woman of knowing that she has this mutation.

> **Suggest** means you need to apply your knowledge and understanding to a new situation. In this case, how it may help a woman to know that she has the harmful mutation in the *BRCA1* gene, and why this knowledge may cause her problems.

....

....

....

....

....

....

.... **(2 marks)**

Genetic terms

1   Describe what is meant by:

(a)   a gamete

> Include what it is and the process by which it forms.

....

....

....   **(2 marks)**

(b)   alleles.

....

....

....   **(2 marks)**

2   Explain the difference between the terms **genotype** and **phenotype**.

Guided

The genotype of an organism is the alleles of a ....

However, an organism's phenotype is its ....

produced by ....   **(3 marks)**

3   People with brown or blue eyes have different combinations of two alleles. The recessive allele b codes for blue eyes, and the dominant allele B codes for brown eyes.

(a)   Some people are heterozygous for eye colour.

(i)   Give the heterozygous genotype for eye colour.

> Use the symbols b and/or B in your answer.

....   **(1 mark)**

(ii)   Explain why a person with the heterozygous genotype has brown eyes.

....

....

....

....   **(2 marks)**

(b)   A girl has blue eyes. Explain what her genotype must be.

....

....

....

....   **(2 marks)**

Genetic crosses

1 *Drosophila* are fruit flies. Most *Drosophila* have normal wings, but some can have poorly formed wings. The allele for normal wings is D, and the allele for poorly formed wings is d. The d allele is recessive.

Drosophila A   *Drosophila* B

(a) The diagram shows two different *Drosophila*. Which alleles are present in *Drosophila* B? Give a reason for your answer.

....

....

....

.... **(2 marks)**

Guided (b) Two *Drosophila* with the alleles Dd are mated together to produce offspring.

Complete the Punnett square diagram to determine the probability of an offspring having badly formed wings. Identify any offspring with poorly formed wings.

> In your completed diagram, circle the genotypes of the offspring with poorly formed wings.

	Parent 1	
	D	d
Parent 2 D		
d		

Probability of poorly formed wings .... **(4 marks)**

2 Fur colour in mice is controlled by two alleles, G and g. A grey mouse and a white mouse produced a total of 40 offspring.

(a) Complete the Punnett square diagram for this cross.

	Parent genotype	
Parent gametes	G	g
Parent genotype g		
g		

(2 marks)

(b) Homozygous recessive mice have white fur. Predict the expected number of offspring with white fur.

> Recessive alleles are shown with lower case letters.

.... **(1 mark)**

(c) Give the genotype of mice with grey fur.

.... **(1 mark)**

Family trees

1 Sickle cell anaemia is a condition caused by a recessive allele.
Two healthy parents have a child who has sickle cell anaemia.
Which one of the following statements is correct? Tick **one** box.

Both parents are homozygous for the sickle cell allele. ☐

One parent is homozygous for the sickle cell allele and the other
is homozygous for the normal allele. ☐

Both parents are heterozygous for the sickle cell allele. ☐

One parent is heterozygous for the sickle cell allele and the other
is homozygous for the normal allele. ☐ **(1 mark)**

2 Cystic fibrosis (CF) is a genetic disorder that affects cell membranes. It is caused by
a recessive allele. The diagram shows a family tree for a family with some affected
individuals.

(a) How many cystic fibrosis alleles must be inherited for an individual to have the disorder?

.... **(1 mark)**

(b) How many males in the family have a homozygous recessive genotype?

.... **(1 mark)**

> **Guided**

(c) Determine the genotype of person 4. Explain your answer using F for the normal
allele and f for the recessive allele.

Person 4 doesn't have cystic fibrosis but she must have inherited an ....

allele from her mother. So she must have inherited an .... allele from

her father. This means that person 4's genotype is .... **(3 marks)**

(d) Explain how the family tree provides evidence
that cystic fibrosis is caused by a recessive allele.

> Look for patterns of inheritance in the family
> tree to work out how CF is inherited.

....

....

.... **(2 marks)**

Inheritance

1 (a) Give the number of pairs of chromosomes found in the nucleus of a human body cell.

.... **(1 mark)**

(b) Complete the Punnett square diagram to show how sex is determined in humans.

Father

	X	
Mother X		

(2 marks)

(c) Give the sex of a child represented by the genotype in the shaded box.

.... **(1 mark)**

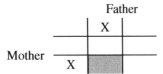

2 Embryo screening may be used to test for the presence of certain inherited disorders. This allows parents to make informed decisions about an embryo or pregnancy. The graph shows how the chance of having a child with Down's syndrome varies with the age of the mother.

Use the information in the graph to suggest why women of different ages are given different advice on embryo screening for Down's syndrome.

The graph shows that the chance of a woman having a child with Down's

syndrome .... as the woman's age increases. So pregnant women

over the age of 40 are .... likely to be offered embryo screening.   **(2 marks)**

Graph: vertical axis "Chance of having child with Down's syndrome (%)" marked 1, 3, 5, 7, 9; horizontal axis "Maternal age in years" marked 20, 30, 40, 50.

3 Polydactyly is an inherited disorder that results in extra fingers or toes. It is caused by a dominant allele, P.

(a) Complete the Punnett square diagram below.

Father

	P	p
P		
p	Pp	

Mother

(1 mark)

(b) Give the genotype of a homozygous dominant child.

> Dominant alleles are shown with upper case letters.

.... **(1 mark)**

(c) Draw a circle around each offspring in the Punnett square diagram **without** polydactyly.   **(1 mark)**

(d) Give the probability of producing a child **with** polydactyly.

.... **(1 mark)**

Variation and evolution

1 All variants in a population arise from mutations. In the sentences below, circle the correct word in each pair of **bold** words.

   (a) **Most | Few** mutations have no effect on the phenotype.   **(1 mark)**

   (b) **Some | Few** mutations determine the phenotype.   **(1 mark)**

2 Variation may have genetic causes, environmental causes, or a combination of genetic and environmental causes. Give the type of cause of the following:

   (a) a scar on the skin

   ....   **(1 mark)**

   (b) differences between a pair of identical twins

   ....   **(1 mark)**

   (c) body mass in a class of Year 11 students.

   ....   **(1 mark)**

3 Explain why, when an environment changes, some individuals within a population survive and reproduce, whereas others do not.

   ....

   ....   **(2 marks)**

4 Use words from the box to complete the sentence that explains how species arise.

populations	similar	fertile
animals	infertile	different

   > You will not need to use all the words to answer the question.

   Two new species form when two .... of one species become so

   .... in phenotype that they can no longer interbreed to produce

   .... offspring.   **(3 marks)**

5 Adult giraffes are 4.5–5 m tall, and nearly half of this height is due to their necks. These long necks allow giraffes to reach leaves for food in high trees. Giraffes are believed to have evolved from short-necked creatures similar to antelopes.

   (a) Suggest a reason why giraffes with the longest necks may be more likely to survive to reproduce.

   ....

   ....   **(1 mark)**

   Guided (b) Explain whether the offspring of giraffes with long necks are likely to have long necks too.

   They are likely to have long necks as well because they inherit ....

   ....

   ....   **(2 marks)**

Selective breeding

Guided

1 Describe what is meant by selective breeding.

It is the process by which humans breed ....

for particular .... **(2 marks)**

2 Dairy farming involves producing milk from cows. Suggest a desirable characteristic that dairy farmers may wish to select for in their herd.

.... **(1 mark)**

3 The characteristic chosen in selective breeding can be for usefulness or appearance. For example, resistance to disease is a useful characteristic for food crops.

Suggest **one** characteristic that might be chosen for:

(a) dogs to be kept as pets in families with young children

.... **(1 mark)**

(b) flowering plants to be sold in garden centres.

.... **(1 mark)**

4 Wheat plants produce edible seeds at the end of thin stems. Artificial fertilisers used by farmers encourage wheat stems to grow very quickly. In the last century, long-stemmed wheat plants were crossed with short-stemmed dwarf varieties in a selective breeding programme.

(a) Suggest an advantage to wheat plants of having fast-growing long stems.

| Think about how plants obtain the energy needed for photosynthesis. |

....

.... **(1 mark)**

(b) Suggest a reason why plant breeders selected for wheat plants with short stems.

| Think about the problems caused by heavy seed heads. |

....

.... **(1 mark)**

Guided

5 Describe how selective breeding could be used to produce lean pigs (less body fat).

Select the pigs in the group that have the least body fat, then............................

....

....

....

....

....

.... **(4 marks)**

Genetic engineering

1 Some potato plants have been genetically engineered so that they can resist attack by insect pests. Their cells contain a gene from a different organism that produces a toxic protein. What has genetic engineering done to these potato plants? Tick **one** box.

made no changes to their genome or phenotype ☐

changed their phenotype but not their genome ☐

changed their genome but not their phenotype ☐

changed their genome and their phenotype ☐   **(1 mark)**

2 Scientists have produced genetically modified mice that glow green in blue light. These 'glow mice' contain a gene naturally found in jellyfish. Describe how this genetically modified organism is produced.

The gene from a .... is cut out using ....

This gene is transferred to a .... embryo cell, and inserted into

a chromosome. The embryo is then allowed to develop as normal.   **(3 marks)**

3 People with Type 1 diabetes need to inject themselves with insulin. This can be extracted from the pancreas of pigs, or produced by GM bacteria. Suggest **two** advantages of using GM bacteria to produce the insulin for treating people with Type 1 diabetes.

1 ....

....

2 ....

....   **(2 marks)**

4 Vitamin A deficiency causes a poor immune response and difficulty seeing at night. Humans need beta-carotene to produce vitamin A. 'Golden rice' is genetically modified to contain the gene for making beta-carotene.

(a) Explain why golden rice might be useful in countries where people have a poor diet.

....

....

....

....   **(2 marks)**

(b) Explain **one** reason why some people are opposed to the production of GM crops, such as golden rice.

> There are different reasons why people may not agree with the growing of GM crops. Choose one and say why people might have this concern.

....

....

....

....   **(2 marks)**

Fossils

Guided

1 Scientists may find preserved remains of woolly mammoths in frozen soil in the Arctic.

(a) Give **two** conditions that prevent the decay of dead organisms.

1 low temperatures

2 .... **(2 marks)**

(b) Describe what is meant by a fossil.

> You do not need to say how a fossil forms.

....

.... **(2 marks)**

2 When people first settled on Christmas Island in the Pacific Ocean, scientists noted two species of rat that were unique to the island. In 1899, black rats escaped on to the island from a ship. These rats carried a parasite. The number of native rats decreased and by 1908 there were none left on the island.

Explain why the introduction of black rats led to the extinction of the native rats.

....

....

.... **(2 marks)**

3 Dinosaurs are thought to have become extinct around 65 million years ago, whereas mammoths became extinct about 4000 years ago. Modern humans evolved around 200 000 years ago.

(a) The extinction of the dinosaurs is often referred to as a mass extinction, in which all species became extinct. Give **two** causes of extinction, other than a single catastrophic event.

1 ....

2 .... **(2 marks)**

(b) Explain why it is unlikely that mammoths became extinct because of a single catastrophic event.

> Use the information in the question to help you.

....

....

.... **(2 marks)**

4 Scientists study fossils to provide evidence for evolution in different species. Despite this research, scientists still cannot be certain about how life began on Earth. There are difficulties for scientists in studying the fossil record to provide evidence for evolution and for early life on Earth. Give **two** reasons for these difficulties.

1 ....

....

2 ....

.... **(2 marks)**

Resistant bacteria

Guided

1   Evolution may be described as a change in the inherited characteristics of a population over time through a process of natural selection. Suggest whether evolution always results in a new species, and a give a reason for your answer.

No, because evolution can also produce new .... **(1 mark)**

2   MRSA is meticillin-resistant *Staphylococcus aureus*, a strain of bacterium. Meticillin is a similar substance to penicillin, used to treat bacterial infections.

   (a)   What type of substance is meticillin? Give a reason for your answer.

       ....

       .... **(2 marks)**

   (b)   Vancomycin is the most common and most effective antibiotic used in the treatment of MRSA infections. A new strain of MRSA is beginning to develop a resistance to vancomycin.

      (i)   Suggest why vancomycin-resistant MRSA is causing concern among doctors and scientists.

           ....

           ....

           ....

           .... **(2 marks)**

      (ii)   Describe how populations of vancomycin-resistant MRSA developed from non-resistant populations of the bacteria.

> Why does the number of resistant bacteria increase and the number of non-resistant bacteria decrease?

           ....

           ....

           ....

           ....

           ....

           ....

           .... **(4 marks)**

3   Give **one** way in which doctors or their patients can help to reduce the rate of development of antibiotic-resistant strains of bacteria.

   ....

   .... **(1 mark)**

Classification

1   The table shows how three different organisms are classified.

(a) Complete the table to give the correct classification group or binomial name for the organisms shown.

Classification group	Humans	Wolf	Panther
kingdom	Animalia	Animalia	Animalia
	Chordata	Chordata	Chordata
class	Mammalia	Mammalia	Mammalia
order	Primate	Carnivora	Carnivora
	Hominidae	Canidae	Felidae
genus	Homo	Canis	Panthera
	sapiens	lupus	pardus
binomial name	*Homo sapiens*		

(6 marks)

(b) Explain which **two** organisms in the table are most closely related.

> Look for the lowest shared classification group.

....

.... **(2 marks)**

2   Honey badgers (*Mellivora capensis*), North American badgers (*Taxidea taxus*), Eurasian badgers (*Meles meles*), stink badgers (*Mydaus javanensis*) and ferret badgers (*Melogale personata*) are all members of the same mammalian family, but are otherwise not closely related to each other.

(a) Name the genus to which the ferret badger belongs.

.... **(1 mark)**

(b) Using evidence from the passage above, suggest an explanation for why the common names for the badgers are misleading.

....

....

....

.... **(2 marks)**

(c) Give **two** reasons why a binomial naming system for each living organism is useful to scientists.

....

....

....

.... **(2 marks)**

Evolutionary trees

1   Bacteria and amoebae are unicellular (single-celled) organisms. However, bacteria are placed in the prokaryota kingdom and amoebae in the eukaryota kingdom.

bacteria

amoeba

Suggest **one** reason why bacteria and amoebae are placed in different kingdoms.

> Think about the differing features of bacterial cells and animal cells.

....

....

....

.... **(2 marks)**

Guided

2   Carl Woese proposed that organisms should be classified into three domains. Complete the table to give the types of organism in each domain.

> There is one type of organism in the archaea domain and four in the eukaryota domain.

Domain	Type(s) of organism in domain
archaea	
bacteria	true bacteria and cyanobacteria
eukaryota	protists,

(6 marks)

3   The diagram shows an evolutionary tree.

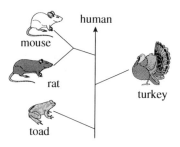

(a)   Which organism shares the oldest common ancestor with humans?

.... **(1 mark)**

(b)   Give the names of the **two** organisms on this tree that are most closely related.

....

.... **(1 mark)**

69

Extended response – Inheritance, variation and evolution

The peppered moth, *Biston betularia*, rests on the trunks of trees during the daytime. Some species of birds eat these moths. There are two forms of the peppered moth, a dark form and a light form. Dark moths became much more common during the nineteenth century. One theory suggested that pollution from factories had blackened the light tree trunks with soot. Birds could not easily see the dark moths. Air pollution is now tightly controlled by law and soot emissions have sharply decreased. The graph below shows how the numbers of dark moths has changed.

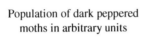

Population of dark peppered moths in arbitrary units

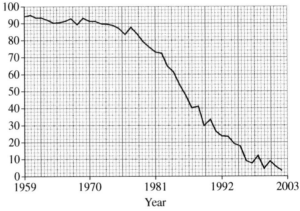

Explain the change in the number of dark moths using Darwin's theory of evolution by natural selection.

> You will be more successful in extended response questions if you plan your answer before you start writing.
>
> You may wish to consider:
>
> • What did the moth population look like in the mid-twentieth century?
>
> • How has the moth population changed over time? Use data from the graph to help you.
>
> • What does the theory of evolution say, and how does it relate to changes in *Biston betularia*?
>
> You should try to use the information given in the question.

....

....

....

....

....

....

....

....

....

.... **(6 marks)**

Ecosystems

1 Light intensity is an abiotic factor in a community.

(a) Plants may compete with each other for light. Give **two** other abiotic factors that plants may compete for.

....

.... **(2 marks)**

Guided (b) Give **two** things that animals may compete for.

> These could be biotic factors and/or abiotic factors.

territory and .... **(2 marks)**

2 Draw **one** line from each term to its meaning.

Term	Meaning
community	a single living individual
organism	all the living organisms and non-living parts in an area
population	all the different populations in a habitat
ecosystem	all the organisms of the same species in a habitat

(4 marks)

3 Lichens are organisms that consist of a fungus closely associated with an alga. The fungus can digest plant material and absorb nutrients, and the alga can make food by photosynthesis. Lichens can grow on the trunks of trees and on other surfaces.

Scientists looked at the distribution of lichens on a tree and on a concrete post next to the tree. The bar chart shows the results.

(a) Describe what the results show.

> What are the differences between the results for the tree and the post, and for the different sides?

....

....

.... **(2 marks)**

(b) Explain the results.

> Think about why the cover is different between the tree and the concrete, and why the cover is different on different sides.

....

....

....

....

....

....

.... **(4 marks)**

Interdependence

Guided

1 Give the meaning of a stable community.

All the species and .... are in balance so that

the population sizes .... **(2 marks)**

2 The diagram shows an interdependent community of plants and animals.

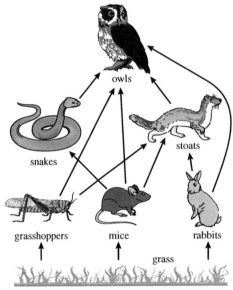

(a) Which animal has the most sources of food in the community?

.... **(1 mark)**

(b) Identify **two** sources of food for stoats in the community.

.... **(2 marks)**

(c) Use the diagram to predict the effect on the number of snakes if the number of mice decreased. Explain your answer.

....

....

.... **(2 marks)**

(d) Use the diagram to predict the effect on the number of mice if all the owls were removed from the community. Explain your answer.

> Work through all the feeding relationships that lead from mice to owls. Explain clearly how and why the number of mice is affected by removing the owls.

....

....

....

....

....

.... **(3 marks)**

Adaptation

1 Hydrothermal vents are found on the seabed. Water that comes out of these vents is very hot. A species of bacteria survives in this hot water. Several other different organisms are found nearby.

(a) Give the name used for organisms that are adapted to survive in hostile conditions.

.... **(1 mark)**

(b) The seabed is cold and dark. There are usually few organisms there. Explain why there is a large variety of life around hydrothermal vents.

> Think about the type of organism that usually produces food that other organisms can consume.

....

....

.... **(2 marks)**

2 Many plants, such as roses, need to attract insects so that the plants can be pollinated and produce seeds.

> **Guided**

(a) Suggest how these plants are adapted in order to attract insects.

Roses produce flowers to attract insects. These flowers have very bright

...., and they also give off a strong .... **(2 marks)**

(b) The diagram shows the seeds that are produced by dandelions. Suggest how these seeds are adapted to make sure that they can be dispersed.

....

....

....

....

.... **(2 marks)**

3 The diagram shows two different species of animal, A and B.

dark skin on face

thick coat

large ears

thin coat

wide feet

Animal A   Animal B

> **Justify** means that you need to use evidence from the information supplied to support your answer.

Determine which animal, A or B, would be better adapted to survive in a cold environment. Justify your answer.

....

....

....

.... **(3 marks)**

Food chains

1 The diagram shows an interdependent community of plants and animals.

> Make sure that your answers name organisms from the community shown in the diagram.

(a) Identify **one**:

   (i) primary consumer:

   ....**(1 mark)**

   (ii) tertiary consumer:

   ....**(1 mark)**

(b) Write a food chain that involves snakes.

   ....

   ....**(1 mark)**

(c) Give the function of the grass in this food chain: grass → rabbit → owl.

.... **(1 mark)**

2 Aphids are insects that feed on plant sap in phloem. Ladybirds are insects that eat aphids.

Guided

The graph shows how the population sizes of aphids and ladybirds in a community change over time.

(a) Explain why the number of ladybirds rises **after** the number of aphids rises.

There is plenty of food for the ladybirds, so more ....

....

.... **(2 marks)**

(b) Explain why the number of aphids falls **before** the number of ladybirds falls.

....

....

.... **(2 marks)**

Fieldwork techniques

1 A gardener went into his garden every night at 7 pm. He counted the number of slugs in the same 1 m² area of his flower bed. The table shows his results.

Day	1	2	3	4	5	6	7
Number of slugs	11	12	7	12	8	8	12

(a) Calculate the mean number of slugs seen each day.

> 🖩 **Maths skills** To calculate the mean, add the values together then divide the total by the number of values.

....

....

Mean number of slugs = ...   **(1 mark)**

(b) Determine the median number of slugs.

> 🖩 **Maths skills** The median is the middle value in a range. If there is an even number of values, you calculate the mean of the middle two values. Remember to put the numbers in order first.

....

....

Median number of slugs = ...   **(1 mark)**

(c) Give **two** reasons why a quadrat would be suitable to use in this investigation.

1   ....

....

2   ....

....   **(2 marks)**

2 A species of broad-leaved plants is growing in a small field between a path and a woodland. Describe how you would use a belt transect to investigate the distribution of this species growing between the path and the woodland.

> Make sure that you describe the use of quadrats, the measurements you would take and what you would record.

....

....

....

....

....   **(3 marks)**

3 A group of students investigated the number of clover plants on a football pitch. The pitch measured 100 m by 65 m. The students used a 1 m × 1 m quadrat. They found that the mean number of clover plants in each quadrat was 7. Estimate the number of clover plants on the whole football pitch.

> **Guided**

Area of the football pitch = 100 × 65 = ... m²

Number of clover plants = 7 × ....

= ....   **(2 marks)**

Required practical – Field investigations

1 A student surveyed the distribution of a species of lichen growing on the trunk of a tree. He used a small quadrat to measure the percentage cover by these lichens on the south-facing and north-facing sides of the tree. He used a light meter to measure the light intensity on each side. The table shows his results.

	South-facing side	North-facing side
Mean percentage cover	39	4
Light intensity in units	320	228

The student concluded that the lichen was better adapted to growing in areas with higher light intensities. Explain whether his conclusion was correct.

> You are asked to say only whether he was right or not, and why. Do not try to explain his results.

....

....

....

.... **(2 marks)**

2 Limpets are animals that have a shell. They live on rocks that are underwater for some or all of the time. They can be found attached to rocks on the seashore.

A scientist investigated the distribution of limpets on a beach. She set up three different transects, and measured the number of limpets inside quadrats placed at regular intervals. The table shows her results.

Distance from the sea in m	Number of limpets			Mean number of limpets
	Transect 1	**Transect 2**	**Transect 3**	
0.5	20	23	20	21
1.0	18	16	17	17
1.5	13	13	13	13
2.0	10	8	9	9
2.5	5	6	4	5
3.0	1	2	0	1

(a) Determine the median number of limpets in Transect 2.

> **Maths skills** The median is the middle value in a range. If there is an even number of values, you calculate the mean of the middle two values.

....

....

Median number of limpets in Transect 2 = ... **(1 mark)**

> **Guided**

(b) Give a suitable conclusion that can be made from the results of this investigation.

> What pattern can you see, and what does it mean for the survival of limpets on the seashore?

As the distance from the sea increases, the number of limpets ....

....

....

....

.... **(3 marks)**

Cycling materials

1   Complete the diagram of the carbon cycle by writing the names of the processes in the boxes.

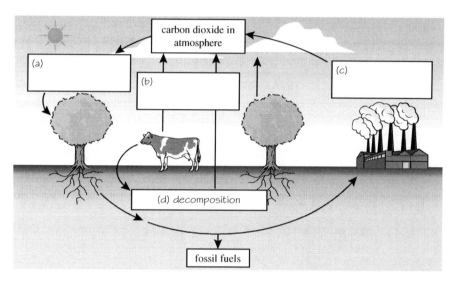

(4 marks)

2   In parts of California there is often a lack of rainfall. Water is taken from rivers and used to water lawns and golf courses. When there is a drought, restrictions are placed on the number of days each week that golf courses can be watered. Suggest an explanation for restricting water use.

> Think about the process involved in the water cycle, which provides plants and animals with fresh water.

Water vapour escapes from plants by .... and from

rivers and soil by .... If the water is not replaced by

rainfall, ...

.... (3 marks)

3   Give a reason why microorganisms are important in recycling carbon.

....

.... (1 mark)

4   The diagram shows a community of plants and fish in a fish tank. Explain how carbon is recycled between these organisms.

> You do not need to describe the role of microorganisms here, but you must mention carbon dioxide.

....

....

....

....

....

.... (4 marks)

Waste management

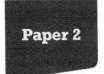

1 Sulfur dioxide pollution is a major cause of acid rain.

Guided

(a) Describe what is meant by pollution.

Pollution is the release or presence in the environment of ....

.... **(1 mark)**

(b) A scientist studied the pattern of growth of a species of lichen on the bricks of two walls. One wall was in an area with air polluted by sulfur dioxide, and the other in an area with unpolluted air. The diagram shows these two walls.

polluted air   **unpolluted air**

☐ no lichen
▨ covered in lichen

Describe what the results show.

....

....

.... **(2 marks)**

2 The rapid increase in the world's human population has caused an increased use of resources.

(a) Give **one** other reason why the use of resources has increased over time.

.... **(1 mark)**

(b) Give **two** ways in which human activities can lead to reduced space for animals and plants.

1 ....

2 .... **(2 marks)**

3 The overuse of artificial fertilisers can cause pollution in water. Water plants absorb mineral ions from the fertilisers and grow very quickly. They cover the surface of the water and prevent light reaching plants below. These plants die and are decomposed. The decomposer organisms use dissolved oxygen to respire.

(a) Explain why oxygen levels may fall in river water polluted by artificial fertilisers.

> Use evidence from the information supplied to support your answer.

....

....

.... **(2 marks)**

(b) The number of fish can decrease if river water is polluted by artificial fertilisers. Suggest a reason to explain this.

....

....

.... **(2 marks)**

Deforestation

1 What is meant by 'deforestation'?

....

.... **(1 mark)**

2 Rainforests in Indonesia are being cut down. The pie chart shows how the deforested land is used.

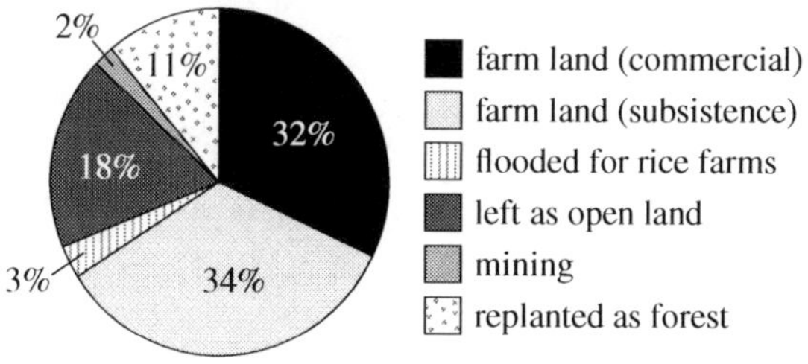

- ■ farm land (commercial)
- ☐ farm land (subsistence)
- ▥ flooded for rice farms
- ▨ left as open land
- ▤ mining
- ⬚ replanted as forest

2% 11% 32% 18% 3% 34%

> Add together the percentages in the pie chart for all farm uses.

(a) Calculate the total percentage of land that is used for farming after deforestation.

....

Percentage used for farming = ... **(1 mark)**

(b) Suggest **one** use for the trees that are cut down in rainforests.

.... **(1 mark)**

Guided (c) Of the land that is cleared, 11% is replanted as forest. Replanting some trees is important in terms of controlling the levels of carbon dioxide in the atmosphere. Explain why.

Planting trees .... the rate at which carbon dioxide is taken

from the atmosphere. The carbon dioxide is 'locked up' as .... **(2 marks)**

3 Deforestation often leads to a loss of biodiversity.

(a) What is meant by 'biodiversity'?

....

.... **(1 mark)**

(b) Give **two** reasons why deforestation can lead to a loss of biodiversity.

1 ....

....

2 ....

.... **(2 marks)**

Global warming

1 Scientists drill into the ice near the Vostok research station in Antarctica. They analyse the ice and ancient air trapped in it. This lets them determine average world temperatures and atmospheric carbon dioxide levels in the distant past. The graph shows their results.

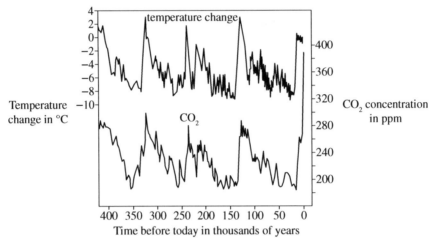

(a) Describe the relationship between average world temperatures and carbon dioxide levels, as shown by the graph.

> A positive gradient in the temperature change line shows that the average world temperature increased.

....

....

.... **(3 marks)**

(b) There has been a very large increase in carbon dioxide levels in the past few decades. Suggest a possible consequence of this for average temperatures.

....

.... **(1 mark)**

2 Carbon dioxide is a greenhouse gas. Increased levels of this gas in the atmosphere contribute to global warming.

(a) A different greenhouse gas is released because of human activities such as rice farming and cattle farming. Name this gas.

.... **(1 mark)**

Guided

(b) Describe what is meant by global warming.

an increase in the Earth's average ....

due to rising levels of .... **(2 marks)**

3 Global warming may cause climate change and increases in sea levels. Describe **one** biological consequence of global warming.

> Make sure that you answer in terms of its effects on living things.

....

.... **(1 mark)**

Maintaining biodiversity

1 Give **two** reasons, other than to ensure the stability of an ecosystem, why it is important to maintain biodiversity.

1 ....

2 .... **(2 marks)**

2 Hedgerows were originally planted to mark the boundaries of fields or to stop farm animals escaping. A typical hedgerow contains several different species of shrubs, and may also contain trees. Beginning in the middle of the last century, hedgerows were removed to form larger fields. It is estimated that the total length of hedgerows in England decreased by more than half in just 50 years.

(a) Suggest a reason why farmers wanted to increase the size of their fields.

> Think about the differences between modern farming and traditional farming.

....

.... **(1 mark)**

(b) Explain why removing hedgerows may reduce biodiversity.

> Do not just answer in terms of the hedgerow plants themselves.

....

....

....

.... **(2 marks)**

(c) Suggest a benefit of replanting hedgerows:

(i) to farmers

.... **(1 mark)**

(ii) to biodiversity.

.... **(1 mark)**

3 The area of woodland in the UK has increased from less than 5% of the land surface just over 100 years ago to over 12% today. Describe **two** benefits for the environment of reforestation such as this.

....

....

.... **(2 marks)**

4 Hedgehogs roam up to 2 km each night, looking for food. Explain why building small tunnels under new roads may help to conserve the numbers of hedgehogs.

> **Guided**

Hedgehogs may be run over by traffic if they ....

....

.... **(3 marks)**

Extended response – Ecology

The graph shows how the area of land being deforested in Brazil changed between 1992 and 2009.

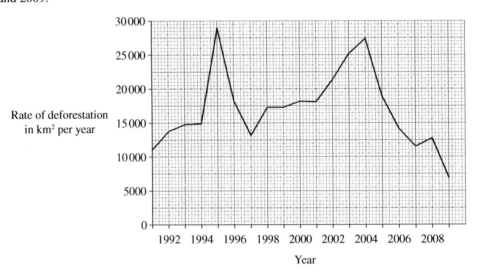

Rate of deforestation in km² per year

Year

It is estimated that about half the world's tropical forests have been cleared for farmland and timber. The remaining forests are estimated to store around 280 billion tonnes of carbon in their biomass.

Explain how deforestation can contribute to climate change.

> You will be more successful in extended response questions if you plan your answer before you start writing.
>
> You may wish to consider:
>
> - what the graph shows about how the area of forest has changed over time
> - the uses of the cleared land and the wood from the felled trees
> - relevant parts of the carbon cycle.
>
> Think about how climate change may be linked to these points.
>
> You should try to use the information given in the question.

....

....

....

....

....

....

....

....

....

....

.... **(6 marks)**

Elements, mixtures and compounds

1 Which substance is an element?

> Always answer multiple-choice questions, even if you don't actually know the answer.

Tick **one** box.

air ☐   iron sulfide ☐

copper ☐   water ☐   **(1 mark)**

2 The diagram shows particles present in three different substances. Circles represent atoms and different colours represent different elements.

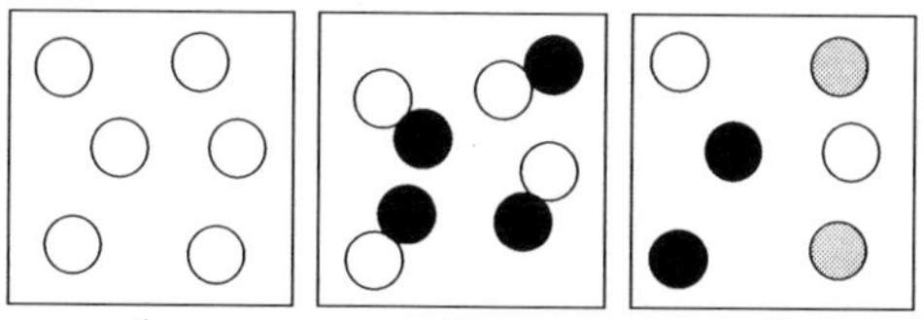

A   B   C

(a) Which box, A, B or C, represents a mixture of different elements? .... **(1 mark)**

(b) Which box, A, B or C, represents an element? .... **(1 mark)**

3 What is a compound?

Tick **one** box.

a substance made up of only one element ☐

a substance made up of two or more elements chemically joined together ☐

a substance made up of only metallic elements chemically joined together ☐

a substance made up of two or more elements physically mixed in a fixed ratio ☐   **(1 mark)**

4 Some symbols and formulae are given in the box below.

NaOH	Al_2O_3	H_2O	Na	S	NH_3	CO

Write a formula or symbol from the box for:

(a) a metallic element .... **(1 mark)**

(b) a compound containing four atoms .... **(1 mark)**

(c) a compound containing three different elements. .... **(1 mark)**

5 When a mixture of the elements iron and sulfur is heated, a compound is formed.

(a) Name the compound formed. .... **(1 mark)**

Guided

(b) Describe the difference between an element and a compound in terms of the atoms they contain.

An element contains one type of atom only. A compound ....

....

.... **(2 marks)**

Filtration, crystallisation and chromatography

 1 The diagram shows some different apparatus used to separate mixtures.

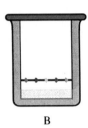

A   B   C

(a) Name the methods of separation that could be carried out using the apparatus in A, B and C.

A ....

B ....

> Remember: 15% of the marks for your GCSE
> are for questions on practical work.

C ....   **(3 marks)**

(b) Choose the most suitable apparatus (A, B or C shown in the diagram) for separating:

(i) sand from a mixture of sand and water   ....   **(1 mark)**

(ii) copper sulfate crystals from a copper sulfate solution   ....   **(1 mark)**

(iii) copper carbonate from a suspension of insoluble copper
carbonate and water   ....   **(1 mark)**

(iv) the different dyes in black ink   ....   **(1 mark)**

2 Rock salt is a mixture of insoluble sand and a soluble salt, sodium chloride.

> Insoluble means
> that the solid does
> not dissolve.

Guided

The steps needed to separate sodium chloride from rock salt are shown in the box. They are not in order.

| filtration   crystallisation / evaporation   addition of water   heating and stirring |

Place the steps in the order in which they must be carried out in the experiment.
Give a reason for each step.

step 1   addition of water

reason   to dissolve the sodium chloride

step 2 ....

reason ....

step 3 ....

reason ....

step 4 ....

reason .... **(5 marks)**

Distillation

1 What is the best method to get water from a salt solution?

Tick **one** box.

More than one of the methods can be used to obtain salt from a salt solution, but only one method obtains water.

(1 mark)

crystallisation ☐   evaporation ☐

distillation ☐   filtration ☐

2 Ethanol and water mix together completely. Ethanol and water have different boiling points.

(a) What is the boiling point of water?

.... **(1 mark)**

(b) Name a method of separation used to separate a mixture of ethanol and water.

Think about which method is used to separate a mixture of liquids.

.... **(1 mark)**

3 Two separation techniques are shown below. The diagrams are not labelled.

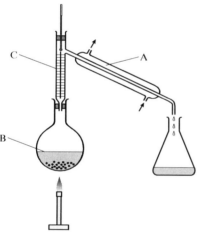
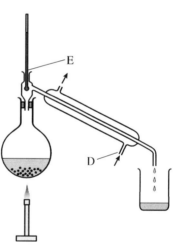

(a) What is the name of the technique carried out using the apparatus on the left?

.... **(1 mark)**

(b) What is the purpose of the piece of apparatus labelled **A**?

.... **(1 mark)**

(c) What change of state happens at **B**?

.... **(1 mark)**

(d) No labels have been included in the diagrams. Name the labels that should be placed at:

Practical skills It is important that you know how to label diagrams for all methods of separation.

C ....

D ....

E ....   **(3 marks)**

(e) Name a different way of heating the apparatus shown in the diagrams.

.... **(1 mark)**   **85**

Historical models of the atom

1 The 'plum pudding' model of an atom, as shown below, suggested that the atom was a charged ball.

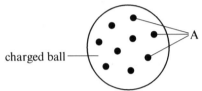

charged ball ——

(a) What type of charge was thought to be on the ball in the plum pudding model?

.... **(1 mark)**

(b) Name particle A in the diagram.

.... **(1 mark)**

〉**Guided**〉 (c) New evidence about atoms meant that the nuclear model has now replaced the plum pudding model. Describe the nuclear model of an atom.

The atom has a nucleus which contains ....

....

.... **(2 marks)**

2 The diagram shows Bohr's model of an atom.

(a) What is the name for the part of the atom labelled A?

.... **(1 mark)**

(b) What is the charge of the part of the atom labelled A?

.... **(1 mark)**

> Remember one particle had not been discovered at the time of Bohr's model.

(c) Name the type of particle found in A.

.... **(1 mark)**

(d) What is the name for the particle labelled B?

.... **(1 mark)**

3 Which scientist discovered the neutron?

Tick **one** box.

Bohr   ☐   Einstein   ☐

Chadwick   ☐   Rutherford   ☐   **(1 mark)**

Particles in an atom

1 (a) What is the symbol for the element calcium? Use the periodic table on page 260 to help you answer this question.

.... **(1 mark)**

(b) What is the atomic number of calcium?

.... **(1 mark)**

2 An atom of sodium has an atomic number of 11 and a mass number of 23.

(a) Define mass number.

.... **(1 mark)**

(b) In terms of subatomic particles, why has a sodium atom no overall charge?

....

.... **(1 mark)**

(c) Give the number of protons, neutrons and electrons in this atom of sodium.

number of protons ....

number of neutrons ....

number of electrons .... **(3 marks)**

> Remember for an atom the number of protons equals the number of electrons.
> To find the number of neutrons subtract the atomic number from the mass number.

(d) Name the two subatomic particles found in the nucleus of a sodium atom.

.... **(1 mark)**

3 (a) Complete the table below to give the number of protons, neutrons and electrons in each of four different atoms, A, B, C and D.

Atom	Atomic number	Mass number	Number of electrons	Number of neutrons	Number of protons
A	27	59	27	59 − 27 = 32	27
B	28	59			
C	13	27			
D	19	39			

(4 marks)

> **Guided**

(b) Use the periodic table on page 260 to give the name of each atom.

A *cobalt*

B ....

C ....

D ....

> The atomic number identifies an atom.
> For A the atomic number is 27, which is cobalt.

(4 marks)

Atomic structure and isotopes

1 An atom of potassium has the symbol $^{39}_{19}$K.

(a) Complete the table to show the relative mass and charge of each particle present in a potassium atom.

Particle	Relative mass	Relative charge
electron		
neutron		
proton		

(3 marks)

> Remember that number of protons = number of electrons.
> Remember also that number of neutrons = mass number minus atomic number.

(b) Give the number of protons, neutrons and electrons in this atom of potassium.

number of protons ....

number of neutrons ....

number of electrons ....   **(3 marks)**

(c) State the approximate radius of a potassium atom.

Give your answer in metres.

....   **(1 mark)**

(d) Another atom of potassium has the symbol $^{41}_{19}$K. Explain why atoms of $^{41}_{19}$K and $^{39}_{19}$K are isotopes.

....

....   **(2 marks)**

2 Carbon has two naturally occurring isotopes, ^{12}C and ^{13}C.

(a) Why are ^{12}C and ^{13}C isotopes?

Tick **one** box.

They are atoms of the same element with a different number of electrons.   ☐

They are atoms with the same atomic number and a different number of neutrons.   ☐

They are atoms with a different atomic number and a different number of neutrons.   ☐

They are atoms of the same element with a different number of protons.   ☐   **(1 mark)**

> **Guided**

(b) Use the information about the two isotopes of carbon in the table below to calculate the relative atomic mass of carbon to one decimal place.

Mass number	12	13
Abundance	99	1

> **Maths skills** Remember, when rounding to one decimal place, if the second decimal place number is five or more, round up.

$$\text{relative atomic mass} = \frac{(\text{mass number isotope 1} \times \text{abundance}) + (\text{mass number isotope 2} \times \text{abundance})}{\text{total abundance}}$$

$$= \frac{(12 \times 99) + \text{................}}{(99 + 1)} = \text{................}$$ **(2 marks)**

Electronic structure

1 Which element has an electronic structure of 2,5?

Tick **one** box.

oxygen ☐   nitrogen ☐   silicon ☐   sulfur ☐

(1 mark)

2 Complete the energy level (shell) diagrams for the elements with the following number of electrons.

Guided

13 electrons   17 electrons   20 electrons

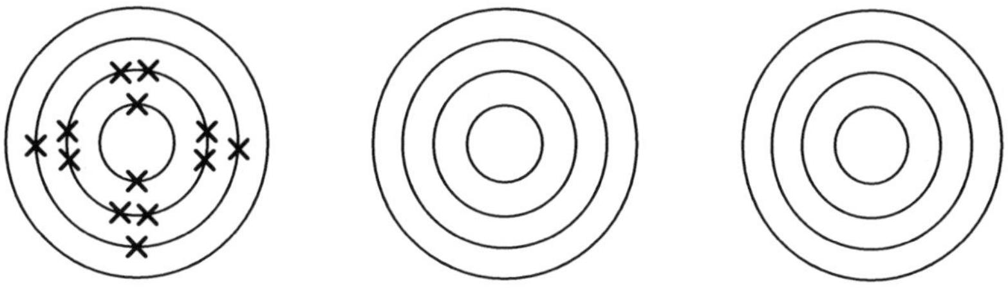

(3 marks)

3 Use the periodic table on page 260 to help you answer this question.

The diagram shows the electron structure of the atoms of an element.

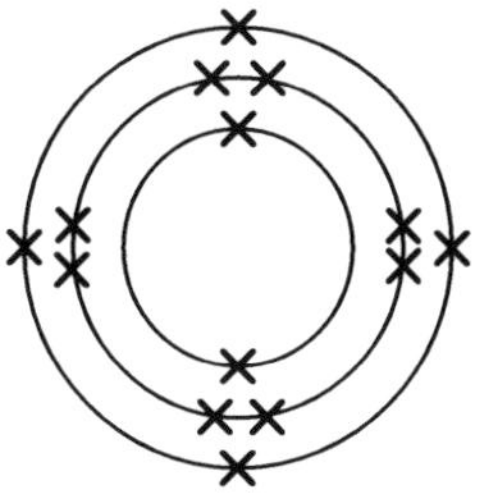

> To find the number of neutrons, you need to get the mass number from the periodic table and subtract the atomic number from it.

(a) What is the name and atomic number of this element?

.... **(2 marks)**

(b) Give the number of protons and electrons in the atoms of this element.

.... **(1 mark)**

(c) What other information is needed to allow us to work out the number of neutrons in the nucleus of the atoms?

.... **(1 mark)**

4 The electronic structure of magnesium can be written as 2,8,2. Write the electronic structures for the following elements in the same way.

(a) potassium .... **(1 mark)**

(b) phosphorus .... **(1 mark)**

(c) calcium .... **(1 mark)**

Development of the periodic table

1 Below is part of Mendeleev's periodic table. Mendeleev left gaps in the table, marked by an asterisk (*).

H						
Li	Be	B	C	N	O	F
Na	Mg	Al	Si	P	S	Cl
K Cu	Ca Zn	* *	Ti *	V As	Cr Se	Mn Br
Rb Ag	Sr Cd	Y In	Zr Sn	Nb Sb	Mo Te	* I

(a) How many groups are in Mendeleev's periodic table?

.... **(1 mark)**

(b) Name a group in the modern periodic table that is not present in Mendeleev's periodic table.

.... **(1 mark)**

(c) Give **one** difference between Group 1 in Mendeleev's periodic table and Group 1 in the modern periodic table.

.... **(1 mark)**

(d) Give **two** differences between Mendeleev's periodic table and the modern periodic table.

....

.... **(2 marks)**

(e) The element in the fourth column marked by an asterisk (*) has the atomic number 32. Name this element.

> Each element in the periodic table has two numbers; the atomic number is the smaller one of the two. On the periodic table on page 260 find the element that has the atomic number 32.

.... **(1 mark)**

(f) Complete the sentence below by choosing the two most appropriate words from the list.

allotropes	isotopes	number	protons	mass	weight

The order of elements in Mendeleev's table is similar but not the same as in the modern periodic table.

> The modern periodic table is organised in order of atomic number.

Knowledge of .... made it

possible to explain why the order based on atomic .... was not

always correct. **(2 marks)**

2 Mendeleev listed the elements in his periodic table in an order. Which property did he use to list the elements?

Tick **one** box.

atomic number ☐   mass number ☐

atomic weight ☐   number of neutrons ☐   **(1 mark)**

The modern periodic table

1   The periodic table contains metals and non-metals.

(a)   Classify the elements below as metals or non-metals.

barium ....

potassium ....

phosphorus .... **(3 marks)**

(b)   Name a metal that is a liquid at room temperature.

.... **(1 mark)**

(c)   Use the periodic table on page 260 to help you complete the table below.

Element	Group number	Number of electrons in outer shell
calcium		
fluorine		

(4 marks)

2   How are elements arranged in the modern periodic table?

Tick **one** box.

by increasing atomic number ☐   by increasing number of neutrons ☐

by increasing mass number ☐   by increasing reactivity ☐   **(1 mark)**

3   The diagram shows the position of six
different elements in the periodic table.
The letters do not represent the symbols
for the elements.

Use the letters in the diagram to answer
the questions below.

(a)   Identify **two** metals with the same number of electrons in
the outer shell of their atoms.

> Remember that metals are found
> on the left of the periodic table.

.... **(1 mark)**

(b)   Identify a halogen.

.... **(1 mark)**

(c)   Identify a non-metal that has five electrons in the outer shell of its atoms.

.... **(1 mark)**

4   Group 3 of the periodic table contains the elements boron, aluminium and gallium.

(a)   Why do these three elements have similar chemical properties?

.... **(1 mark)**

Guided

(b)   Which of boron, aluminium and gallium has the lowest number of protons in the nucleus?

The element with the smallest atomic number is ....

The atomic number gives the number of protons, so the element with the lowest

number of protons is .... **(1 mark)**

Group 0

1   Neon is a noble gas. The atomic number of neon is 10.

(a) Write the electronic structure of neon.

   .... **(1 mark)**

(b) Use your answer to part (a) to explain why neon is unreactive.

   .... **(1 mark)**

2   Which of the electronic structures below is the structure of an atom of a noble gas?

Tick **one** box.

2 ☐   2,2 ☐   2,8,2 ☐   2,8,7 ☐   **(1 mark)**

3   The table below shows some properties of the noble gases.

Element	Boiling point in °C	Density in g/dm³	Relative atomic mass
helium	−269	0.2	4
neon	−246	0.9	20
argon	−190		40
krypton		3.8	84
xenon	−111	5.9	131

(a) What is the group number of the noble gases?

   .... **(1 mark)**

(b) Predict the boiling point of krypton.

   .... **(1 mark)**

(c) What is the relationship between boiling point and relative atomic mass?

   ....

   .... **(1 mark)**

(d) Estimate the density of argon.

   > Look at the general trend in density. You are asked for an estimate, so a value halfway between 0.9 and 3.8 is a good idea.

   .... **(1 mark)**

(e) Write the electronic structures of helium and neon.

   .... **(2 marks)**

> Guided

4   Why do the atoms of noble gases not easily form molecules?

Tick **one** box.

~~They all have 8 electrons in their outer shell.~~   ☐

They have a full outer shell and are stable.   ☐

They only form covalent bonds.   ☐

Their reactivity decreases down the group.   ☐   **(1 mark)**

> The first answer in this guided question has been crossed out. This is because it is untrue – helium is a noble gas and it has only 2 electrons in its outer shell.

Group 1

1   Some of the elements of Group 1 are listed below.

lithium	sodium	potassium	rubidium

(a) Which metal is the most reactive?

.... **(1 mark)**

(b) Which metal reacts with oxygen to give K_2O?

.... **(1 mark)**

(c) Which metal has the electronic structure 2,8,1?

.... **(1 mark)**

2   Two elements in Group 1 of the periodic table are lithium and potassium.

(a) Explain why lithium and potassium are both in Group 1 of the periodic table. Your answer should be in terms of their electronic structures.

....

.... **(1 mark)**

(b) Very small pieces of lithium and potassium are separately allowed to react with water.

(i) Describe the similarities and differences in what is observed.

....

....

....

....

....

.... **(4 marks)**

(ii) Name the products for the reaction of potassium with water.

.... **(2 marks)**

3   Sodium is a Group 1 metal that reacts with non-metals.

(a) Complete the word equations for some reactions of sodium.

sodium + chlorine → ....

sodium + oxygen → .... **(2 marks)**

> **Guided**

(b) Sodium reacts with water to produce sodium hydroxide and hydrogen.

(i) Balance the equation for this reaction.

.............Na + ...H_2O → $2NaOH + H_2$ **(1 mark)**

(ii) Name the ion that makes the final solution alkaline.

.... **(1 mark)**

> Remember how to balance equations. First a 2 is placed in front of the NaOH. Now there are two oxygens on the right of the equation. Balance the oxygen on the left – you must put a number in front of the H_2O. Then balance the Na.

Group 7

1   What is the name for Group 7 in the periodic table?

Tick **one** box.

alkali metals ☐   noble gases ☐

halogens ☐   transition metals ☐   **(1 mark)**

2   Group 7 elements react with Group 1 metals such as sodium and potassium.

(a) Write a word equation for the reaction of sodium with bromine.

....   **(1 mark)**

(b) How many electrons are in the outer shell of bromine?

> Remember, you do not need to write the electronic structure for this –
> the group number is all that you need.

....   **(1 mark)**

(c) Balance the equation for the reaction of potassium with chlorine.

.........K + Cl$_2$ → ....KCl   **(1 mark)**

(d) Name the product KCl.

....   **(1 mark)**

3   The table shows the results of adding halogens to solutions of halide ions.

Guided

Halogen	Sodium chloride solution	Sodium bromide solution	Sodium iodide solution
chlorine		orange solution produced	brown solution produced
bromine	no reaction		brown solution produced
iodine	no reaction	no reaction	

(a) Explain why there is no reaction between sodium chloride and bromine.

Reactivity decreases down the group and so bromine is less reactive than ....

....

....   **(2 marks)**

(b) Complete the word equation for the reaction between chlorine and sodium iodide.

chlorine + sodium iodide → ....   **(1 mark)**

(c) Give the name of the type of reaction in part (b).

....   **(1 mark)**

(d) What does the information in the table show about the trend in reactivity of the halogens?

....

....   **(1 mark)**

Chemical equations

1 Complete the word equations.

(a) potassium + chlorine → ....

(b) magnesium + oxygen → ....

(c) hydrogen + bromine → ....

(d) copper + oxygen → .... **(4 marks)**

2 The chemical equation for the reaction between methane and oxygen is shown below.

$$CH_4 + 2O_2 \rightarrow CO_2 + 2H_2O$$

(a) Describe this reaction between methane and oxygen in terms of the names of the substances and the number of molecules involved.

One molecule of methane reacts..

.... **(2 marks)**

(b) When 4 g of methane burns, 11 g of carbon dioxide and 9 g of water are produced.

What mass of oxygen was needed to react with the 4 g of methane?

mass of products = 11 + 9

= 20 g

mass of oxygen   = ... g

> Remember: no atoms are gained or lost during a chemical reaction, so the total mass of reactants used up will always equal the total mass of products formed.

(1 mark)

3 Balance the following equations.

(a) .....Mg + ...O_2 → .....MgO   **(1 mark)**

(b) .....HCl + ...Ca → .....$CaCl_2$ + ...H_2 **(1 mark)**

(c) .....N_2 + ...H_2 → .....NH_3 **(1 mark)**

(d) .....SO_2 + ...O_2 → .....SO_3 **(1 mark)**

(e) .....H_2 + ...F_2 → .....HF   **(1 mark)**

4 Sodium metal burns in oxygen to form sodium oxide.

$$...............Na + O_2 \rightarrow ....Na_2O$$

(a) Balance the above symbol equation for the reaction of sodium and oxygen.   **(2 marks)**

(b) Potassium burns in oxygen in a similar way to sodium.

> Remember that oxygen is diatomic. Work out the formula of potassium oxide first.

Write a balanced symbol equation for the reaction of potassium and oxygen.

.... **(2 marks)**

5 $C_2H_5OH + yO_2 \rightarrow 2CO_2 + 3H_2O$

What is the value of y in the equation above?

Tick **one** box.

2 ☐   3 ☐   3½ ☐   6 ☐   **(1 mark)**

Extended response – Atomic structure

 Describe the trend in reactivity down Group 1 and Group 7 of the periodic table.

> You will be more successful in extended response questions if you plan your answer before you start writing.
>
> The question asks you to explain, so make sure that you do this by considering the outer shell electrons of the atoms in each group. Do the atoms need to gain or lose electrons?

....

....

....

....

....

....

....

....

....

....

....

....

....

....

....

....

....

....

....

....

....

.... **(6 marks)**

> Check your answer and make sure that you have fully answered the question.
>
> Make sure that you have answered for both groups.

Forming bonds

1 What holds the ions in sodium chloride together?

Tick **one** box.

covalent bonds ☐   metallic bonds ☐

electrostatic forces ☐   magnetic forces ☐   **(1 mark)**

2 (a) Complete the table by inserting each of the elements listed below into the correct column.

> **Guided**

| chlorine   oxygen   hydrogen   calcium   magnesium   sulfur   nitrogen |

Metal	Non-metal
	chlorine

Find chlorine on the periodic table on page 260 – it is on the right of the periodic table so it is a non-metal. Now find oxygen on the periodic table.

(2 marks)

(b) Complete the table by ticking (✓) the correct type of bonding in the compound.

Ionic bonding occurs in compounds formed from metals combined with non-metals.
Covalent bonding occurs in most non-metal elements and compounds.

Compound	Ionic bonding	Covalent bonding
calcium oxide	✓	
hydrogen chloride		
hydrogen sulfide		
magnesium chloride		

(4 marks)

3 The diagram shows the bonding in a compound of nitrogen and hydrogen.

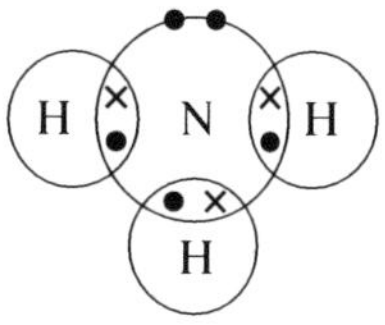

(a) Write the formula of the compound shown in the diagram.

....

(1 mark)

(b) Name and describe the type of bonding shown in the diagram.

....

.... **(2 marks)**

(c) What type of bonding is represented in the diagram to the right?

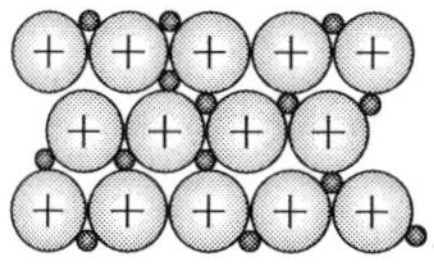

....

(1 mark)

4 Which pair of elements forms a covalent compound?

Tick **one** box.

lithium and chlorine ☐   nitrogen and hydrogen ☐

magnesium and oxygen ☐   potassium and bromine ☐   **(1 mark)**

Ionic bonding

1 What is the charge on an oxide ion?

> Oxygen has atomic number 8 so its electronic structure is 2,6. Now work out how many electrons it needs to lose or gain to obtain a full outer shell.

Tick **one** box.

1– ☐   2– ☐

1+ ☐   2+ ☐   **(1 mark)**

2 (a) Write the electronic structure of a sodium atom.

.... **(1 mark)**

(b) Write the electronic structure of a sodium ion.

.... **(1 mark)**

3 What happens when calcium reacts with chlorine to form calcium chloride?

Tick **one** box.

Each chlorine atom loses one electron. ☐

Each chlorine atom gains one electron. ☐

Each calcium atom gains one electron. ☐

Each calcium atom gains two electrons. ☐   **(1 mark)**

4 Sodium forms an ionic compound with oxygen. Describe what happens when two atoms of sodium react with one atom of oxygen. Give the formulae of the ions formed.

> **Guided**

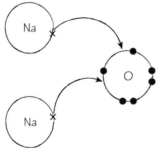

> You need to work out the number of electrons in the outer shell of each atom, and think about their transfer, as shown in the diagram. Then describe in words where the electrons transfer from and to, and how many electrons are involved.

Two sodium atoms each lose ....

....

....

....

....

....

....

....

....

.... **(5 marks)**

Giant ionic lattices

1   Sodium chloride is an ionic compound. Tick (✓) two properties of ionic compounds.

Property	Tick
usually dissolve in water	
high melting point	
low boiling point	
never conduct electricity	

(2 marks)

2   What surrounds each sodium ion in a sodium chloride crystal?

Tick **one** box.

one chloride ion ☐

two chloride ions ☐

four chloride ions ☐

six chloride ions ☐

(1 mark)

3   The structure of caesium chloride can be represented using the ball-and-stick model shown in the diagram.

(a)   What type of bonding is found in caesium chloride?

.... **(1 mark)**

(b)   What is the name for this type of structure?

.... **(1 mark)**

(c)   The ball-and-stick model is not a good representation of an ionic compound.

Give one reason why. | Think about how the ions fit together in the crystal. |

....

.... **(1 mark)**

(d)   What holds the ions together in caesium chloride?

....

.... **(2 marks)**

Guided   (e)   Why does calcium chloride solid not conduct electricity?

The ions are held tightly in the ....

.... **(2 marks)**

Covalent bonding

1 The dot-and-cross diagrams of some molecules are shown below.

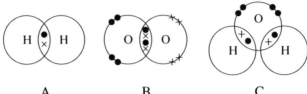

A   B   C

(a) Which substance, A, B or C, contains a double covalent bond?

.... **(1 mark)**

(b) Which substance, A, B or C, contains no lone pairs?

.... **(1 mark)**

(c) Which substance, A, B or C, contains two lone pairs?

.... **(1 mark)**

(d) What is the name of substance C?

.... **(1 mark)**

2 Complete the dot-and-cross diagram to show the bonding in a molecule of hydrogen chloride. Show the outer shell electrons only.

H ( ) **Cl**

(2 marks)

3 A dot-and-cross diagram for the bonding in a molecule of the gas phosphine is shown below.

> Remember that a lone pair is an unbonded pair of electrons and a covalent bond is a shared pair of electrons.

(a) Complete the diagram by labelling:

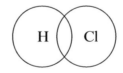

(i) a lone pair **(1 mark)**

(ii) a covalent bond. **(1 mark)**

(b) Give the formula of phosphine.

.... **(1 mark)**

(c) Is phosphine a compound or an element?

.... **(1 mark)**

(d) What is a covalent bond?

.... **(1 mark)**

Small molecules

1 Phosphine (PH_3) is a gas made of small molecules.

(a) Name the type of bonding in phosphine.

.... **(1 mark)**

(b) Explain if phosphine conducts electricity.

> To conduct electricity, free electrons or ions are needed to carry the charge. Are there any in phosphine?

....

.... **(2 marks)**

2 The molecules of two chlorine compounds are shown below.

A   B

(a) Write the molecular formula of the compound shown in:

(i) A .... **(1 mark)**

(ii) B .... **(1 mark)**

(b) Draw a diagram of the compound in diagram A above. Use letters to represent the atoms and a
   line to represent each single bond.

(1 mark)

3 Complete the dot-and-cross diagram to represent the
   compound ammonia NH_3. Show outer electrons only
   and the hydrogen electrons as crosses.

> Nitrogen has atomic number 7 and electronic
> structure 2,5. The 5 outer electrons of nitrogen
> are shown. Hydrogen has atomic number 1 and
> electronic structure 1. To complete NH_3, use
> the outer electron on each of the 3 hydrogen
> atoms so that nitrogen has a full outer shell of
> 8 electrons.

$$\bullet\bullet$$
$$\bullet \quad N \quad \bullet$$
$$\bullet$$

(1 mark)

4 Why does hydrogen chloride have a low boiling point?

Tick **one** box.

It is covalently bonded. ☐   The covalent bonds between the atoms are weak. ☐

It is ionically bonded. ☐   The forces between the molecules are weak. ☐ **(1 mark)**

Polymer molecules

1 (a) What is a polymer?

....

.... **(1 mark)**

(b) Name the elements present in the polymer shown in the diagram below.

$$-\overset{\displaystyle F}{\underset{\displaystyle F}{C}}-\overset{\displaystyle F}{\underset{\displaystyle F}{C}}-\overset{\displaystyle F}{\underset{\displaystyle F}{C}}-\overset{\displaystyle F}{\underset{\displaystyle F}{C}}-\overset{\displaystyle F}{\underset{\displaystyle F}{C}}-\overset{\displaystyle F}{\underset{\displaystyle F}{C}}-$$

.... **(2 marks)**

(c) What type of bonding is present between the atoms in the polymer shown in the diagram above?

.... **(1 mark)**

2 Draw the bonds to complete the displayed formula of the polymer PVC shown in the diagram below.

> Remember that this is just the repeating unit and the bonds need to go through the brackets to represent this.

$$\begin{bmatrix} \overset{\displaystyle H}{\underset{\displaystyle H}{C}} - \overset{\displaystyle H}{\underset{\displaystyle Cl}{C}} \end{bmatrix}_n$$

(1 mark)

3 Circle the correct word to complete the sentences below.

> **Guided**

Polymers have very **large** / **small** molecules.

The **atoms** / **ions** in the polymer molecules are linked to others by **strong** / **weak** covalent bonds.

The intermolecular forces between polymer molecules are relatively **strong** / **weak** and so these substances are solids at room temperature.

(4 marks)

4 The structure of poly(ethene) is represented in the diagram.

$$\begin{bmatrix} \overset{\displaystyle H}{\underset{\displaystyle H}{C}} - \overset{\displaystyle H}{\underset{\displaystyle H}{C}} \end{bmatrix}_n \leftarrow B$$

(a) What does n represent?

.... **(1 mark)**

(b) What label should be placed at B?

.... **(1 mark)**

(c) In what physical state does this polymer exist at room temperature and pressure?

.... **(1 mark)**

Diamond and graphite

1 The diagram shows the structure of an element.
What is the name of this element?

Tick **one** box.

argon ☐   carbon ☐

calcium ☐   silver ☐

(1 mark)

2 Why does the element in the diagram for question **1** not conduct electricity?

Tick **one** box.

It has covalent bonds. ☐   It has ionic bonds. ☐

It has no free electrons or ions. ☐   It has a rigid shape. ☐   **(1 mark)**

3 Many substances have giant covalent structures or simple molecular structures.

Choose the correct structure, giant covalent or simple molecular, for each of the following substances.

> Your specification only expects you to know of three giant covalent structures: graphite, diamond and silicon dioxide.

ammonia ....

carbon dioxide ....

diamond ....

silicon dioxide ....

water .... **(5 marks)**

4 The diagram shows the structure of graphite.
Complete the diagram by inserting the correct labels.

> Guided

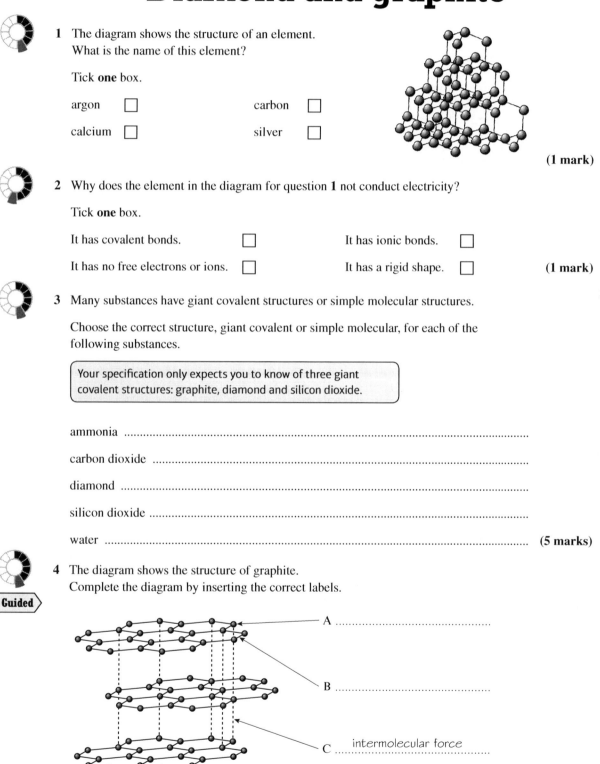

A ....

B ....

C intermolecular force ....

(3 marks)

Graphene and fullerenes

1 Tick (✓) **two** correct statements about graphene.

Statement	Tick (✓)
Graphene is a cylindrical fullerene.	
Graphene is a single layer of graphite.	
Graphene has rings of five carbon atoms.	
Graphene has hexagonal rings of carbon.	

(2 marks)

2 Which structure is shown in the diagram?

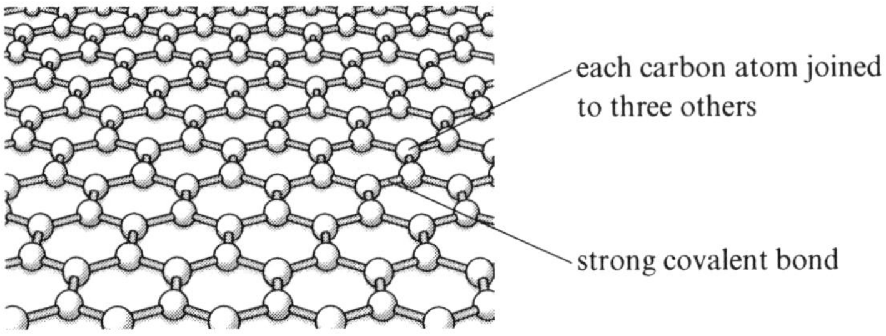

each carbon atom joined to three others

strong covalent bond

Tick **one** box.

buckminsterfullerene ☐   graphene ☐

diamond ☐   graphite ☐   **(1 mark)**

3 Fullerenes are molecules of carbon atoms with hollow shapes. The structure of fullerenes is based on rings of carbon atoms.

(a) How many carbon atoms do most rings of a fullerene contain? Choose **two** numbers from the box.

4	5	6	7	8	20	60

(1 mark)

⟩ **Guided** ⟩   (b) Name two fullerenes.

    carbon nanotubes and .... **(2 marks)**

4 The diagram shows the structure of a type of cylindrical fullerene.

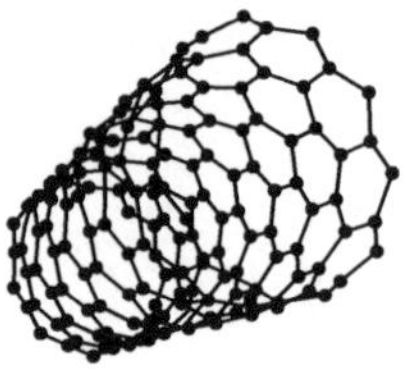

(a) Name this type of fullerene.

.... **(1 mark)**

⟩ **Guided** ⟩   (b) Complete the sentence below about the fullerene in the diagram.

    This fullerene is a .... conductor of electricity and has a ....

    tensile strength. **(2 marks)**

> To successfully answer questions on this topic you need to remember that the molecules are all made of carbon and try to remember their shapes – graphene (layer), fullerene (sphere) and nanotubes (cylinder).

Metallic bonding

1 (a) In which way are the atoms arranged in a metal?

Tick **one** box.

in a sphere ☐   in a hexagon shape ☐

in layers ☐   in a tetrahedral arrangement ☐   **(1 mark)**

(b) The electrons in the outer shell of metal atoms are free to move through the whole structure. What term is used to describe this?

.... **(1 mark)**

2 The diagram shows the structure of the metal sodium.

(a) Describe the structure of the metal sodium.

....

....

.... **(2 marks)**

(b) What is a metallic bond?

....

....

.... **(2 marks)**

3 The table below gives some properties of the metal calcium and one of its compounds, calcium chloride.

Property	Calcium	Calcium chloride
Melting point in °C	842	772
Electrical conductivity when solid	conducts	does not conduct
Electrical conductivity when molten	conducts	conducts

Remember there are three types of strong bonding – metallic, ionic and covalent.

(a) Name the type of bonding found in:

(i) calcium .... **(1 mark)**

(ii) calcium chloride .... **(1 mark)**

(b) Apart from its melting point and electrical conductivity, suggest one other physical property of calcium.

.... **(1 mark)**

Had a go ☐ **Nearly there** ☐ **Nailed it!** ☐

Giant metallic structures and alloys

1 Gold (Au) is the most malleable metal.

(a) (i) What does **malleable** mean?

Tick **one** box.

can be drawn into a wire ☐   can conduct electricity ☐

can be hammered into shape ☐   is shiny ☐   **(1 mark)**

(ii) Why can gold conduct electricity?

Tick **one** box.

It contains ions that can move. ☐   It contains delocalised electrons. ☐

It has covalent bonding. ☐   It has layers of atoms. ☐   **(1 mark)**

> **Guided**

(iii) Give the name and the number present of each particle found in the nucleus of a gold atom. You may find the periodic table on page 260 useful.

> The number of protons equals the number of electrons in an atom, and equals the atomic number.

protons ....

> The mass number minus the atomic number equals the number of neutrons.

.... **(2 marks)**

(b) Pure gold is very soft. It is often alloyed with other metals, such as copper or silver, for use in jewellery.

Explain, in terms of its structure, why an alloy is harder than a pure metal.

....

....

.... **(2 marks)**

2 The figure shows an alloy made of metals A and B.

Ⓐ
Ⓑ

> **Maths skills**   Percentage of atom A =
> $$\frac{\text{number of atom A}}{\text{total number of atoms}} \times 100$$

What percentage of the atoms in the alloy are atom A?

....

....

Percentage of atom A = ... **(2 marks)**

The three states of matter

> Melting point is the temperature at which a solid changes to a liquid, and boiling point is the temperature at which a liquid changes to a gas.

1 The table below shows the melting point and boiling point of four substances, W, X, Y and Z.

Substance	Melting point in °C	Boiling point in °C
W	−95	9
X	325	1755
Y	800	1412
Z	−38	356

What state is each of the substances in at room temperature (20 °C)?

W ....

X ....

Y ....

Z .... **(4 marks)**

2 The diagram shows the arrangement of particles in a solid, in a liquid and in a gas.

> Guided

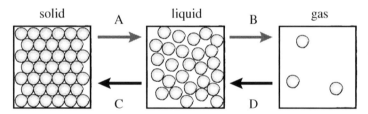

(a) Name each change of state, A, B, C and D.

A melting ....

B ....

C ....

D .... **(4 marks)**

(b) Describe what happens to the movement and arrangement of the particles when the solid is heated until it changes to a liquid.

....

....

....

.... **(2 marks)**

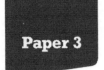

Extended response – Bonding and structure

 Copper is a metal. Some of the physical properties of copper are shown in the table below.

Physical properties of copper
high melting point
good conductor of electricity
good conductor of heat
soft and malleable

Explain, in terms of structure and bonding, the physical properties of copper.

> You will be more successful in extended response questions if you plan your answer before you start writing.
>
> Before you begin, think about the type of bonding present in copper and the type of particles that make up the structure. Make sure that you use the correct terminology in your answer.
>
> You should try to use the information given in the question.

....

....

....

....

....

....

....

....

....

....

....

....

....

....

....

....

....

.... **(6 marks)**

> When you have finished your answer, read it through and tick each of the physical properties you have explained to ensure that you have not left any out.

Relative formula mass

Use the periodic table on page 260 to help answer the following questions.

1 Calculate the relative formula mass of each substance in the table.

> You need to look up the relative atomic mass of each element in the periodic table – it is the larger of the two numbers.

Substance	Relative formula mass
Cl_2	
HF	
NaOH	
K_2O	

(4 marks)

2 Calculate the relative formula mass (M_r) of the following:

> **Guided**

(a) sodium oxide, Na_2O

   Na_2O

   $\longrightarrow$ 1 × 16 = 16

   $\longrightarrow$ 2 × 23 = ...

   M_r = ... **(1 mark)**

(b) sucrose, molecular formula = $C_{12}H_{22}O_{11}$

   M_r = ... **(1 mark)**

(c) ethyl ethanoate, structural formula =

```
    H   O      H   H
    |   ||     |   |
H — C — C — O — C — C — H
    |          |   |
    H          H   H
```

   M_r = ... **(1 mark)**

(d) sulfuric acid, H_2SO_4

   M_r = ... **(1 mark)**

(e) calcium nitrate, $Ca(NO_3)_2$

> **Maths skills** Remember that brackets mean you multiply everything inside the brackets by the number outside – there are 2 N atoms and 6 O atoms.

   M_r = ... **(1 mark)**

(f) aluminium sulfate, $Al_2(SO_4)_3$

   M_r = ... **(1 mark)**

Balanced equations and masses

1 An antacid tablet for indigestion contains sodium hydrogen carbonate and citric acid. When added to water the tablet fizzes as the sodium hydrogen carbonate reacts with the citric acid to produce a salt, called a citrate.

(a) (i) Complete the word equation for the formation of a salt, carbon dioxide and water from citric acid:

> Remember to name the salt.

sodium hydrogen carbonate + citric acid →

.... + ... + ... **(1 mark)**

(ii) Use the equation in part (a)(i) to explain what causes the fizz.

.... **(1 mark)**

(b) In an experiment an antacid tablet is added to $50\,cm^3$ of water in a conical flask. The flask is loosely stoppered with a cotton-wool plug and placed on a balance. The initial reading is $103.261\,g$.

Guided

(i) Draw a labelled diagram of the apparatus.

> The balance has been drawn for you. Read the description and think of the other things you need to draw.

top-pan balance

(3 marks)

(ii) Why did the balance reading decrease?

Tick **one** box.

A The tablet broke down. ☐   **C** A gas was lost from the flask. ☐

B A salt was produced in the reaction. ☐   **D** Water was produced in the reaction. ☐

(1 mark)

2 Copper carbonate and hydrochloric acid react as shown in the equation:

$$CuCO_3 + 2HCl \rightarrow CuCl_2 + H_2O + CO_2$$

(a) Complete the table.

Reactant	Relative formula mass	Product	Relative formula mass
$CuCO_3$		$CuCl_2$	
HCl		H_2O	
		CO_2	

(5 marks)

Guided

(b) Use your calculated values in part (a) to show that the equation for the reaction is balanced.

> 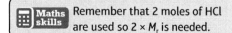 Remember that 2 moles of HCl are used so $2 \times M_r$ is needed.

total formula mass of reactants =..

....

.... **(2 marks)**

Concentration of a solution

1 Sea water contains dissolved salts.

Which row (**A**, **B**, **C** or **D**) correctly describes the components of sea water? Tick **one** box.

A ☐
B ☐
C ☐
D ☐

	Solute	Solvent	Solution
A	water	salt	sea water
B	salt	sea water	water
C	sea water	salt	water
D	salt	water	sea water

(1 mark)

Guided

2 Calculate the following volumes in dm^3:

$\boxed{\text{Maths skills}}$ $1\,dm^3 = 1000\,cm^3$

(a) $2500\,cm^3$

$volume = \dfrac{2500}{1000} = $ .... dm^3

(1 mark)

(b) $500\,cm^3$

.... **(1 mark)**

(c) $25\,cm^3$

.... **(1 mark)**

3 Calculate the concentrations of the following solutions in g/dm^3:

(a) $50\,g$ of sodium hydroxide dissolved in $2\,dm^3$ of water

.... **(1 mark)**

(b) $14.6\,g$ of hydrogen chloride dissolved in $0.400\,dm^3$ of water

.... **(1 mark)**

(c) $0.25\,g$ of glucose dissolved in $0.050\,dm^3$ of water.

.... **(1 mark)**

Guided

4 A student dissolves $10\,g$ of copper sulfate in $250\,cm^3$ of water. Calculate the concentration of the solution formed in g/dm^3.

$concentration = \left(\dfrac{10}{250}\right) \times 1000 = $ .... **(1 mark)**

5 A student dissolves $2.0\,g$ of silver nitrate in $125\,cm^3$ of water. Calculate the concentration of the solution formed in g/dm^3.

.... **(1 mark)**

6 A school technician wants to make $2.5\,dm^3$ of a $40\,g/dm^3$ aqueous solution of sodium hydroxide.

(a) Describe the meaning of the term '**aqueous solution**'.

.... **(1 mark)**

(b) Calculate the mass of sodium hydroxide that the technician must dissolve to make her solution.

....

....

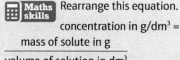

$\boxed{\text{Maths skills}}$ Rearrange this equation.

concentration in $g/dm^3 = \dfrac{\text{mass of solute in g}}{\text{volume of solution in } dm^3}$

.... **(1 mark)**

Extended response – Quantitative chemistry

Copper carbonate thermally decomposes. Plan an experiment to show that when 0.62 g of copper carbonate is heated, 0.22 g of carbon dioxide gas is produced.

> You will be more successful in extended response questions if you plan your answer before you start writing.
>
> Remember that thermal decomposition means breaking down a substance using heat.
>
> copper carbonate(s) → copper oxide(s) + carbon dioxide(g)
>
> The loss in mass is due to carbon dioxide escaping.

....

....

....

....

....

....

....

....

....

....

....

....

....

....

....

....

....

....

....

....

....

....

.... **(6 marks)**

Reactivity series

1 In an experiment, some metals were placed into a metal salt solution and any reaction that occurred was recorded.

Metal \ Solution	Copper sulfate solution	Zinc sulfate solution	Iron sulfate solution
copper		✗	✗
zinc	✔		✔
iron	✔	✗	

✔ means a reaction occurred   ✗ means a reaction did not occur

(a) Use these results to put the metals in order from most reactive to least reactive.

> A good way of tackling this question is to look at the results for each metal and note how many solutions it reacts with; the more ticks there are, the more reactive the metal.

most reactive ....

....

least reactive .... **(1 mark)**

(b) State **one** observation when zinc reacts with copper sulfate solution.

.... **(1 mark)**

2 Complete the following word equations.

> Guided

(a) magnesium + water → magnesium hydroxide + ... **(1 mark)**

(b) calcium + nitric acid → calcium nitrate + ... **(1 mark)**

(c) zinc + hydrochloric acid → .... + ... **(1 mark)**

3 Potassium reacts with water at room temperature to produce an alkaline solution and a gas.

(a) Name the gas produced .... **(1 mark)**

(b) Name the alkaline solution .... **(1 mark)**

(c) State **two** observations for this reaction.

1 ....

2 .... **(2 marks)**

4 The table below shows the results when a piece of each metal was placed in separate test tubes containing dilute hydrochloric acid.

Metal	zinc	magnesium	copper	calcium
Observations	some bubbles	bubbles and metal disappears	no reaction	vigorous bubbling, metal disappears

Which list gives the correct order of reactivity for the four metals, starting with the most reactive?

Tick **one** box.

zinc, copper, magnesium, calcium ☐   calcium, magnesium, zinc, copper ☐

magnesium, zinc, calcium, copper ☐   copper, zinc, magnesium, calcium ☐

(1 mark)

Oxidation, reduction and the extraction of metals

1 What is meant by the term oxidation?

Tick **one** box.

gain of oxide ☐   loss of oxygen ☐

gain of oxygen ☐   loss of oxide ☐   **(1 mark)**

2 Choose an element from the box to answer the following questions. Each element may be used once, more than once or not at all.

| hydrogen | silver | carbon | aluminium | gold | calcium |

(a) Name a metal that is found in the Earth's crust as the uncombined element.

> Think about the reactivity series to help with this question.

.... **(1 mark)**

(b) Name **two** metals that are likely to be found as compounds.

.... **(2 marks)**

(c) Name an element that can be used to reduce some metal ores.

.... **(1 mark)**

(d) Name an element that is extracted using electrolysis.

.... **(1 mark)**

3 Most metals are extracted from metal oxides found in rocks. Some metals are found as the uncombined elements.

(a) Why are some metals found as the uncombined elements?

.... **(1 mark)**

(b) In industry, iron is manufactured in the blast furnace from iron(III) oxide.

(i) Balance the equation for the reaction.

......Fe_2O_3 + ...C → ......Fe + ...CO_2 **(1 mark)**

(ii) Write the formula of a substance that is reduced in this reaction.

.... **(1 mark)**

> **Guided**

(iii) State and explain if any substance is oxidised in this reaction.

C has been oxidised because ....

....

....

.... **(2 marks)**

Reactions of acids

1 What type of reaction occurs when sodium hydroxide reacts with hydrochloric acid?

Tick **one** box.

crystallisation ☐   neutralisation ☐

decomposition ☐   polymerisation ☐

(1 mark)

2 Indigestion is caused by too much hydrochloric acid in the stomach. Some indigestion remedies contain the insoluble compounds magnesium hydroxide and aluminium hydroxide to react with the excess hydrochloric acid.

(a) What one-word term can be used to describe magnesium hydroxide and aluminium hydroxide?

.... **(1 mark)**

(b) Name the **two** salts formed when magnesium hydroxide and aluminium hydroxide react with the excess hydrochloric acid.

.... **(2 marks)**

3 Complete the table below.

> Guided

> The name of the metal in the base becomes the first word in the name of the salt. The second part of the name of the salt (chloride, nitrate or sulfate), comes from the name of the acid used. The name of the first salt in the table has been completed for you.

Acid	Base	Salt
hydrochloric acid	lithium hydroxide	lithium chloride
	calcium oxide	calcium nitrate
sulfuric acid	sodium hydroxide	
	magnesium oxide	magnesium chloride

(4 marks)

4 Complete the word equations.

> Remember that oxides and hydroxides are bases, and both react with acids to give a salt and water only.

(a) hydrochloric acid + ... → magnesium chloride + hydrogen   **(1 mark)**

(b) sulfuric acid + potassium hydroxide → .... + water   **(1 mark)**

(c) nitric acid + sodium carbonate → sodium nitrate + water + ...   **(1 mark)**

(d) copper oxide + sulfuric acid → water + ...   **(1 mark)**

Required practical – Salt preparation

1   In the preparation of copper sulfate crystals, a student initially added excess copper oxide to dilute sulfuric acid in a beaker with warming.

(a)   What colour are copper sulfate crystals?

.... **(1 mark)**

(b)   Complete the labelled diagram to show how the excess copper oxide would be removed.   **(2 marks)**

(c)   Describe how crystals of copper sulfate can be obtained from the salt solution.

....

....

.... **(2 marks)**

2   Sodium produces a salt when it reacts with dilute sulfuric acid.

> Think about the position of sodium in the reactivity series.

(a)   Name the salt formed between sodium and sulfuric acid.

.... **(1 mark)**

(b)   Explain why the addition of sodium metal to sulfuric acid would not be used as a method of preparing sodium sulfate in the laboratory.

....

....

....

.... **(2 marks)**

3   Describe how a sample of cobalt chloride crystals could be made from cobalt oxide and dilute hydrochloric acid.

Guided

Measure out some dilute hydrochloric acid into a beaker. Add a spatula measure

of cobalt oxide, with stirring. ....

....

....

....

....

.... **(4 marks)**

The pH scale

> Remember that the lower the pH the stronger the acid and the higher the pH the stronger the alkali.

1 The pH of some solutions is recorded in the table below.

Solution	A	B	C	D	E
pH	2	6	7	10	13

(a) Describe how a student could find the pH of an unknown solution.

....

....

.... **(2 marks)**

(b) Which solution in the table could be water?

.... **(1 mark)**

(c) Which solution(s) are acidic?

.... **(1 mark)**

(d) Which solution is the strongest alkali?

.... **(1 mark)**

(e) What is an aqueous solution?

....

.... **(1 mark)**

⟩ Guided ⟩ (f) Complete the table.

Name of ion present in acid solutions	Name of ion present in alkaline solutions
	hydroxide ion

(2 marks)

2 Sulfuric acid neutralises potassium hydroxide.

(a) Write a word equation for this reaction.

.... **(1 mark)**

(b) What is neutralisation?

Tick **one** box.

a reaction in which oxygen is removed ☐

a reaction in which a base and alkali cancel each other out ☐

a reaction between hydrogen ions and hydroxide ions to produce water ☐

a reaction between an acid and universal indicator ☐　**(1 mark)**

(c) What colour is universal indicator in water?

.... **(1 mark)**

Electrolysis

1 Molten lead bromide breaks down when it conducts electricity.

(a) Using the apparatus shown, how would you know
if an electric current was passing?

.... **(1 mark)**

> **Guided**

(b) Explain why the lead bromide needs to be molten.

Solid lead bromide ....

....

....

....**(2 marks)**

(c) Name the products at each of the electrodes during this process.

....

.... **(2 marks)**

(d) Explain why graphite is used for the electrodes.

....

.... **(2 marks)**

graphite
electrodes

molten
lead
bromide

2 When molten sodium chloride is electrolysed, reactions occur at both the cathode and the anode.

(a) Complete the table.

	Anode	Cathode
Product for electrolysis of molten sodium chloride		

(2 marks)

(b) Explain how the results are different when solid sodium chloride is used.

....

....

.... **(2 marks)**

(c) Explain what happens to metal ions during electrolysis.

> You need to mention which electrode the different ions move to, and what happens
> when they get there.

....

....

.... **(2 marks)**

118

Aluminium extraction

1   Aluminium is extracted from molten aluminium oxide by electrolysis.

(a)   Name the ions present in molten aluminium oxide and identify the electrode to which each ion moves.

> First you need to find the charge of each ion present.

name of ion:... It moves to the ....

name of ion:... It moves to the .... **(2 marks)**

(b)   Write the formula of aluminium oxide.

.... **(1 mark)**

2   Aluminium is extracted from its ore using electricity. The ore, which mainly contains aluminium oxide, is mixed with cryolite before it is melted and electrolysed.

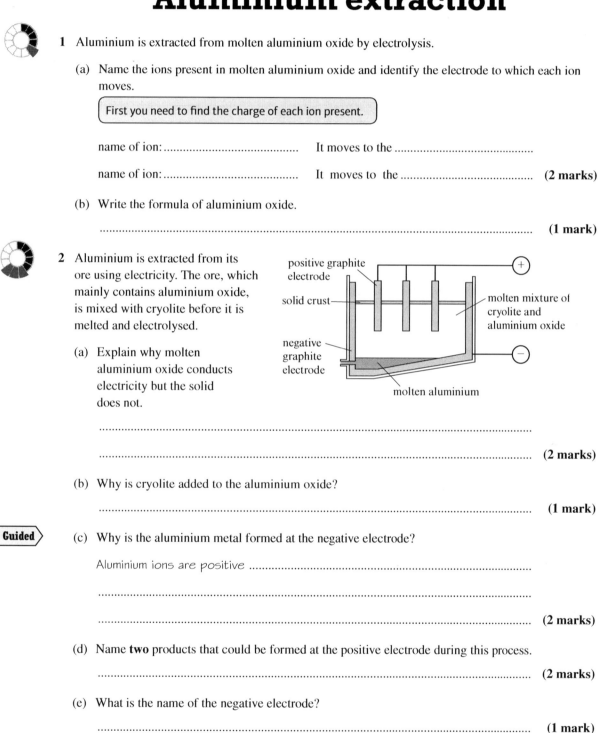

positive graphite electrode

solid crust

negative graphite electrode

molten aluminium

molten mixture of cryolite and aluminium oxide

(a)   Explain why molten aluminium oxide conducts electricity but the solid does not.

....

.... **(2 marks)**

(b)   Why is cryolite added to the aluminium oxide?

.... **(1 mark)**

> Guided

(c)   Why is the aluminium metal formed at the negative electrode?

Aluminium ions are positive ....

....

.... **(2 marks)**

(d)   Name **two** products that could be formed at the positive electrode during this process.

.... **(2 marks)**

(e)   What is the name of the negative electrode?

.... **(1 mark)**

(f)   Explain why the positive electrode must be continually replaced.

....

....

....

.... **(3 marks)**

Electrolysis of solutions

1 Why does calcium chloride solution conduct electricity?

Tick **one** box.

It contains electrons which can move. ☐

It contains ions which can move. ☐

It contains a metal. ☐

It contains water. ☐   **(1 mark)**

2 Name the products of electrolysis of potassium bromide solution.

Tick **one** box.

at the cathode	at the anode	
hydrogen	bromine	☐
hydrogen	oxygen	☐
potassium	bromine	☐
potassium	oxygen	☐ **(1 mark)**

3 (a) When calcium nitrate solution is electrolysed, the product at the cathode gives a pop with a burning splint, and the product at the anode relights a glowing splint.

    (i) Identify the product at the cathode.

    .... **(1 mark)**

    (ii) Identify the product at the anode.

    .... **(1 mark)**

> **Guided**

(b) Complete the table below to show the products at the electrodes during the electrolysis of some electrolyte solutions.

> Remember to use the reactivity series. At the cathode, hydrogen is produced if the metal is higher than hydrogen in the series. At the anode, oxygen is produced, unless the solution contains halide ions, when the halogen is produced.

Electrolyte solution	Anode	Cathode
copper chloride	chlorine	
potassium bromide	bromine	
sodium iodide		
sodium sulfate		

                                     (4 marks)

Required practical – Electrolysis

1 The apparatus shown can be used to electrolyse some aqueous solutions.

(a) Name electrodes A and B and suggest a suitable material for the electrodes.

....

....

....**(3 marks)**

(b) Name the solute and solvent in potassium chloride solution.

solute ....

solvent .... **(2 marks)**

> **Guided**

(c) The table below gives the observations and results of tests carried out on the products when some aqueous solutions were electrolysed.

Complete the table.

electrolyte

electrolyte

A   B

power supply
−   +

> Remember, if a halide ion is present, then a halogen is always produced at the anode.

Solution	Potassium chloride	Calcium nitrate	Sulfuric acid	Zinc bromide	Silver nitrate
Observations at cathode	colourless gas	colourless gas	colourless gas	grey solid	white solid
Observations at anode	greenish gas	colourless gas	colourless gas	orange solution	colourless gas
Test used for product at cathode	Insert a lighted splint. result – pop	Insert a lighted splint. result – pop	Insert a lighted splint. result – pop	*no reaction*	*no reaction*
Test used for product at anode	Universal indicator paper turns red and bleaches.		relights a glowing splint	Universal indicator paper turns red and bleaches.	relights a glowing splint
Identity of product at cathode				zinc	silver
Identity of product at anode				*bromine*	

(9 marks)

(d) Explain **one** important safety instruction that must be followed in this practical.

....

.... **(2 marks)**

121

Extended response –
Chemical changes

Dilute hydrochloric acid reacts with calcium hydroxide solution and with solid calcium.
Compare these two reactions in terms of observations, products and equations.

> You will be more successful in extended response questions if you plan your answer before you start writing.
>
> Think first of the general reactions for acids:
>
>   acid + base → salt + water
>
>   acid + metal → salt + hydrogen
>
> Then write word and balanced equations for the specific reactions.
>
> You should try to use the information given in the question.

....

....

....

....

....

....

....

....

....

....

....

....

....

....

....

....

....

....

....

....

....

....

.... **(6 marks)**

Exothermic reactions

1 In an experiment some solids were dissolved in water. The temperature of the water was initially 21 °C. The figure shows the thermometer readings after dissolving the solids in water.

A
```
-20 -10   0   10  20  30  40  50
                °C
```
B
```
-20 -10   0   10  20  30  40  50
                °C
```
C
```
-20 -10   0   10  20  30  40  50
                °C
```

> **Maths skills** First record the temperatures on the thermometers. Then calculate the temperature change.

Complete the table.

Solid	Initial temperature in °C	Final temperature in °C	Temperature change in °C
A	21	26	increased by 5
B	21		
C	21		

(6 marks)

2 (a) What is the law of conservation of energy?

The amount of energy in the Universe at the end of a chemical reaction is ....

.... **(2 marks)**

(b) In an exothermic reaction energy is transferred to the surroundings. Do the products have more or less energy than the reactants?

.... **(1 mark)**

3 (a) What is an exothermic reaction?

....

.... **(2 marks)**

(b) Name **two** everyday uses of exothermic reactions.

1 ....

2 .... **(2 marks)**

4 Combustion reactions occur when substances react with oxygen and burn.

(a) Balance the equation for the combustion of methane, CH_4.

......CH_4 + ...O_2 →..........CO_2 + ...H_2O

(1 mark)

(b) Describe what would happen to the temperature of the surroundings during this reaction.

.... **(1 mark)**

Endothermic reactions

1   Chemical energy changes have many uses in industry and the home. These changes, which can be exothermic or endothermic, all involve a transfer of heat energy from one place to another.

(a) Describe the difference between exothermic and endothermic reactions.

An exothermic reaction .... heat energy while an endothermic

reaction .... heat energy.   **(2 marks)**

(b) How could you tell if an endothermic reaction was taking place in a solution?

....

.... **(2 marks)**

(c) Give **one** example of a chemical reaction that is endothermic.

.... **(1 mark)**

2   The equation for the combustion of glucose is shown below.

$$C_6H_{12}O_6 + 6O_2 \rightarrow 6CO_2 + 6H_2O \text{ (+ energy)}$$

The reaction in plants that forms glucose, called photosynthesis, is shown below.

$$6CO_2 + 6H_2O \rightarrow C_6H_{12}O_6 + 6O_2$$

Use the information given above to explain if photosynthesis is an exothermic or endothermic reaction.

....

....

.... **(2 marks)**

3   Some reactions are exothermic and some are endothermic.

(a) Complete the table to classify the following reactions as exothermic or as endothermic.

Think about the temperature – if it increases, heat has been given out, or **ex**ited to the surroundings – an **ex**othermic reaction.

Reaction	Temperature at start in °C	Temperature at end in °C	Exothermic or endothermic
A	21	50	
B	18	14	
C	20	26	
D	10	−1	

(4 marks)

(b) Calculate the temperature change for reaction A and for reaction D.

....

....

temperature change for A = ... °C

temperature change for D = ... °C   **(2 marks)**

Required practical – Energy changes

1   In an experiment, 25 cm^3 of sodium hydroxide solution was placed, at room temperature (20 °C), in a polystyrene cup, and an excess (40 cm^3) of hydrochloric acid was added. The mixture was stirred with a thermometer and the highest temperature recorded.

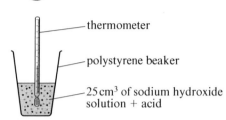

thermometer

polystyrene beaker

25 cm^3 of sodium hydroxide solution + acid

> Remember that this is an acid and base reaction producing a salt and water.

(a)   Write a word equation for the reaction of sodium hydroxide, with hydrochloric acid.

....

.... **(1 mark)**

(b)   Why was a polystyrene cup used rather than a glass beaker?

.... **(1 mark)**

(c)   Why was the solution stirred after adding the hydrochloric acid?

.... **(1 mark)**

(d)   Describe one improvement that could be made to the apparatus set up as shown above.

....

.... **(2 marks)**

(e)   The experiment was repeated, adding 40 cm^3 of different dilute acids to 25 cm^3 of sodium hydroxide solution, and the results recorded below.

	Hydrochloric acid	Ethanoic acid	Nitric acid	Sulfuric acid
Maximum temperature in °C	26.0	23.9	25.9	26.1

   (i)   Explain whether the reaction of sodium hydroxide with an acid is exothermic or endothermic.

....

.... **(2 marks)**

   (ii)   What is the independent variable in this experiment?

     Tick **one** box.

     time taken ☐   volume of acid ☐

     type of acid ☐   temperature ☐   **(1 mark)**

   (iii) State **one** controlled variable in this experiment.

.... **(1 mark)**

Activation energy

1 A reaction profile for a reaction is shown below.

   (a) Use the words below to label each axis correctly.

       • Progress of reaction   • Energy   **(2 marks)**

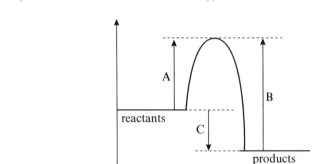

   (b) Which arrow, A, B or C, represents the activation energy?

      .... **(1 mark)**

   (c) Which arrow, A, B or C, represents the overall energy change for this reaction?

      .... **(1 mark)**

   (d) Is this an exothermic reaction or an endothermic reaction?

      .... **(1 mark)**

2 Classify each reaction in the energy level diagram below as exothermic or endothermic.

> Look at the position of the reactants and products.

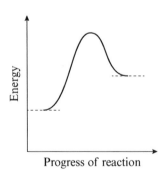 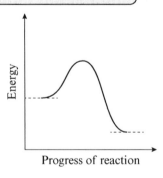

      reaction 1 ....   reaction 2 ....   reaction 3 ....

                                                  (3 marks)

3 (a) What is activation energy?

       It is the energy needed ....

      .... **(1 mark)**

   (b) What must particles do, in order for a reaction to occur?

      .... **(1 mark)**

Extended response – Energy changes

Combustion and thermal decomposition are two reactions that have an energy change. Explain whether each reaction is exothermic or endothermic. Describe how the temperature of the surroundings would change.

> You will be more successful in extended response questions if you plan your answer before you start writing.
>
> Remember that combustion is the reaction of a fuel with oxygen to release energy and thermal decomposition is the breakdown of a compound using heat.

....

....

....

....

....

....

....

....

....

....

....

....

....

....

....

....

....

....

....

....

.... **(6 marks)**

Rate of reaction

1 In a reaction between magnesium and hydrochloric acid the mass loss was 1.2 g in 2 minutes. Calculate the mean rate of reaction in g/s.

> Always look at the units – the rate is needed in g/s so your first step must be to convert 2 minutes to seconds.

time taken = 2 x 60 = 120 seconds

$$rate = \frac{change}{time} = \frac{1.2}{120}$$

mean rate of reaction = ... g/s   **(2 marks)**

2 A student carried out an experiment to investigate the rate of reaction between marble chips and hydrochloric acid. To follow the reaction rate the student measured the mass lost by the reaction mixture with time. The results of the experiment are shown below.

Time in min	0	1	2	3	4	5	6	7	8	9	10
Mass lost in g	0.00	0.12	0.22	0.30	0.36	0.40	0.42	0.45	0.45	0.45	0.45

(a) Calculate the mean rate of reaction in g/min between:

   (i)   2 and 4 minutes $rate = \dfrac{change}{time} = \dfrac{0.36 - 0.22}{4 - 2}$

     rate of reaction = ... g/min   **(2 marks)**

   (ii)   4 and 6 minutes

     rate of reaction = ... g/min   **(2 marks)**

(b) Draw a labelled diagram of the apparatus used to carry out this experiment.

(3 marks)

Rate of reaction on a graph

1 A student measured the loss in mass every minute during the reaction of magnesium and dilute hydrochloric acid.

> Remember that an acid and a metal produce a salt and hydrogen.

(a) Write a word equation for the reaction of magnesium and hydrochloric acid.

.... **(1 mark)**

(b) The table below shows the student's results.

Time in min	0	1	2	3	4	5	6	7	8	9	10
Mass lost in g	0	0.12	0.22	0.30	0.36	0.40	0.42	0.45	0.45	0.45	0.45

Plot the results from the table on the grid below and draw a line of best fit.

Mass lost in g

Time in min

> **Maths skills** Often there are 3 marks for drawing a graph: 1 mark for sensible scales, 1 mark for using at least half the grid and plotting all points, and 1 mark for drawing a correct best fit line.

(3 marks)

2 The rate of reaction between calcium carbonate and hydrochloric acid was investigated. The graph shows the results for two different experiments.

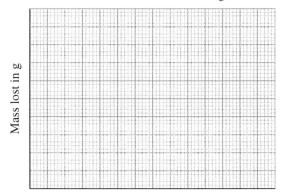

(a) What volume of gas is produced at 20 seconds?

experiment A ....

experiment B ....

(2 marks)

> experiment A
> experiment B
> Volume in cm³
> Time in seconds

> Guided

(b) Calculate the difference in volume of gas produced at the end between experiment A and experiment B.

> The experiment is over when no more gas is produced and the graph is horizontal.

end volume for experiment A = ... end volume for experiment B = ...

difference in volume = ... **(3 marks)**

(c) (i) use the graph for experiment B to complete the table opposite.

Volume of gas in cm³	
Time taken in s	40

(1 mark)

(ii) calculate the mean rate of the reaction using the results in the table and the equation:

$$\text{mean rate of reaction} = \frac{\text{volume in cm}^3}{\text{time taken in seconds}}$$

Mean rate of reaction = ...cm³/s   **(2 marks)**

Collision theory

1 When do chemical reactions occur?

Tick **one** box.

when particles collide or touch   ☐

when particles collide for a sufficient amount of time   ☐

when particles collide with sufficient energy   ☐

when particles mix together in a reaction vessel   ☐   **(1 mark)**

2 In an experiment the mass lost in a reaction between calcium carbonate and hydrochloric acid changed with time as shown in the graph.

> The rate of reaction is given by the gradient of the graph.

(a) Describe the change in the rate of reaction as time increases.

....

....

....

.... **(2 marks)**

(b) The reaction was carried out again using the same mass of calcium carbonate and the same volume of dilute hydrochloric acid at a higher temperature. Give **two** reasons why the rate of reaction increases.

Tick **two** boxes.

The particles are more concentrated.   ☐

The particles have a greater mass.   ☐

The particles have a larger surface area. ☐

The particles have more energy.   ☐

The particles move faster.   ☐   **(2 marks)**

> Guided

(c) The experiment was repeated using the same mass of calcium carbonate and the same volume of hydrochloric acid, but the acid was more concentrated.

Describe what would have happened to the rate of the reaction.

The rate of reaction would have increased. The acid was more concentrated so there were

.... particles in the .... volume so there were more ....

....

.... **(4 marks)**

Rate: pressure, surface area

1 Why does rate of reaction generally increase if the pressure is increased?

Tick **one** box.

The particles move faster and there are more collisions. ☐

There are fewer particles in the same volume and there are more collisions. ☐

There are more particles in the same volume and there are more collisions. ☐

The particles have more energy and there are more collisions. ☐ **(1 mark)**

2 Which reaction will be fastest at the start of the reaction?

Tick **one** box.

calcium carbonate lumps reacting with dilute nitric acid ☐

calcium carbonate lumps reacting with concentrated nitric acid ☐

calcium carbonate powder reacting with dilute nitric acid ☐

calcium carbonate powder reacting with concentrated nitric acid ☐ **(1 mark)**

3 In an experiment, a mass of magnesium ribbon reacted with excess dilute hydrochloric acid at room temperature. The volume of gas produced was recorded every 10 seconds. The results are shown in the graph as line B.

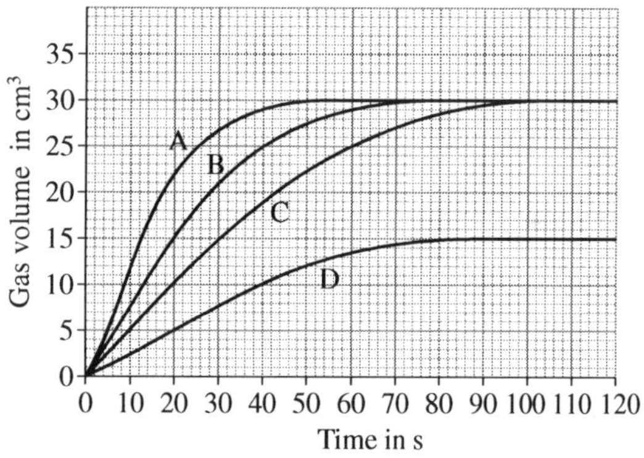

(a) At what time does the reaction for line B end?

.... **(1 mark)**

(b) Which line, A, C or D, on the graph shows the results obtained when the experiment was repeated using the same mass of magnesium powder, rather than ribbon? Give a reason for your answer.

....

.... **(2 marks)**

Guided (c) Complete the diagram to show how the experiment is carried out in the laboratory.

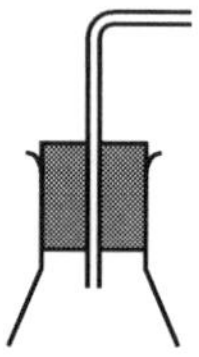

> You need to complete the conical flask and then add a gas syringe to collect the gas.

> What separate piece of apparatus is needed to record the volume of gas every 20 seconds?

(4 marks)

Rate: temperature

1   A group of students was investigating the reactions between two metals and dilute hydrochloric acid. The metals used were magnesium and zinc, and they set up the experiments as shown below. (Note: the concentration of the acid is measured in g/dm^3.)

Flask A	**Flask B**	**Flask C**	**Flask D**
$36.5\ g/dm^3$ hydrochloric acid at 20 °C and zinc lump	$36.5\ g/dm^3$ hydrochloric acid at 25 °C and zinc powder	$73\ g/dm^3$ hydrochloric acid at 20 °C and magnesium lump	$73\ g/dm^3$ hydrochloric acid at 55 °C and magnesium lump

(a) (i)   In which flask would the reaction be slowest? ....   **(1 mark)**

    (ii)   Give **two** reasons for your answer to (i).

       ....

       ....   **(2 marks)**

(b) The students wanted to investigate how changing temperature affected the rate of reaction between metals and acid.

    (i)   Which **two** flasks could be used to investigate the effect of temperature?

       ....   **(1 mark)**

    (ii)   Suggest **two** other variables that would need to be kept the same to make this test fair.

> Think about the other factors that could affect the rate of reaction.

       ....   **(2 marks)**

2   The time taken for a piece of magnesium to fully react with excess hydrochloric acid was recorded at different temperatures. The results are shown in the table.

Temperature in °C	**Time for reaction in s**
20	90
30	70
40	58

(a) Use the results to determine the effect of temperature on rate of reaction.

Increasing the temperature makes the reaction ....   **(1 mark)**

(b) Explain, in terms of particles, the effect of temperature on the rate of reaction.

       ....

       ....

       ....

       ....

       ....   **(3 marks)**

Required practical – Rate of reaction

A student used the apparatus shown to investigate the effect of changing acid concentration on the rate of reaction between magnesium and dilute hydrochloric acid. Excess hydrochloric acid of different concentrations was allowed to react with 0.1 g of magnesium ribbon, and the volume of gas produced in each case was recorded every minute.

hydrogen   gas syringe

hydrochloric acid and magnesium

Look at what the student needs to record.

(a) Name one other piece of apparatus that **must** be used in this experiment.

....

(1 mark)

(b) State **two** things that would be observed occurring in the flask during the reaction.

....

....

(2 marks)

Guided

(c) State **two** ways to ensure that this experiment was a fair test.

The ....

and the .... of the

hydrochloric acid must be kept the

same in all the experiments.

(2 marks)

The results from this experiment are plotted in the graph.

Gas volume in cm³

Time in minutes

(d) Which reaction is fastest, A, B or C?

.... **(1 mark)**

(e) Which reaction, A, B or C, is carried out using the most concentrated acid?

.... **(1 mark)**

(f) Identify any anomalous results in the graph.

.... **(1 mark)**

(g) Describe another method, other than measuring the volume of gas collected, that could be used to investigate the rate of reaction between magnesium and hydrochloric acid.

Could you use a balance?

....

....

.... **(3 marks)**

133

Catalysts

1 A reaction profile is shown for a catalysed reaction and an uncatalysed reaction. Label the reaction profile by adding the labels:

- Activation energy with catalyst
- Reactants
- Products
- Energy   **(4 marks)**

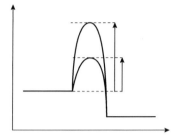

Progress of reaction

2 The volume of oxygen produced when a solution of hydrogen peroxide decomposes with manganese(IV) oxide as a catalyst can be measured using the apparatus shown.

(a) What is A?

....

(1 mark)

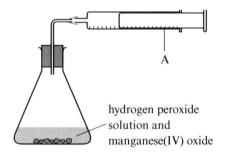

A

hydrogen peroxide solution and manganese(IV) oxide

(b) The graph shows data obtained at 25 °C using hydrogen peroxide solution with 1.0 g of powdered manganese(IV) oxide.

(i) What was the total volume of gas collected?

volume = ... cm^3

(1 mark)

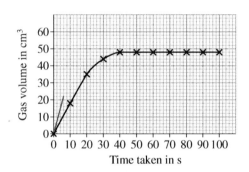

(ii) The reaction was repeated using 1.0 g samples of powdered metal oxides as catalysts and hydrogen peroxide solution of the same concentration at the same temperature. The time taken for the reaction was recorded for each sample in the table on the right.

Metal oxide	Time for complete decomposition in s
manganese(IV) oxide	40
copper oxide	127
zinc oxide	360

Which one of the metal oxides was the least effective catalyst? Give a reason for your answer.

....

.... **(2 marks)**

> **Guided**

(iii) The reaction was repeated with manganese(IV) oxide at 40 °C and all other factors were kept the same. Sketch the graph line you would expect on the graph above.

> This reaction is at a higher temperature so the reaction is faster. The gradient will be steeper. The first part of the line has been drawn. Now draw the rest of the line. Remember that the same volume of gas will be produced but the reaction finishes faster.

(1 mark)

Reversible reactions

1 What is a reversible reaction?

Tick **one** box.

a reaction in which heat is alternately given out and taken in as the reaction proceeds   ☐

a reaction in which heat is taken in   ☐

a reaction in which the products of the reaction can react to produce the original reactants   ☐

a reaction in which the reactants are converted into products   ☐

(1 mark)

2 In the Haber process the reaction forming ammonia from nitrogen and hydrogen can be written as shown below:

nitrogen + hydrogen $\rightleftharpoons$ ammonia

(a) Complete the balanced equation below.

> Remember to fill in the formula first and then balance.

N_2 + ... $\rightleftharpoons$ ....   **(2 marks)**

(b) How does the equation show that this reaction is reversible?

....   **(1 mark)**

3 Methane can be formed when carbon monoxide reacts with hydrogen:

$$CO(g) + 3H_2(g) \rightleftharpoons CH_4(g) + H_2O(g)$$

> **Guided**

(a) What does the double arrow ($\rightleftharpoons$) between reactants and products mean?

This means that the reaction goes ....   **(1 mark)**

(b) Name the molecules that will be present when this reaction has been left for some time.

....

....   **(2 marks)**

4 The reaction between anhydrous copper sulfate and water to give hydrated copper sulfate is a reversible reaction. It is exothermic in one direction and endothermic in the opposite direction.

anhydrous copper sulfate + water $\rightleftharpoons$ hydrated copper sulfate

(a) Which direction of the reaction is the endothermic direction?

....   **(1 mark)**

(b) What is the colour change when water is added to anhydrous copper sulfate?

....   **(2 marks)**

(c) What does hydrated mean?

....   **(1 mark)**

Equilibrium

1 Hydrogen can be made by reacting methane with steam as shown in the equation below:

methane + steam → hydrogen + carbon monoxide

$$CH_4(g) + H_2O(g) \rightarrow 3H_2(g) + CO(g)$$

This reaction is reversible and an equilibrium can be reached.

(a) What does 'equilibrium' mean?

....

.... **(2 marks)**

(b) State a necessary condition for equilibrium to occur in a reversible reaction.

.... **(1 mark)**

2 The graph shows how the yield of ammonia, in the Haber process, is affected by changes to temperature and pressure.

(a) State the effect of increasing the pressure on the yield of ammonia at 400 °C.

....

....

....

.... **(1 mark)**

Graph: Percentage ammonia (y-axis, 0 to 100) against Pressure in atmospheres (x-axis, 0 to 1000). Curves labelled 200 °C, 300 °C, 400 °C, 500 °C, 600 °C, 700 °C.

> Look at the yield for the same pressure but different temperatures.

(b) State the effect of changing the temperature on the yield of ammonia.

....

.... **(1 mark)**

(c) What is the percentage yield of ammonia when the temperature is 400 °C and the pressure 200 atm?

.... **(1 mark)**

(d) What type of reaction *must* the Haber process be if equilibrium is to occur?

Tick **one** box.

exothermic ☐

endothermic ☐

neutralisation ☐

reversible ☐   **(1 mark)**

Extended response – Rates of reaction

Magnesium reacts with dilute hydrochloric acid. A student has been asked to investigate how the rate of this reaction changes when the concentration of hydrochloric acid is changed.
Plan a method the student could use.

> You will be more successful in extended response questions if you plan your answer before you start writing.
>
> Write a word equation for the reaction, and study it to help you decide what to measure.
>
> Make sure that your plan includes how you will ensure that the experiment is a fair test.

....

....

....

....

....

....

....

....

....

....

....

....

....

....

....

....

....

....

....

.... **(6 marks)**

> For a fair test, make sure that you have controlled all the factors that might affect the rate.

Crude oil

1 Which word below best describes crude oil?

Tick **one** box.

compound   ☐

electrolyte ☐

mixture   ☐

polymer   ☐
(1 mark)

2 The first process in oil refining separates the crude oil into fractions.

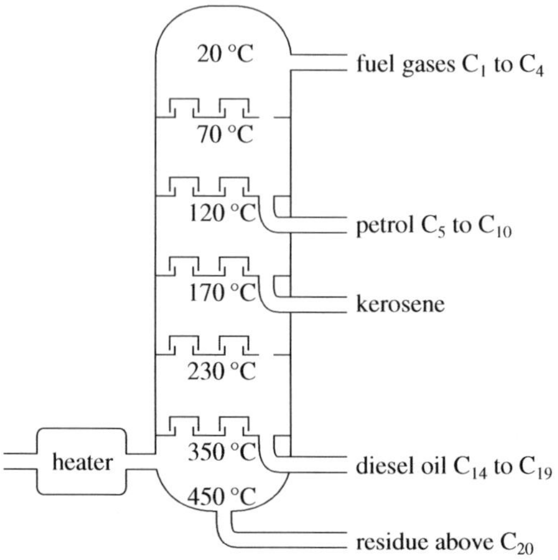

(a) Suggest a range of molecular sizes for kerosene.

....

(1 mark)

(b) (i) Which fraction has the highest boiling point?

....

(1 mark)

20 °C — fuel gases C_1 to C_4

70 °C

120 °C — petrol C_5 to C_{10}

170 °C — kerosene

230 °C

heater   350 °C — diesel oil C_{14} to C_{19}

450 °C

residue above C_{20}

(ii) Which fraction will contain the molecules shown below?

> Count the carbon atoms in the structures.

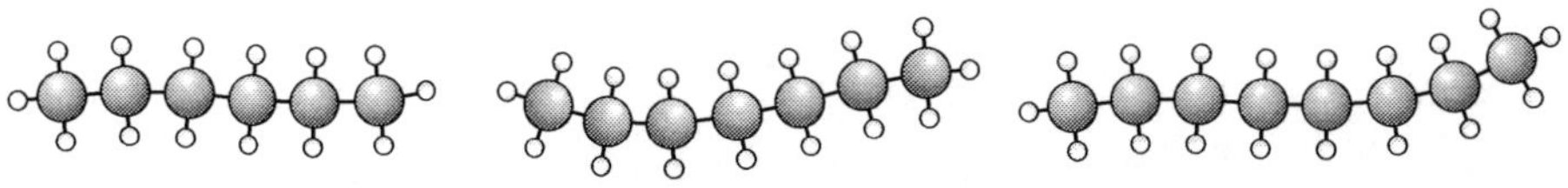

.... **(1 mark)**

(c) What is the name for the method of separation shown in the diagram?

.... **(1 mark)**

(d) How does the number of carbon atoms in each fraction affect the boiling point range of the fraction?

.... **(1 mark)**

(e) The fractions can be processed to produce fuels and feedstock for the petrochemical industry.

(i) Name **two** fractions that can be processed to produce fuel.

1 .... 2 .... **(2 marks)**

> Guided

(ii) Name **three** useful materials besides fuel on which modern life depends that are produced by the petrochemical industry.

1 solvents   2 .... 3 .... **(3 marks)**

Alkanes

1 Crude oil is a mixture of different hydrocarbons.

(a) What is a hydrocarbon?

....

.... **(2 marks)**

(b) The table gives information about hydrocarbons called alkanes.

Alkanes	Formula	Boiling point in °C
	CH_4	−162
ethane	C_2H_6	−89
propane		
butane	C_4H_{10}	0
pentane	C_5H_{12}	+36

(i) Give the name for the alkane with the formula CH_4 .... **(1 mark)**

(ii) Estimate the boiling point of propane in °C .... **(1 mark)**

(iii) Give the formula for propane .... **(1 mark)**

2 Draw the structure of:

(a) butane

> Butane has four carbon atoms in each molecule. These have been drawn for you. Now complete the structure by making sure that each carbon atom has four bonds, with hydrogen atoms attached.

C — C — C — C

(1 mark)

(b) ethane

(1 mark)

(c) an alkane with five carbon atoms in its molecule

(1 mark)

3 Which hydrocarbon is not an alkane?

Tick **one** box.

CH_4 ☐ C_3H_8 ☐ C_4H_8 ☐ C_5H_{12} ☐

> Use the general formula for alkanes to help.

(1 mark)

Properties of hydrocarbons

1 (a) Balance the equation for the hydrocarbon burning:

$$.......C_3H_8 + ...O_2 \rightarrow ....CO_2 + ...H_2O$$ **(1 mark)**

(b) Name the hydrocarbon C_3H_8.

.... **(1 mark)**

Guided

2 The diagram shows the apparatus a student used to investigate the products of combustion of hydrocarbons.

(a) Describe what the student would observe happening in tube A and tube B when the hydrocarbon had been burning for a few minutes.

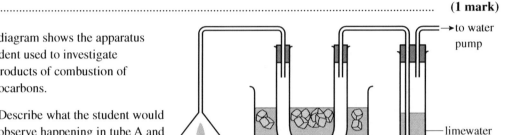

In tube A, a colourless .... is formed.

In tube B, the limewater changes from ....

to ....

(3 marks)

> **Practical skills** When describing observations, describe what you **see** happening rather than giving the names of products.

(b) Name a substance that could be used to show that water is present in tube A and state the observations.

....

....

.... **(3 marks)**

(c) Complete the equation below:

hydrocarbon + oxygen → .... **(2 marks)**

3 Pentane (C_5H_{12}) and octane (C_8H_{18}) are both alkanes.

(a) Which of these alkanes has the higher boiling point? Give a reason for your answer.

....

.... **(2 marks)**

(b) Which of these alkanes is more flammable?

.... **(1 mark)**

(c) Petrol is liquid fuel used to power motor car engines. Give **two** properties of petrol that make it suitable to be used in this way.

....

.... **(2 marks)**

Cracking

1 What type of reaction is cracking?

Tick **one** box.

displacement ☐

exothermic ☐

neutralisation ☐

thermal decomposition ☐

(1 mark)

2 Hydrocarbons can be cracked.

(a) What does 'cracking' mean?

....

.... **(2 marks)**

(b) Complete the equation for the cracking of octane, C_8H_{18}.

$$C_8H_{18} \rightarrow C_6H_{14} + \quad ....$$ **(1 mark)**

> **Guided**

(c) Name **two** methods of cracking.

1 catalytic

2 .... **(2 marks)**

(d) Suggest **two** reasons why there is greater demand for the products of cracking than for C_8H_{18}.

....

.... **(2 marks)**

3 Fractional distillation separates crude oil into fractions of similar hydrocarbons. The table below compares the fractions obtained from crude oil from three different sources.

Fraction	Crude oil A content in %	Crude oil B content in %	Crude oil C content in %
fuel gases	6	4	9
petrol and naphtha	10	6	19
diesel and kerosene	15	10	18
fuel oil	17	20	21
bitumen and residue	52	60	33

> Check back to page 138 if you have forgotten the sizes of molecules present in the different fractions.

(a) Which fraction has the largest molecules?

.... **(1 mark)**

(b) Which crude oil, A, B or C, has the highest viscosity?

.... **(1 mark)**

141

Alkenes

1 Which of the following shows the structure of an alkene molecule?

Tick **one** box.

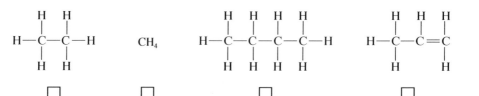

☐   ☐   ☐   ☐   **(1 mark)**

2 The diagram shows some examples of hydrocarbons that could be found in products from crude oil.

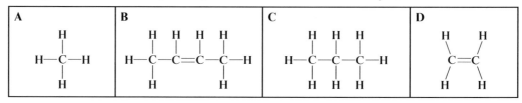

(a) The two hydrocarbons that are alkenes are .... and .... **(1 mark)**

(b) The chemical name for compound A is methane. Give the chemical name for compound C.

.... **(1 mark)**

(c) Why are substances A, B, C and D all described as hydrocarbons?

....

.... **(2 marks)**

> **Guided**

(d) Complete and balance the equation for the complete combustion of substance A, CH_4.

$CH_4 + ...O_2 \rightarrow$ ....

(2 marks)

> All hydrocarbons burn to form carbon dioxide and water. Write the formulae of these products, and then balance the equation.

3 A hydrocarbon, **Z**, has the formula C_xH_y. The hydrocarbon undergoes complete combustion as shown in the equation:

$$C_xH_y + 5O_2 \rightarrow 3CO_2 + 4H_2O$$

(a) Determine the values of x and y using the equation given above.

.... **(2 marks)**

(b) Name hydrocarbon **Z**. .... **(1 mark)**

(c) Draw a displayed structure of a molecule of hydrocarbon **Z**.

(1 mark)

Extended response – Organic chemistry

 The many hydrocarbons in crude oil can be separated into fractions using fractional distillation. The hydrocarbons can then be cracked. Describe the processes of fractional distillation and cracking. You should also give two differences between fractional distillation and cracking.

> You will be more successful in extended response questions if you plan your answer before you start writing.
>
> Remember to note any differences between the two methods.
>
> You should try to use the information given in the question.

....

....

....

....

....

....

....

....

....

....

....

....

....

....

....

....

....

....

....

....

....

....

.... **(6 marks)**

Pure substances and formulations

1 Describe the difference between a pure substance in chemistry and a pure substance in everyday life.

....

....

.... **(2 marks)**

2 A solid is thought to be pure aspirin. Which is the best way to test its purity?

Tick **one** box.

Determine its density. ☐   Determine its melting point. ☐

Determine the pH. ☐   Determine its flame colour. ☐

(1 mark)

3 Which substance is a formulation?

Tick **one** box.

air ☐   steel ☐

iron ☐   gold ☐

(1 mark)

4 The table shows some data about elements and formulations.

Substance	Melting point in °C	Boiling point in °C
A	420	913
B	1420–1536	2535–2545
C	−33	355

(a) Classify the substances in the table as solids, liquids or gases at room temperature (20 °C).

> If the melting point is above 20 °C, then the substance is a solid at room temperature.

....

.... **(3 marks)**

(b) Classify the substances in the table as elements or formulations. Give reasons for your answers.

....

....

.... **(3 marks)**

5 The melting point of a substance was determined. How can this melting point be used to identify the substance?

.... **(1 mark)**

Required practical – Chromatography

1 A student used the apparatus shown to separate the substances mixed together in some purple food dye.

> Guided

(a) Describe each part of the apparatus set-up.

A ....

B ....

C beaker

D ....   **(4 marks)**

(b) Describe what is wrong with the set-up and give a reason why it will not work as shown.

....

.... **(2 marks)**

2 A student investigated an orange drink in the laboratory using chromatography, to determine whether the drink contained dyes X, Y and Z. The results are shown, right.

(a) How many dyes were in the orange drink?

....

(1 mark)

(b) Why is the start line drawn in pencil?

.... **(1 mark)**

(c) Explain if dye Z is a pure substance.

....

.... **(1 mark)**

(d) Use the figure to complete the table.

	Distance in cm
distance moved by dye X	
distance moved from start line by solvent	

Use the equation:

$$R_f = \frac{\text{distance moved by dye X}}{\text{distance moved by solvent}}$$

> You need to use a ruler to help you.

Calculate the R_f value for dye X.

R_fX = ... **(4 marks)**

Tests for gases

1 Which of the following is used to test for the presence of chlorine?

Tick **one** box.

Put a glowing splint into a test tube of the gas. ☐

Put a burning splint into a test tube of the gas. ☐

Bubble the gas through limewater. ☐

Put a piece of damp litmus paper into the gas. ☐   **(1 mark)**

2 A burning splint is lowered into a gas jar. Which gas, if present in the jar, will allow the splint to burn vigorously?

Tick **one** box.

carbon dioxide ☐

helium ☐

neon ☐

oxygen ☐   **(1 mark)**

3 Calcium carbonate and dilute hydrochloric acid were reacted in a test tube and the gas produced was bubbled into limewater.

calcium carbonate + hydrochloric acid

test tube A   test tube B

(a) Write a word equation for the reaction of calcium carbonate with hydrochloric acid.

> What gas is produced when an acid and carbonate react?

.... **(1 mark)**

(b) State what was observed in test tube B.

....

.... **(2 marks)**

Guided

(c) Write the chemical name and formula for limewater.

name *calcium hydroxide solution*

formula .... **(2 marks)**

Practical skills

Extended response – Chemical analysis

Plan an experiment to positively identify each gas in unlabelled samples of each of the following:

- carbon dioxide
- chlorine
- helium
- hydrogen
- oxygen.

> You will be more successful in extended response questions if you plan your answer before you start writing.
>
> Try to give chemical tests and describe the observations that would be seen.

....

....

....

....

....

....

....

....

....

....

....

....

....

....

....

....

....

....

....

....

....

....

.... **(6 marks)**

The early atmosphere and today's atmosphere

1 Which unreactive gas makes up most of the Earth's atmosphere today?

Tick **one** box.

carbon dioxide ☐

helium ☐

nitrogen ☐

oxygen ☐   **(1 mark)**

> **Guided**

2 The proportions of the main gases in our atmosphere have not changed much over the past 200 million years.

(a) Complete the table to show the percentages of the **two** main gases in the Earth's atmosphere.

Main gas	Percentage in atmosphere
	20

       (2 marks)

(b) The atmosphere also contains small amounts of other gases, for example argon, water vapour, carbon dioxide and hydrogen.

Which of these other gases is a noble gas? .... **(1 mark)**

(c) Name **two** gases that were present in the early atmosphere, which are not present in today's atmosphere.

....

.... **(2 marks)**

3 A group of students burned some magnesium in air. The volume of air reduced as the magnesium reacted with the oxygen in the air. The students recorded the volumes of air.

The results of their experiment are shown below.

Starting volume in cm³	Temperature in °C	Final volume in cm³	Temperature in °C
200	20	172	20

(a) Complete the balanced symbol equation for the reaction of magnesium with oxygen.

..............Mg + ... → ....MgO   **(2 marks)**

(b) What is the volume of oxygen in the sample?

> Write down the volume of oxygen at the start, and subtract the volume of oxygen at the end.

.... **(1 mark)**

(c) Calculate the percentage of oxygen in the sample.

....

....

.... **(2 marks)**

Evolution of the atmosphere

1 The table below shows the main gases in the Earth's atmosphere today and 3.5 billion years ago.

Earth's atmosphere today	Early Earth's atmosphere (3500 million years ago)
nitrogen 78%	carbon dioxide 95.5%
oxygen 20%	nitrogen 3.1%
argon 0.9%	argon 1.2%
carbon dioxide 0.04%	methane 0.2%

(a) Compare the composition of gases in the Earth's early atmosphere with the atmosphere today.

The early atmosphere contained no oxygen, but ....

....

....

....

.... **(3 marks)**

(b) Explain why the data on the Earth's atmosphere today will be more accurate than the data on the early Earth's atmosphere.

....

.... **(1 mark)**

(c) Scientists think that the atmosphere has changed due to the presence of plants and algae on the Earth. Explain how the presence of algae and plants could change the atmosphere.

> Think about the chemical reactions in plants that use gases from the air for life processes.

....

....

.... **(2 marks)**

2 When carbon dioxide dissolves in water carbonic acid is formed.

(a) Complete the balanced symbol equation for this chemical reaction, including state symbols.

$$H_2O(l) + ... \rightarrow H_2CO_3(aq)$$ **(1 mark)**

(b) Some sea creatures need the carbon dioxide for growth.

   (i) What do some marine animals make with the dissolved carbon dioxide?

     .... **(1 mark)**

   (ii) What kind of sedimentary rocks do they eventually form?

     .... **(1 mark)**

(c) Algae and plants produced the oxygen that is now in the atmosphere by photosynthesis. Balance the equation for this reaction.

$$....CO_2 + ...H_2O \rightarrow ....C_6H_{12}O_6 + ...O_2$$ **(1 mark)**

Greenhouse gases

1 Which is **not** a greenhouse gas?

Tick **one** box.

carbon dioxide ☐   oxygen ☐

methane ☐   water vapour ☐   **(1 mark)**

2 The graph shows how the percentage of carbon dioxide in the atmosphere has changed over the past 4500 million years.

(a) What was the percentage of carbon dioxide in the atmosphere 4000 million years ago?

.... **(1 mark)**

> **Guided**

(b) Carbon dioxide is a greenhouse gas. Name, and give the formula of, **two** other greenhouse gases.

water vapour, which has formula ...., and ....

.... **(4 marks)**

(c) Give **two** conclusions that can be drawn from the graph.

> Look at what is happening to the percentage of carbon dioxide – does it increase or decrease?

....

....

....

.... **(2 marks)**

(d) It is thought that the percentage of carbon dioxide in the atmosphere has changed in the last 100 years.

State **two** human activities that may have contributed to this change.

1 ....

2 .... **(2 marks)**

Global climate change

Guided >

1 Due to human activity the levels of carbon dioxide in our atmosphere have been increasing over the last 100 years.

(a) Explain why destroying large areas of forest causes increased levels of carbon dioxide in the atmosphere.

During photosynthesis plants take in ....

.... **(2 marks)**

(b) Describe how one other human activity is thought to be responsible for increasing carbon dioxide levels in the atmosphere.

....

.... **(2 marks)**

(c) Describe **two** environmental problems caused by the increased levels of carbon dioxide.

....

.... **(2 marks)**

2 The graph shows the changes in average world temperatures and carbon dioxide levels over the past few thousand years.

(a) Describe the relationship between carbon dioxide levels and average world temperatures shown by the graph.

> From the graph decide what happens to temperature if the carbon dioxide level increases.

Vostok (Antarctica) ice core records

Temperature change in °C: 4, 2, 0, 22, 24, 26, 28, 210

CO_2 concentration in ppm: 400, 360, 320, 280, 240, 200

400 350 300 250 200 150 100 50 0
Years before present in thousands

....

....

.... **(2 marks)**

(b) An increase in global temperature may cause climate change. What is one possible effect of climate change?

Tick **one** box.

acid rain   ☐   ice caps melting   ☐

global dimming   ☐   volcanic activity   ☐   **(1 mark)**

(c) Define global warming.

....

.... **(1 mark)**

Carbon footprint

1 What is meant by the term 'carbon footprint'?

Tick **one** box.

the amount of carbon in a substance ☐

the total amount of carbon dioxide emitted over the full life cycle of a substance ☐

the total amount of all greenhouse gases emitted over the full life cycle of a substance ☐

the percentage of carbon dioxide formed from burning a substance ☐   **(1 mark)**

2 The graph shows some factors that contribute to the carbon footprint of an average person living in the UK.

(a) What percentage of the footprint comes from water heating?

.... **(1 mark)**

(b) What percentage of the footprint comes from travel?

⬡ Remember to include all types of travel.

.... **(1 mark)**

(c) State **two** ways in which the percentage in part (b) could be reduced.

....

.... **(2 marks)**

⮞ **Guided** ⮞ (d) To reduce the carbon footprint due to electricity generation from fossil fuels, alternative energy sources can be used, or carbon capture and storage could be introduced.

State **two** alternative energy sources.

1. solar power

2. .... **(2 marks)**

(e) A carbon footprint can be reduced by reducing emissions of two different gases. Name these **two** gases.

.... **(2 marks)**

Atmospheric pollution

1 The gas emitted from a power station chimney contained the gases shown in the table.

Gas	Abundance in %
nitrogen	66
carbon dioxide	18
oxygen	10
sulfur dioxide	

(a) Calculate the percentage of sulfur dioxide present in the chimney gas.

Maths skills Add up the total abundance. Remember % means out of 100.

....

....

.... **(2 marks)**

(b) Name **one** pollutant gas from the table.

.... **(1 mark)**

2 Burning fuels that contain carbon can produce carbon dioxide, carbon monoxide and soot (carbon).

(a) Which of these products are **not** formed by complete combustion of the fuel?

.... **(1 mark)**

(b) All three of the products can cause different environmental problems.

Describe **one** problem caused by each of the three products.

....

....

.... **(3 marks)**

3 When petrol burns in an engine, several pollutants are formed.

(a) Complete the table.

Name of pollutant	Formula	Effect of pollutant
sulfur dioxide		acid rain / respiratory problems
	CO	toxic – can cause suffocation
	C	
nitrogen oxides	NO_x	

(5 marks)

(b) How does sulfur dioxide form when petrol burns?

.... **(1 mark)**

(c) How does CO form when petrol burns?

.... **(1 mark)**

Extended response – The atmosphere

 The graph shows how the concentration of carbon dioxide in the atmosphere has changed from the year 1000 to the year 2000.

Describe and account for the change in concentration of carbon dioxide in the atmosphere and why it is an area of concern.

> You will be more successful in extended response questions if you plan your answer before you start writing.
>
> What human activities increase the amount of carbon dioxide in the atmosphere?
>
> You should try to use the information given in the question.

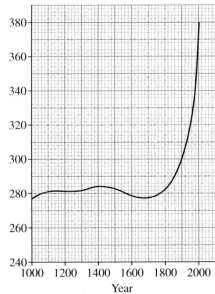

Concentration of CO_2 in the atmosphere in ppm

....

....

....

....

....

....

....

....

....

....

....

....

....

....

.... **(6 marks)**

The Earth's resources

1 Energy resources that, once used, can replenish themselves and so more can be used are called:

Tick **one** box.

finite ☐

kinetic ☐

non-renewable ☐

renewable ☐   **(1 mark)**

2 Which of the energy sources listed is **not** a renewable source of energy?

Tick **one** box.

oil ☐

solar ☐

tidal ☐

wind ☐   **(1 mark)**

Guided

3 We use energy for transport, power generation, and in our factories and homes. Some energy sources are shown in the table below. Complete the table.

> Renewable means that it can be replaced in a human lifetime.

	Energy source	Finite or renewable
biodiesel	processing of plant oils	
coal	deep mining or opencast mining	Finite
ethanol	fermentation of sugars from plants	
wind power	wind driving turbines	
petrol	fractional distillation of crude oil	

(5 marks)

Guided

4 Products can be classified as natural or as synthetic. Draw one line from each product to the correct classification.

Product   **Classification**

wool

plastic   natural

cotton

                                            synthetic

wood

(4 marks)

Water

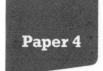

1 Water that is safe to drink is called potable water.

(a) Why is potable water not pure?

....

.... **(1 mark)**

(b) In the UK most potable water comes from rainwater that collects in the ground and in lakes and rivers. Give the **two** main steps used to treat groundwater to make it potable. Give a reason for each step.

step 1

....

....

step 2

....

.... **(4 marks)**

(c) In the UK, 1.5% of the water requirement is produced by the Thames Water desalination plant.

  (i) What is desalination?

  .... **(1 mark)**

  (ii) Name **two** methods of desalination.

            | One of these requires the use of membranes. |

  ....

  .... **(2 marks)**

  (iii) Why is desalination expensive?

  ....

  .... **(1 mark)**

2 Sewage and agricultural wastewater require removal of organic matter and harmful microbes. Sewage treatment includes the different stages shown in the box below.

> **Guided**

| sedimentation   anaerobic digestion of sewage sludge   screening and grit removal |

(a) Place these stages in the order in which they occur.

1 ....

2 ....

3 *anaerobic digestion of sewage sludge*   **(1 mark)**

(b) What is the purpose of screening and grit removal?

....

.... **(1 mark)**

Required practical – Analysis and purification of water

1 Drinking water has been distilled from seawater since at least 200 CE. Distillation involves evaporation and condensation.

The diagram shows the apparatus used by a student to distil salt water.

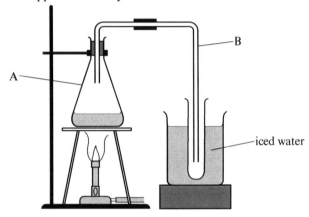

(a) Where does evaporation occur in the apparatus?

.... **(1 mark)**

(b) Where does condensation occur in the apparatus?

.... **(1 mark)**

> **Guided**

(c) What is the purpose of the beaker of iced water?

to cool the .... **(1 mark)**

(d) Name the pieces of apparatus A and B.

.... **(1 mark)**

(e) Suggest **one** piece of equipment that could be used to improve the distillation.

> This piece of apparatus would mean that the iced water is not necessary.

.... **(1 mark)**

(f) Describe a test that could be carried out to show that the water produced is pure. Give the expected result.

....

....

.... **(2 marks)**

(g) Explain why obtaining potable water in this way is not good for the environment.

....

....

.... **(2 marks)**

Life cycle assessment

1   Why are life cycle assessments carried out on products?

....

....

....

.... **(2 marks)**

2   The table shows data about plastic and glass fizzy drink bottles.

	Energy needed for manufacture in J	Energy needed for filling and delivery in J
Plastic fizzy drink bottle	4 500 000	2 200 000
Glass fizzy drink bottle	7 520 000	2 000 000

(a) How much energy is needed to manufacture a glass fizzy drink bottle?

.... **(1 mark)**

Guided

(b) Give **three** processes that are considered when creating a life cycle assessment to assess the environmental impact of the plastic and glass fizzy drink bottles.

1 extracting and processing raw materials

2 ....

3 .... **(3 marks)**

(c) Calculate the energy saving when the glass bottle is reused four times compared with using four new plastic bottles.

> First work out the energy to reuse the glass bottle four times, and add the cost of the manufacture. Then work out the cost for manufacturing and filling four plastic bottles.

....

....

....

....

....

....

....

Energy saving = ... **(5 marks)**

(d) Give **two** methods of reducing the carbon footprint of a plastic bottle.

> Refer to page 152 to remind you about carbon footprints.

....

.... **(2 marks)**

Conserving resources

1 The bar chart shows information about the proportion of different metals that are recycled.

(a) Which **two** metals have the highest proportion recycled?

.... **(1 mark)**

 Guided

(b) Suggest **two** reasons why one metal might be recycled more than another metal.

1   Its ore might be ....

2   It might be ....to extract the metal.

(2 marks)

(c) In 2010 the total world lead consumption was approximately 4.6 million tonnes.
Use this information and the data from the chart to calculate the mass of lead recycled that year.
Give your answer to two significant figures.

....

mass of lead recycled = ... tonnes

(2 marks)

(d) State **three** advantages of recycling metals.

....

....

.... **(3 marks)**

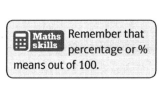
Maths skills Remember that percentage or % means out of 100.

2 Aluminium is extracted from the ore bauxite, which is aluminium oxide.

(a) The formula of aluminium oxide is Al_2O_3. Calculate the relative formula mass of aluminium oxide. Relative atomic masses A_r: O = 16; Al = 27.

....

.... **(1 mark)**

 Guided

(b) Calculate the percentage of aluminium in aluminium oxide by mass.
Give your answer to three significant figures.

$$\% \text{ aluminium} = \frac{\text{mass of aluminium}}{\text{relative formula mass}} \times 100$$

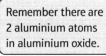
Remember there are 2 aluminium atoms in aluminium oxide.

$$\frac{27 \times 2}{\text{relative formula mass}} \times 100$$

percentage of aluminium = ...% **(2 marks)**

(c) In the USA 31% of aluminium metal is recycled. It is melted and reformed into different products.

Why is aluminium recycled?

....

.... **(2 marks)**

Extended response – Using resources

A packaging company have decided to use cardboard cartons to package food, because they think using cardboard cartons will have less environmental impact than using plastic cartons. Evaluate their decision. Use your own knowledge and information from the table.

The table shows data from a life cycle assessment to make a cardboard carton, and a similar-sized plastic carton.

raw material	wood	crude oil
mass of carbon dioxide produced during manufacture in kg	0.5	0.3
maximum temperature used in production in °C	365	850
volume of water used in manufacture in dm³	4500	250

> You will be more successful in extended response questions if you plan your answer before you start writing.
>
> You should try to use the information given in the question.

....

....

....

....

....

....

....

....

....

....

....

....

....

....

....

....

....

.... **(6 marks)**

Energy stores and systems

1 Identify which of the following is an energy store.

Tick **one** box.

elastic potential ☐

light ☐

radiation ☐

wind ☐   **(1 mark)**

2 Identify the correct energy stores that occur in the following examples by drawing lines to show your answers. The first one has been done for you.

A	a container box lifted by a crane
B	hot water in a saucepan
C	bag of coal
D	moving wind turbine

chemical

gravitational

kinetic

thermal

(1 mark)

3 The principle of the conservation of energy states that energy can be usefully transferred to other stores. Complete the energy flow diagram below to show the changes in energy stores and transfers for a battery-operated music system, when it is switched on. Write the correct description of energy in each box.

> Your answer should include the following terms: 'electrical current', 'heating', 'chemical energy', 'sound waves'.

(a) Store of	(b) Energy transfer by	(c) Energy transfer to
....	....	....
....	....	....

(3 marks)

4 A basket of apples is lowered to the ground from an apple tree using a rope and pulley. The total energy transferred is 250 J. Describe the energy transfers taking place, including the useful and wasteful energy components that result.

The total energy available initially in this closed system, in the gravitational potential

store, is ....

....

....

....

....

....

.... **(4 marks)**

Changes in energy

1   Choose the correct equation for calculating gravitational potential energy.

Tick **one** box.

$E_p = m\,v\,h$ ☐ $E_p = m\,F\,a$ ☐

$E_p = \frac{1}{2}\,m\,v^2$ ☐ $E_p = m\,g\,h$ ☐   **(1 mark)**

2   A cyclist and her bicycle are travelling at 6 m/s.

> **Guided**

The mass of the cyclist and bicycle is 70 kg.

Calculate the kinetic energy of the cyclist. Choose the correct unit from the box.

m/s²	J	W

Kinetic energy = ...

so   ....

Kinetic energy = ... unit .... **(3 marks)**

3   A spring has a spring constant of 200 N/m.

It is stretched 15 cm when a mass is applied.

Calculate the energy transferred to the spring. Use the correct equation from the Physics Equation Sheet.

....

....

Energy transferred = ... J **(3 marks)**

4   A dancer with a mass of 60 kg practises chin-ups during training and raises her body 0.7 m.

Calculate the gravitational potential energy gained by the dancer between the bottom and top of the chin-up.

> Use $g = 10$ N/kg in the equation that links m, g and h.

....

....

Gravitational potential energy = ... J **(2 marks)**

Energy changes in systems

1 Give the equation for specific heat capacity.

.... **(1 mark)**

2 Calculate how much energy is needed to heat 0.8 kg of water from 30 °C to 80 °C. The specific heat capacity of water is 4200 J/kg °C. Use the correct equation from the Physics Equation Sheet.

....

....

....

Energy required = ... J **(3 marks)**

3 A 1.2 kg block of copper is supplied with 20 000 J of electrical energy. Calculate the change in temperature of the copper. The specific heat capacity of copper is 385 J/kg °C. Use the correct equation from the Physics Equation Sheet.

> You will need to rearrange the equation you used in Question 2.

$\Delta\theta = \dfrac{\Delta E}{(m\ c)}$ so $\Delta\theta = \dfrac{20\,000}{\rule{3cm}{0.4pt}} = $ ....

....

....

....

Change in temperature of the copper = ... °C **(3 marks)**

4 A metal block of mass 0.8 kg is connected to a heater which transfers 16 200 J of energy to the block. The temperature increase is 25 °C. Calculate the specific heat capacity of the block of metal. Use the correct equation from the Physics Equation Sheet.

thermometer · · · · · ·

low voltage supply

V

A

metal block

lagging

heater

....

....

....

....

Specific heat capacity = ... J/kg °C **(3 marks)**

Required practical – Specific heat capacity

1 Water is widely used in cooling systems because of its relatively high specific heat capacity compared with some other liquids.

   (a) Write the definition of the term 'specific heat capacity'.

      .... **(1 mark)**

   (b) Give the **three** quantities that need to be measured to calculate the specific heat capacity of a substance.

      .... **(1 mark)**

2 (a) Describe an experiment that could be set up to measure the specific heat capacity of water using an electric water heater, a beaker and a thermometer.

> Remember 'pre-experiment' steps, e.g. zero the balance to eliminate the mass of apparatus before measuring substances, take a starting temperature reading before heating and decide on the range or type of measurements to be taken.

      ....

      ....

      ....

      ....

      ....

      ....

      ....

      .... **(5 marks)**

   (b) Suggest how you can determine the amount of thermal energy supplied to the heater by the electric current.

      ....

      ....

      .... **(2 marks)**

   (c) Describe how this experiment could be improved to give more accurate results.

      ....

      ....

      .... **(2 marks)**

3 A known mass of ice is heated until it becomes steam. The temperature is recorded every minute. Describe how to use the data to identify when there are changes of state.

      ....

      ....

      .... **(2 marks)**

Power

1 A kettle transfers 12 500 J of electrical energy in 5 seconds. What is the power rating of the kettle?

Tick **one** box.

2500 W   ☐   25 000 W   ☐

12 500 W   ☐   62 500 W   ☐   **(1 mark)**

2 A microwave heats a drink in 20 seconds using 15 000 J of electrical energy. Calculate the power of the microwave.

> **Guided**

Energy transferred = ... J, time taken = ... s

$P = \dfrac{E}{t} =$ .... W

Power = ... W   **(2 marks)**

3 A student with a mass of 60 kg climbs 20 stairs to a physics lab. Each stair is 0.08 m high; g is 10 N/kg.

(a) Calculate the gravitational potential energy gained in climbing the 20 stairs to the lab. Select the correct unit from the box.

watts	newtons	joules

> You need to remember that $E_P = m\,g\,h$ because it's not on the Physics Equation Sheet.

....

....

Gravitational potential energy = ... unit ....   **(3 marks)**

(b) Calculate the power of the student's muscles to climb the stairs in 12 seconds. Include the unit in your answer.

....

Power = ...   **(1 mark)**

4 Two students investigate the time taken for two different winch motors to transfer energy.

> You will need to recall and rearrange the equation $P = E\,/\,t$

(a) Calculate the time taken for a 3 W winch motor to transfer 360 J of energy.

....

.... **(2 marks)**

(b) Calculate the time taken for a 5 W winch motor to transfer 360 J of energy.

....

.... **(2 marks)**

Energy transfers and efficiency

1 (a) Identify the most suitable material, from the table below, for building an energy-efficient garage.

Material	Relative thermal conductivity
brick	1.06
concrete	1.00
sandstone	2.20
granite	2.75

.... **(1 mark)**

(b) Define the term 'low relative thermal conductivity' of a material.

....

.... **(2 marks)**

> **Guided**

2 (a) Some houses are built with very thick walls. Explain how these walls help to keep the houses warm in the winter.

Thicker walls provide more material for ....

to travel through from the inside to outside, so the ....

.... is less, keeping the houses warmer.   **(2 marks)**

(b) In hot countries, some traditional houses have thick walls with small windows. Explain why.

Thicker walls provide more material for ....

to travel through from the outside to inside, so the ....

.... is less, keeping the houses cool.   **(2 marks)**

3 A student uses four beakers containing hot water, each wrapped with different insulating materials, to investigate the transfer of thermal energy. Which factor will **not** affect the rate of transfer of thermal energy?

Tick **one** box.

rate of data collection ☐   temperature of the room ☐

starting temperature of water ☐   thickness of the insulators ☐ **(1 mark)**

4 A box gains 100 J of energy in its gravitational potential energy store when it is lifted from the floor to a lab desk. The motor lifting the box transfers 400 J as kinetic energy.

> Remember: efficiency = $\dfrac{\text{useful energy transferred by the machine}}{\text{total energy supplied to the machine}}$

Calculate the efficiency of the motor.

....

....

.... **(2 marks)**

Energy resources

1 Name **three** non-renewable energy resources.

1 ....

2 ....

3 .... **(1 mark)**

2 A hydroelectric power station is used to produce electricity when demand is high.

(a) Explain why the hydroelectric power station is a reliable producer of electricity.

> Hydroelectric power relies on water power; you need to explain why this is reliable.

....

....

....

.... **(2 marks)**

(b) Explain why hydroelectric power stations are not used in more places in the UK.

....

....

....

.... **(2 marks)**

3 For each of the following statements about fossil fuels, describe the negative environmental impacts.

Guided

> Think about the possible consequences of the statements describing the use of fossil fuels.

(a) Carbon dioxide is released as a result of burning fossil fuels.

When carbon dioxide is released into the atmosphere it contributes to ....

....

.... **(2 marks)**

(b) Burning fossil fuels produces sulfur dioxide and nitrogen oxides.

....

....

.... **(2 marks)**

(c) Fossil fuels need to be extracted from the ground and transported to the power station.

Coal mines / oil / gas wells create environmental ....

....

.... **(2 marks)**

Patterns of energy use

Guided

1 The graphs show patterns of energy use and human population growth.

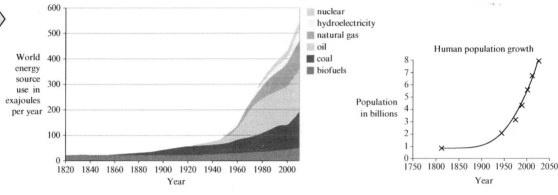

(a) Give **three** reasons why energy consumption rose significantly after the year 1900.

1 After 1900, the world's energy demand .... as the population grew.

2 There was development in ....

3 The rise of power stations using fossil fuels added to .... **(3 marks)**

(b) (i) Identify the **three** main energy resources used to provide the world's energy between the years 1000 and 2000.

.... **(1 mark)**

(ii) Suggest **two** reasons why the use of energy resources has increased in the developed world.

1 ....

2 .... **(2 marks)**

(iii) Suggest why nuclear energy resources appear only after 1950.

.... **(1 mark)**

(iv) Identify a renewable resource from the graph that makes use of gravitational potential energy.

.... **(1 mark)**

2 In the graph in question 1, the patterns in energy consumption are similar to the pattern in the world's population growth. Describe the issues that may result from the continuing use of energy in the future, at the same rate as shown in the graph.

> Consider the finite resources and increasing demand.

....

....

....

....

....

.... **(4 marks)**

Extended response – Energy

A girl plays on a swing in the park. The swing seat is initially pulled back by her friend to 30° to the vertical position and then released. Describe the energy changes in the motion of the swing as it swings backwards and forwards.

Your answer should also explain, in terms of energy, why the swing eventually stops.

> You will be more successful in extended response questions if you plan your answer before you start writing.
>
> The question asks you to give a detailed explanation of the energy changes as the swing moves backwards and forwards. Think about:
>
> - how gravitational potential energy changes as the swing is pulled back
> - points where gravitational potential energy (E_p) and kinetic energy (E_k) are at maximum and at 0
> - where some energy may be lost from the system
> - why the swing will eventually stop.
>
> You should try to use the information given in the question.

....

....

....

....

....

....

....

....

....

....

....

....

....

.... **(6 marks)**

Circuit symbols

1 Select the component that is designed to respond to changes in levels of light.

Tick **one** box.

diode ☐ LDR ☐

LED ☐ thermistor ☐

(1 mark)

2 (a) The three symbols below represent three components. Write the name of each component in the corresponding box.

1	2	3

(3 marks)

(b) Identify which component in part (a) is commonly found in a household plug connected to the live wire.

.... **(1 mark)**

3 Complete the table of circuit symbols below:

Component	Symbol	Purpose
ammeter		
		provides a fixed resistance to the flow of current
	⊸▷⊢	
		allows the current to be switched on / off

(4 marks)

4 Draw a circuit that could be used to measure the resistance of an unknown resistor.

> Consider whether each component should be connected in series or in parallel.

(4 marks)

Electrical charge and current

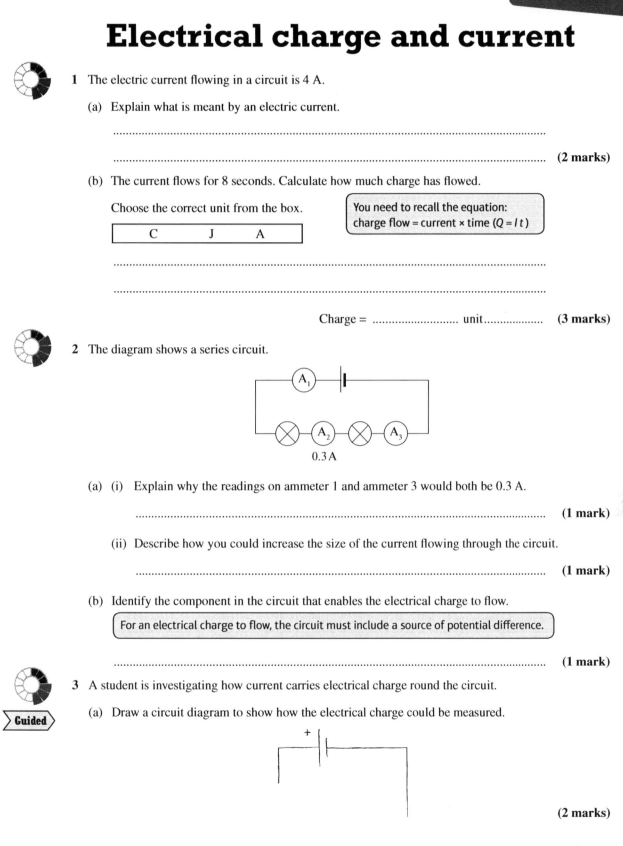

1 The electric current flowing in a circuit is 4 A.

(a) Explain what is meant by an electric current.

....

.... **(2 marks)**

(b) The current flows for 8 seconds. Calculate how much charge has flowed.

Choose the correct unit from the box.

C	J	A

> You need to recall the equation:
> charge flow = current × time ($Q = I\,t$)

....

....

Charge = ... unit.................. **(3 marks)**

2 The diagram shows a series circuit.

0.3 A

(a) (i) Explain why the readings on ammeter 1 and ammeter 3 would both be 0.3 A.

.... **(1 mark)**

(ii) Describe how you could increase the size of the current flowing through the circuit.

.... **(1 mark)**

(b) Identify the component in the circuit that enables the electrical charge to flow.

> For an electrical charge to flow, the circuit must include a source of potential difference.

.... **(1 mark)**

3 A student is investigating how current carries electrical charge round the circuit.

> **Guided**

(a) Draw a circuit diagram to show how the electrical charge could be measured.

+

(2 marks)

(b) Give **one** other piece of equipment the student would need to calculate electrical charge.

.... **(1 mark)**

Current, resistance and pd

1 Choose the quantity that the ohm (Ω) is the unit of.

Tick **one** box.

current ☐   potential difference ☐

energy ☐   resistance ☐   **(1 mark)**

Guided

2 Give the relationship between current and potential difference for a resistor.

The current flowing through a .... at constant temperature is

.... to the potential difference across the resistor. **(2 marks)**

3 (a) Calculate the potential difference across a resistor which has a resistance of 60 Ω and a current of 0.20 A passing through it.

> You will need to recall the equation: $V = I R$

....

....

....

Potential difference = ... V **(2 marks)**

(b) Calculate the current passing through a 55 Ω resistor with a potential difference of 22 V across it.

....

....

....

Current = ... A **(2 marks)**

4 (a) Sketch two lines on the graph to show two ohmic conductors of different resistances. Label these A and B. **(2 marks)**

Current in A

0   Potential difference in V

(b) From your graph, identify which line represents the resistor with the higher resistance.

.... **(1 mark)**

Required practical – Investigating resistance

1 Which of these is the correct method of connecting an ammeter and a voltmeter to determine resistance of a component in a circuit?

Tick **one** box.

Ammeter and voltmeter are both connected in series with the component. ☐

Ammeter is connected in series but voltmeter is connected in parallel across the component. ☐

Ammeter and voltmeter are both connected in parallel across the component. ☐

Voltmeter is connected in series but ammeter is connected in parallel across the component. ☐

(1 mark)

2 Calculate the resistance of a lamp supplied with a current of 1.5 A and a potential difference of 90 V.

....

....

Resistance of lamp = ... Ω **(2 marks)**

3 Complete the circuit diagram to show how the resistance of a lamp may be obtained using an ammeter and a voltmeter.

Use the components in the box to help you.

(3 marks)

4 Suggest which components have been tested by looking at the graphs (below) of the data collected.

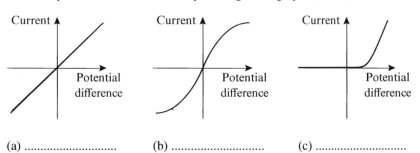

(a) ....   (b) ....   (c) .... **(3 marks)**

Resistors

1 The *I–V* graphs below show **two** types of component.

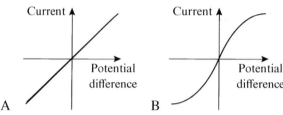

      A   B

(a) Describe what happens to the current through the component shown in graph A as the potential difference increases.

....

....

.... **(2 marks)**

(b) Describe what happens to the current through the component shown in graph B as the potential difference increases.

....

....

.... **(2 marks)**

2 (a) Complete the *I–V* graphs for a fixed resistor and a filament lamp.

           Fixed resistor   Filament lamp

     Current   Current

                  Potential   Potential

                  difference   difference

(2 marks)

(b) Explain why the filament lamp graph has a different shape to the fixed resistor graph (at constant temperature).

> A fixed resistor (at constant temperature) is an ohmic conductor but a filament lamp is not.

....

....

.... **(2 marks)**

3 Describe an experiment to collect data to enable the calculation of the resistance of a wire.

Data can be collected using an ammeter to measure ....

and a voltmeter to measure ....

A wire should be included and a fixed .... to prevent overheating.

A range of .... measurements should be made so that

resistance can be calculated using the equation .... **(5 marks)**

LDRs and thermistors

1 Identify the variable that will affect the resistance of an LDR.

Tick **one** box.

current ☐

humidity ☐

light ☐

temperature ☐ **(1 mark)**

2 Draw the circuit symbols for the components in the boxes provided.

light-dependent resistor (LDR)	thermistor

(2 marks)

3 The sketch graphs below illustrate the relationship between two variables.

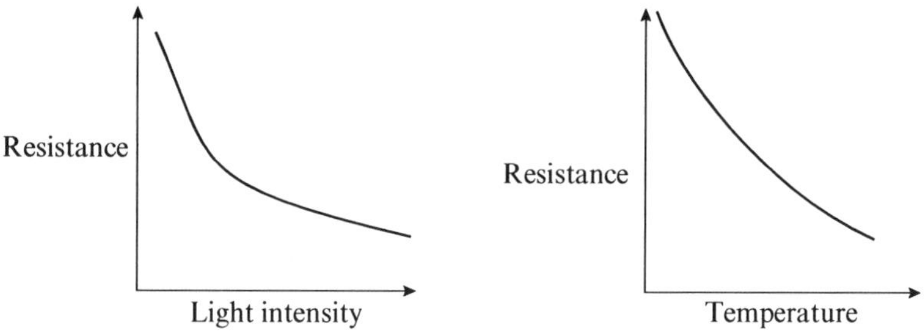

(a) Describe how resistance changes with light.

.... **(1 mark)**

(b) Describe how resistance changes with temperature.

.... **(1 mark)**

4 A car stops at traffic lights. While the car is stationary, the engine is no longer cooled by moving air. A thermistor forms part of a circuit connected to a cooling fan near the engine. Explain the role of the thermistor in the circuit.

The thermistor reacts to a rise in .... in the engine.

Above a certain temperature, it allows .... in the circuit

to flow to a fan, which.. the engine. **(3 marks)**

Guided

Required practical – Investigating *I–V* characteristics

1 (a) Complete the diagram below to show how the circuit could be used to investigate the *I–V* characteristics of a range of components.

(2 marks)

  (b) Suggest the type of data that should be collected using the circuit above by completing headings for the table below.

> These are the dependent and independent variables that you are recording in your experiment.

(i)	(ii)
Data	Data

(2 marks)

  (c) Explain why the terminal connections should be reversed to collect additional data.

.... **(1 mark)**

  (d) Write the labels you would give to the axes on your graph.

    y-axis ....

    x-axis .... **(1 mark)**

2 (a) Write the equation linking potential difference, resistance and current in symbols, including the units used.

    ....

    .... **(2 marks)**

  (b) Describe what an ohmic conductor is.

    ....

    ....

    .... **(2 marks)**

3 Identify **one** safety hazard when using resistors in a circuit.

.... **(1 mark)**

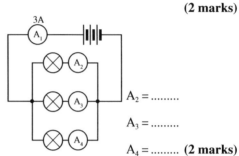

Series and parallel circuits

1 (a) Explain the rules for current in series and parallel circuits.

In a series circuit the current flowing through each component is ....

In a parallel circuit, the current is ....

the components. **(2 marks)**

(b) Each lamp in these circuits is identical. Write the
current for each ammeter on the circuit diagrams.

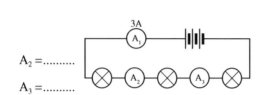

A_2 =..........

A_3 =..........

A_2 = ...

A_3 = ...

A_4 = ... **(2 marks)**

2 (a) Describe the rules for potential difference in series and parallel circuits.

In a series circuit, the total potential difference supplied is ....

....

In a parallel circuit, the potential difference across each component is ....

.... **(2 marks)**

(b) Each lamp in these circuits is identical.
Write the potential difference for each
voltmeter on the circuit diagrams.

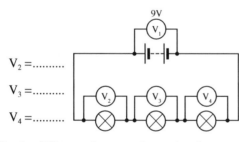

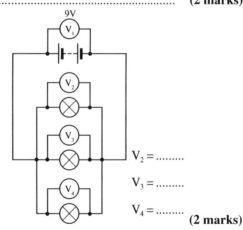

V_2 =..........

V_3 =..........

V_4 =..........

V_2 = ...

V_3 = ...

V_4 = ... **(2 marks)**

3 Describe the difference between the total resistance
of a series circuit and the total resistance of a parallel
circuit, as illustrated below.

> You may find the equation for series
> circuits $R = R_1 + R_2$ helpful in considering
> how current flows.

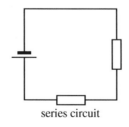

series circuit

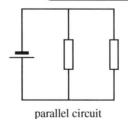

parallel circuit

....

....

....

.... **(4 marks)**

ac and dc

1 Circuits can operate using either a direct potential difference and current or an alternating potential difference and current.

  (a) Explain what is meant by **direct** potential difference and current.

    Direct potential difference is constant and the current flows in the ....

    direction. **(2 marks)**

  (b) Explain what is meant by **alternating** potential difference and current.

    Alternating potential difference is .... and the current constantly

    .... direction. **(2 marks)**

2 Identify the correct values for potential difference and frequency of the mains supply in the UK.

  Tick **one** box.

  120 V and 50 Hz ☐   50 V and 230 Hz ☐

  230 V and 20 Hz ☐   230 V and 50 Hz ☐   **(1 mark)**

3 A cell in an electric circuit causes electrons to move along the wires as shown in the diagram.

  (a) State the type of current supplied by the cell and give a reason for your answer.

    Use the diagram to help you.

cell

    ....

    .... **(2 marks)**

  (b) Complete the graph to show what the trace of the current supplied by the cell would look like on an oscilloscope.

Volts

Time

(1 mark)

Mains electricity

1 (a) Add labels to complete the diagram of a household plug. Use words from the box.

| earth wire | fuse | live wire | neutral wire |

....
(yellow and green)   (brown)

....
(blue)   ....

(4 marks)

(b) Explain which wire the fuse is connected to and why.

....

.... **(2 marks)**

2 The UK domestic mains electricity supply has certain characteristics.

(a) Give the type of current that is delivered through the mains electricity National Grid.

.... **(1 mark)**

(b) Give the potential difference between the live and neutral wires.

.... **(1 mark)**

(c) Give the potential difference and purpose of the earth wire.

....

.... **(2 marks)**

(d) Give the frequency of the domestic electricity supply in the UK.

.... **(1 mark)**

3 Explain how the fuse in a plug works.

> **Guided**

> A large current can cause a heating effect in the fuse, which is connected to the live wire.

When a large current enters the live wire, this produces ....

.... which ....

and the circuit is then .... **(4 marks)**

4 Describe how the earth wire in a plug protects the user if the live wire becomes loose.

....

....

....

.... **(3 marks)**

Electrical power

1 A hotplate is used to heat up a saucepan of water. The hotplate uses mains voltage of 230 V. The electric current through the hotplate is 5 A. Calculate the power of the hotplate in watts.

> **Guided**

$P = I\,V = 5\,A \times$ V

so $P =$ .... W   **(2 marks)**

2 The potential difference across a cell is 6 V. The cell delivers 3 W of power to a filament lamp.

(a) Calculate the current flowing through the lamp.

....

....

....

Current = ... A   **(3 marks)**

(b) A new lamp has a resistance of 240 Ω which draws a current of 0.5 A. Calculate the power rating of the new lamp.

> You need to recall the equation $P = I^2 R$

....

....

....

Power = ... W   **(3 marks)**

3 A coffee maker draws a current of 6 A using a mains voltage of 230 V. The coffee maker is switched on for 15 minutes. Which calculation could be used to determine the power of a coffee maker?

Tick **one** box.

power = (6 × 230 × 15) / 15 (W) ☐   power = 6 × 230 / 15 (W) ☐

power = 6 × 230 / 900 (W) ☐   power = 6 × 230 (W) ☐   **(1 mark)**

4 An 80 V electric drill has a resistance of 8 Ω.

(a) Calculate the current flowing through the drill.

....

....

Current = ... A   **(2 marks)**

(b) Calculate the power of the drill.

....

....

Power = ... W   **(2 marks)**

Electrical energy

1 Identify the quantity that is **not** used to calculate the amount of energy transferred by a device.

Tick **one** box.

current ☐

force ☐

potential difference ☐

time ☐ **(1 mark)**

2 Calculate the amount of energy transferred to a 9 V lamp when a charge of 30 C is supplied.

....

....

Energy transferred = ... J **(2 marks)**

3 A mobile phone has a battery that produces a potential difference of 4 V. When making a call, the phone uses a current of 0.2 A. A student makes a call lasting 30 seconds.

> **Guided**

You need to recall the equations $Q = I\,t$ and $E = Q\,V$

(a) Calculate the charge flow during the phone call.

Charge flow, $Q = $ ....

Charge flow = ... C **(2 marks)**

(b) Calculate the energy transferred by the mobile phone while the call is made. Choose the correct unit from the box.

W	J	V

Energy transferred, $E = $ ....

....

Energy transferred = ... unit................. **(3 marks)**

4 Explain how the energy of a circuit device is related to the following:

(a) Power:

....

.... **(1 mark)**

(b) Potential difference and current:

....

....

....

.... **(2 marks)**

The National Grid

1 The National Grid transmits electricity from power stations at 400 000 volts (400 kV).

(a) Describe the cause of the heating effect of a current.

....

.... **(2 marks)**

(b) Explain why this voltage is used to transmit electricity long distances.

> Remember that increasing the voltage decreases the current.

....

....

....

....

.... **(3 marks)**

(c) Explain how this system can be described as 'efficient'.

....

....

....

.... **(2 marks)**

(d) Give **one** hazard of transmitting electricity at 400 000 V.

.... **(1 mark)**

2 Describe **two** ways in which energy losses from the National Grid may be reduced.

....

....

....

.... **(2 marks)**

3 Transformers are used at various places in the National Grid. Describe the role of transformers.

> **Guided**

Step-up transformers are used to increase the ....

from the power station to the .... then step-down

transformers are used to .... the ....

for domestic use. **(4 marks)**

Extended response – Electricity

Explain how a circuit can be used to investigate the change in resistance for a thermistor and a light-dependent resistor. Your answer should include a use for each component.

> You will be more successful in extended response questions if you plan your answer before you start writing.
>
> The question asks you to give a detailed explanation of how resistance changes in two types of variable resistor. Think about:
>
> - how resistance in a resistor can be measured and calculated
> - the variable that causes a change in resistance in a thermistor
> - the variable that causes a change in resistance in a light-dependent resistor
> - the consequence to the circuit of a change in resistance in a component
> - uses for thermistors and light-dependent resistors.
>
> You should try to use the information given in the question.

....

....

....

....

....

....

....

....

....

....

....

....

....

....

....

....

....

.... **(6 marks)**

Density

1 The diagram below shows the three states of matter for a metal.

(a) Identify the three states of matter. Write the names in the boxes. **(1 mark)**

| 1 | 2 | 3 |

(b) Describe how mass per unit volume varies with particle arrangement for **each** of the states of matter shown in the diagrams.

....

....

....

....

.... **(3 marks)**

2 Which of these statements correctly describes density?

Tick **one** box.

Density is constant for a substance, whether it is a solid, a liquid or a gas. ☐

Density is calculated by dividing mass by volume. ☐

Density can be described by weight per unit area. ☐

Density is calculated by measuring force and volume. ☐ **(1 mark)**

3 A timber centre collects data on the density of different types of wood.

(a) Calculate the density of a large block of pine wood with a mass of 1650 kg and a volume of 3 m^3.

> You will need to learn the equation $\rho = m / V$ as it's not on the Physics Equation Sheet.

....

....

Density = ... kg/m^3 **(2 marks)**

(b) Calculate the density of a block of elm wood that has a mass of 4000 kg and a volume of 5 m^3.

....

....

Density = ... kg/m^3 **(2 marks)**

Practical skills

Required practical – Investigating density

1 When determining the density of a substance you need to measure the volume of the sample.

   (a) Identify which other quantity you need to measure.

   .... **(1 mark)**

   (b) Give an example of how you could measure this quantity.

   .... **(1 mark)**

2 (a) Describe a method that could be used to determine the volume of a regularly shaped solid.

   ....

   ....

   ....

   .... **(2 marks)**

   (b) Describe a method that could be used to determine the volume of an irregularly shaped solid.

   ....

   ....

   ....

   .... **(2 marks)**

3 (a) Describe a method that could be used to find the density of a liquid using a balance.

Guided

   Place a measuring cylinder on a balance and then zero the scales with ....

   ....

   Add the liquid and .... Record the ....

   .... (in g) from the balance and the .... (in cm^3)

   by reading from the ....level in the measuring cylinder. **(3 marks)**

   (b) Describe the technique to read the volume of the liquid accurately.

   ....

   ....

   .... **(2 marks)**

   (c) Calculate the density of a liquid with a mass of 121 g and a volume of 205 cm^3.

> You may find this equation useful
>
> $$\text{density} = \frac{\text{mass}}{\text{volume}} \quad \left(\rho = \frac{m}{V} \right)$$

   ....

   ....

   ....

   Density = ... g/cm^3 **(2 marks)**   **185**

Had a go ☐   Nearly there ☐   Nailed it! ☐

Changes of state

1   Describe the difference between intermolecular forces between particles in a liquid and between particles in a gas.

....

....

.... **(2 marks)**

2   Write the type of change that takes place when a substance changes state.

.... **(1 mark)**

3   Water is commonly used to demonstrate changes of state. Complete the sentences to describe the changes of state using words from the box.

condenses	evaporates	boils	freezes	melts

When ice is heated beyond 0 °C it .... to become water. The water

is heated and it .... at 100 °C. As heating continues the water

.... and turns to water vapour. As the water vapour is cooled it

.... to become water. As the water cools further it

.... at 0 °C to become ice. **(3 marks)**

4   Which statement describes the energy change when ice melts and then refreezes?

Tick **one** box.

energy is transferred to surroundings → further energy is transferred to surroundings ☐

energy is transferred to the ice → energy is transferred to surroundings ☐

energy is transferred to surroundings → energy is transferred to the ice ☐

energy is transferred to the ice → energy remains in the system ☐   **(1 mark)**

5   Explain why the temperature stops rising when a liquid is heated to its boiling point and heating continues.

Guided

At boiling point, the ....

so the energy applied after boiling point is reached goes into ....

....

The particles .... and become a .... **(3 marks)**

Internal energy

1 Choose the correct description of internal energy.

Tick **one** box.

the total number of particles in the system ☐

the total sum of the kinetic and potential energies of the particles inside the system ☐

the total number of energies inside the system ☐

the total sum of the kinetic and potential energies of the particles outside the system ☐

(1 mark)

2 A liquid is heated at boiling point before becoming a gas. Describe the change, if any, in the potential and kinetic energies of the particles.

> Remember that latent heat of vaporisation occurs at the boiling point.

liquid   gas

....

....

....

.... **(2 marks)**

3 (a) Describe how internal energy changes when there is a temperature rise in a substance that is heated.

....

....

....

.... **(2 marks)**

(b) Describe how internal energy changes when there is no change in temperature in a substance that is heated.

....

....

....

.... **(2 marks)**

> Guided

4 Explain the condensation of water vapour in terms of kinetic and potential energies of the particles.

When the water vapour condenses into a liquid there will be no change in the

.... of the water particles so the temperature ....

.... but there will be a .... in the

.... of the water particles as they move

from a gas state to a liquid state. **(3 marks)**

Had a go ☐   Nearly there ☐   Nailed it! ☐

Specific latent heat

1 Define the term 'specific latent heat'.

.... **(1 mark)**

2 Which of the following remains constant during a change of state?

Tick **one** box.

thermal energy of the mass ☐

kinetic energy of the particles ☐

temperature of the mass ☐

energy supplied to the mass ☐ **(1 mark)**

3 Calculate the amount of energy needed to melt 25 kg of ice. Take the specific latent heat of fusion of water to be 336 000 J/kg.

....

....

Energy required = ... J   **(2 marks)**

4 Which of the letters A–E on the graph correspond to the following stages during the temperature rise of water over time?

Temperature in °C

(a) Melting ....

(b) Evaporating ....

(c) Specific latent heat of fusion ....

(d) Specific latent heat of vaporisation .... **(4 marks)**

(e) Describe what is happening at stages B and D when there is no rise in temperature.

> Consider the bonds between particles.

....

.... **(2 marks)**

5 Calculate the energy needed to evaporate 36 kg of water at 100 °C to 36 kg steam at 100 °C.

Take the specific latent heat of vaporisation of water to be 2260 kJ/kg.

....

....

....

Energy needed = ... kJ   **(2 marks)**

Particle motion in gases

1 Describe what is meant by temperature.

> Consider the movement of particles.

....

.... **(1 mark)**

2 The graph below represents the change in pressure with temperature of a gas at constant volume. Describe the relationship shown in the graph between pressure and temperature of the gas.

....

.... **(1 mark)**

3 In an experiment, a fixed-volume container of 100 g of helium gas is warmed from −10 °C to 30 °C.

(a) Describe what happens to the velocity of the helium particles as the temperature increases.

As the temperature increases the particles will move ....

because they gain more .... **(2 marks)**

(b) Explain how this affects the pressure on the container walls.

....

....

.... **(2 marks)**

(c) Describe what happens to the average kinetic energy of the particles as the temperature increases.

.... **(1 mark)**

Extended response – Particle model

 Substances can undergo a change of state. Explain, using the kinetic particle theory, the changes of state of water. In your answer, include reasons to explain why thermal energy input and output are not always linked to changes in temperature.

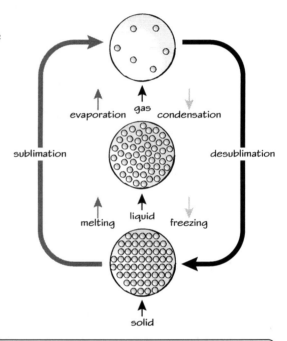

> You will be more successful in extended response questions if you plan your answer before you start writing.
>
> The question asks you to give a detailed explanation of how water changes state in terms of particles. Think about:
>
> - the relative kinetic energy of particles in solids, liquids and gases
> - why a change of state is described as a reversible change
> - how heating the system can result in a change in temperature
> - why heating the system does not always result in a change in temperature
> - how latent heat is involved in the process.
>
> Include equations to help explain your answer. You should try to use the information given in the question.

....

....

....

....

....

....

....

....

....

....

.... **(6 marks)**

The structure of the atom

1 Complete the diagram to show the location and charge of:

(a) protons **(1 mark)**

(b) neutrons **(1 mark)**

(c) electrons **(1 mark)**

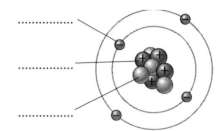

2 (a) Explain why neutral atoms have no overall charge.

> **Guided**

The number of .... in the nucleus is

.... orbiting the nucleus. **(2 marks)**

(b) Describe what will happen to the overall charge if an atom loses an electron.

.... **(1 mark)**

3 Identify the approximate diameter of an atom and a nucleus from the measurements in the box.

10^{-18} m	10^{-15} m	10^{-10} m	10^{-9} m	10^{-6} m	10^{-2} m

Size of an atom: ....

Size of a nucleus: .... **(2 marks)**

4 The diagram below shows the emission of electromagnetic radiation from an atom.
Describe the process of absorption and emission that would cause this to occur.

electron

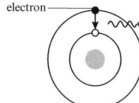

> The diagram shows emission but you will also need to explain the absorption that happens first.

....

....

....

....

....

....

....

.... **(4 marks)**

Had a go ☐ Nearly there ☐ Nailed it! ☐

Atoms, isotopes and ions

1 Describe what is meant by each term.

Guided

   (a) nucleon the name given to particles in the nucleus   **(1 mark)**

   (b) atomic number ....   **(1 mark)**

   (c) mass number ....   **(1 mark)**

2 Here are some isotopes of lithium.

$$^6_3Li, \quad ^7_3Li, \quad ^8_3Li$$

Which statement is true?

Tick **one** box.

The mass numbers of the atoms are the same.   ☐

The proton numbers of the atoms are different.   ☐

The number of neutrons is different.   ☐

The atoms are of different elements.   ☐   **(1 mark)**

3 Explain why different isotopes of the same element will still be neutrally charged.

> Consider all the particles of the isotopes.

....

....

....   **(2 marks)**

4 Some of these symbols show atoms and some show ions. Write each symbol in the correct part of the table.

| F^- | Na^+ | B | K^+ | Cu |

Atoms	Ions

(2 marks)

5 Explain **two** ways in which a neutral atom or molecule can become a positive ion by losing one or more electrons.

....

....

....

....

....

....

....

....   **(4 marks)**

Models of the atom

1 Bohr developed the nuclear model by describing orbits around the nucleus. Which particle did Bohr propose travelled in this way?

Tick **one** box.

the electron ☐

the proton ☐

the neutron ☐

the positron ☐ **(1 mark)**

2 Compare the plum pudding and nuclear models of the atom.

> Guided

The plum pudding model showed the atom as ....

particle containing ....

whereas the nuclear model showed the atom as ....

....

surrounded by .... **(4 marks)**

3 Describe the evidence that led to the nuclear model replacing the plum pudding model.

....

....

....

....

....

.... **(3 marks)**

4 About 20 years after the nuclear model was developed, James Chadwick carried out experiments by firing alpha particles at beryllium atoms. He noticed that a mass was produced close to the size of a proton but was not affected by electrical fields.

(a) Describe the conclusion that Chadwick reached as a result of this observation.

....

....

....

.... **(2 marks)**

(b) Name the particle that was discovered as a result of Chadwick's experiments.

.... **(1 mark)**

Radioactive decay

1 Complete the following sentences to explain the radioactive process.

(a) Activity is the .... at which the unstable nuclei decay

per second.   (1 mark)

(b) The unit of activity is the ....   (1 mark)

(c) Count rate is the ....

....   (2 marks)

2 Caesium-137 undergoes beta decay. Identify the correct statement.

Tick **one** box.

The positive charge of the nucleus is reduced by 2.   ☐

The number of protons decreases by 1.   ☐

The mass number decreases by 1.   ☐

The number of neutrons decreases by 1.   ☐   (1 mark)

3 Identify the correct description of a gamma-ray.

Tick **one** box.

an electron   ☐

electromagnetic radiation   ☐

a neutron   ☐

a proton   ☐   (1 mark)

4 In radioactive decay, changes occur in the nucleus. The changes resulting from two different types of radioactive decay are described below. Describe how each type of radiation is produced and include its name.

> The types of radiation to think about are: α, β, γ and neutron radiation.

(a) The nucleons are reduced by 4.

....

....

....

....   (2 marks)

(b) The positive charge of the nucleus increases by 1.

....

....

....

....   (2 marks)

Nuclear radiation

1   Select the correct description of an alpha particle.

Tick **one** box.

helium nucleus with charge −2   ☐

helium nucleus with charge +2   ☐

high-energy neutron   ☐

ionising electron   ☐   **(1 mark)**

2   Complete the table below.

Type of radiation	Penetrating power
	very low, stopped by 10 cm of air
	low, stopped by thin aluminium
	very high, stopped by very thick lead

                                                                     (2 marks)

3   An atom of carbon-14, with 6 protons and 8 neutrons, undergoes beta decay.

It becomes an atom of nitrogen, with 7 protons and 7 neutrons.

(a)   Give the change in relative atomic mass.

....

.... **(1 mark)**

(b)   Give another description for a beta particle.

....

.... **(1 mark)**

(c)   Name the relative ionising category of a beta particle.

....

.... **(1 mark)**

4   Describe why alpha particles have the shortest ionising range in air, compared with other types of ionising radiation.

> **Guided**

Compared with other types of ionising radiation, the chance of collision with air

particles at close range is high because ....

....

....

....

.... **(3 marks)**

Uses of nuclear radiation

1 Machinery that produces standard sheets of paper uses radiation to check the thickness.

> Recall the properties of alpha, beta and gamma radiation.

(a) Explain which type of radiation is used.

....

....

.... **(3 marks)**

(b) A radiation detector measures a sudden drop in the radiation that passes through the paper.

(i) Suggest the most likely cause of this change in radiation detected.

.... **(1 mark)**

(ii) Suggest how the machine would respond to the change.

.... **(1 mark)**

2 Gamma-rays are used to treat cancers. Describe the property of gamma-rays that makes them useful for treating cancers.

.... **(1 mark)**

3 The diagram of the smoke alarm shows that the radioactive isotope americium-241 is used in the system. It is a source of alpha radiation.

Guided

(a) Explain why it is safe to use smoke detectors in the home.

Alpha particles cannot pass through ....

.... and they are ....

.... **(2 marks)**

(b) Explain why the siren sounds when smoke gets into the smoke alarm.

The smoke particles absorb the alpha

particles ....

....

....

....

....

....

....

smoke entering the alarm   americium-241

siren

air molecules

charged plate

detector

battery

(4 marks)

4 Beta emitters with a short half-life can be used as tracers in the body for medical analysis. Describe the property of beta particles that make them more suitable than alpha particles for monitoring systems in the body.

....

....

.... **(2 marks)**

Nuclear equations

1 Give the symbols used in decay equations to represent the following particles.

   (a) Alpha particle: .... **(1 mark)**

   (b) Beta particle: .... **(1 mark)**

2 Radium-222 undergoes alpha decay. Identify which of the following statements is true for the original atom.

   Tick **one** box.

   The positive charge of the nucleus is
   reduced by 4.   ☐   The atomic number is increased by 1. ☐

   The mass number is reduced by 4.   ☐   The nucleus gains an extra proton.   ☐ **(1 mark)**

3 Using the data in the table, complete the equations below.

7	9	11	12	14	16	19	20
Li	Be	B	C	N	O	F	Ne
lithium	beryllium	boron	carbon	nitrogen	oxygen	fluorine	neon
3	4	5	6	7	8	9	10
23	24	27	28	29	32	35.5	40
Na	Mg	Al	Si	P	S	Cl	Ar
sodium	magnesium	aluminium	silicon	phosphorus	sulfur	chlorine	argon
11	12	13	14	15	16	17	18

   (a) $^{14}_{6}C \rightarrow\ ^{14}_{......}N +\ ^{0}_{-1}e$ **(1 mark)**

   (b) $^{32}_{......}P \rightarrow\ ^{32}_{16}S +\ ^{0}_{-1}e$ **(1 mark)**

4 Identify the type of radiation that would be emitted in each decay.

   > Remember the law of conservation of mass.

   (a) Carbon-10 (6 protons, 4 neutrons) → boron-10 (5 protons, 5 neutrons)

   .... **(1 mark)**

   (b) Uranium-238 (92 protons, 146 neutrons) → thorium-234 (90 protons, 144 neutrons)

   .... **(1 mark)**

   (c) Helium-5 (2 protons, 3 neutrons) → helium-4 (2 protons, 2 neutrons)

   .... **(1 mark)**

5 Complete each equation, naming the type of decay shown.

   > Check that the A and Z numbers obey the conservation laws.

   (a) $^{......}_{84}Po \rightarrow\ ^{4}_{2}He +\ ^{204}_{82}Pb$ Type of decay .... **(2 marks)**

   (b) $^{222}_{......}Rn \rightarrow\ ^{4}_{2}He +\ ^{218}_{84}Po$ Type of decay .... **(2 marks)**

   (c) $^{42}_{19}K \rightarrow\ ^{0}_{-1}e +\ ^{......}_{20}Ca$ Type of decay .... **(2 marks)**

   (d) $^{......}_{4}Be \rightarrow\ ^{1}_{0}n +\ ^{8}_{4}Be$ Type of decay .... **(2 marks)**

Half-life

1 Identify the correct term to describe the radioactive decay of an atom.

Tick **one** box.

methodical ☐   random ☐

regular ☐   systematic ☐   **(1 mark)**

2 Define the term 'half-life'.

....

.... **(1 mark)**

3 A sample of thallium-208 contains 16 million atoms. Thallium-208 has a half-life of 3.1 minutes.

(a) Give the number of nuclei that will have decayed in 3.1 minutes.

Number of nuclei = ... **(1 mark)**

(b) Calculate the number of unstable thallium nuclei left after 9.3 minutes.

> Remember that thallium-208 has a half-life of 3.1 minutes, so there are three half-lives in 9.3 minutes.

....

....

Number of thallium nuclei after 9.3 min = ... **(2 marks)**

Guided

4 A student measured the activity of a radioactive sample for 30 minutes. She plotted the graph of activity against time shown on the right.

Count rate in becquerels

Time in minutes

Use the graph to work out the half-life of the sample.

Starting activity = 480 Bq at .... minutes.

Half this activity = ... Bq, at .... minutes,

so the half-life is .... minutes. **(3 marks)**

Contamination and irradiation

1 Identify the correct term for when a person or object is exposed to nuclear radiation.

Tick **one** box.

decontamination ☐

fusion ☐

irradiation ☐

radioactive decay ☐   **(1 mark)**

2 Define the following terms about exposure to radiation.

(a) External contamination

....

.... **(1 mark)**

(b) Internal contamination

....

.... **(1 mark)**

(c) Irradiation

....

.... **(1 mark)**

3 Give an example of how a person may be subjected to:

(a) external contamination

.... **(1 mark)**

(b) internal contamination

.... **(1 mark)**

4 Explain why alpha particles are more dangerous from a source of internal contamination than external contamination.

> Alpha particles travel only a very short distance before colliding with another particle, losing their energy. This can have serious consequences near to the body.

....

....

....

....

....

.... **(4 marks)**

Hazards of radiation

1 Identify the most ionising radiation.

Tick **one** box.

alpha particles ☐   gamma-rays ☐

beta particles ☐   X-rays ☐   **(1 mark)**

2 Suggest **three** precautions that may be taken by people who may come into contact with ionising radiation to reduce the risk of cell damage.

1 ....

2 ....

3 ....   **(3 marks)**

3 Explain why alpha particles are more dangerous inside the body than gamma-rays.

> **Guided**

A source of alpha particles with high activity inside the body ....

.... because they ....

before transferring all of their ionising energy. Gamma-rays can ....

.... without ....

....   **(4 marks)**

4 When radioactive sources are handled, tongs are often used. Explain why people handling radioactive sources would use tongs.

radioactive source

....

....   **(2 marks)**

5 X-rays can also be ionising to body cells. Suggest why it is considered safe for the patient to be exposed to a controlled amount of X-rays whereas the medical workers have to leave the room.

> Think about what could happen to those working regularly with radioactive sources if they did not leave the room when using these.

....

....

....   **(3 marks)**

Extended response – Radioactivity

Ionising radiation will travel through some materials but will be stopped by others. The diagram shows three different materials and how alpha, beta or gamma radiation may be absorbed by each one.

Use the diagram to help you describe the structure and properties of these three types of radiation. In your answer, name the materials that could be shown in the diagram, and give other examples of how these types of radioactivity may be absorbed.

helium nucleus = α emission

electron = β emission

electromagnetic radiation = γ emission

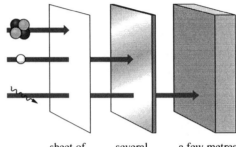

sheet of paper

several millimetres of aluminium

a few metres of concrete or more than 10 cm of lead

> You will be more successful in extended response questions if you plan your answer before you start writing.
>
> The question asks you to give a detailed explanation of the penetrative characteristics of ionising radiation and examples of materials that may stop the radiation. Think about:
>
> - the relative ionising abilities of alpha, beta and gamma radiation
> - how energy is transferred when radiation encounters a particle
> - the effect that particle collisions have on how radiation passes through a material
> - examples of materials that absorb different types of radiation.
>
> You should try to use the information given in the diagram.

....

....

....

....

....

....

....

....

....

....

....

....

....

....

.... **(6 marks)**

Scalars and vectors

1 (a) Complete the table using the examples of scalars and vectors from the box below.

acceleration   displacement   speed   energy   temperature
mass   force   velocity   momentum   distance

Scalars	Vectors

(2 marks)

> **Guided**

(b) Give one example of a scalar from the table, and explain why it is a scalar.

.... is a scalar because it has a size / magnitude but

does not have .... **(3 marks)**

2 (a) Which of the following is **not** a scalar?

Tick **one** box.

energy ☐   temperature ☐   mass ☐   weight ☐   **(1 mark)**

(b) Give a reason for your answer to part (a).

.... **(1 mark)**

3 Two students set off jogging in opposite directions. The first student starts to jog to the east at a velocity of 2 m/s. The second student jogs to the west at a velocity of −2 m/s.

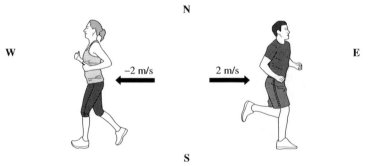

(a) (i) Explain why velocity is used in this example rather than speed.

.... **(1 mark)**

(ii) Explain why the velocity for the student jogging to the west is given a negative value.

.... **(1 mark)**

(b) Explain the importance of the length of the diagram arrows. Describe how you would draw the arrow if the second student sped up to 3 m/s.

....

....

....

.... **(2 marks)**

Interacting forces

1 Name the **three** types of fields that cause objects to interact with each other without making contact.

   1 .... 2 .... 3 .... **(3 marks)**

2 Which of the following statements correctly describes the similarities between magnetic and electrostatic fields?

   Tick **one** box.

   Like poles and charges repel. ☐

   Like poles and charges attract. ☐

   Opposite poles and charges have a null point. ☐

   Opposite poles and charges repel. ☐ **(1 mark)**

3 Describe the differences and similarities between weight and normal contact force.

   Weight and normal contact force are both vectors because ....

   ....

   Weight is measured .... whereas normal contact force is

   measured .... **(3 marks)**

4 A student pulls a wheeled suitcase, as shown in the diagram, at constant velocity.

   (a) Name the contact forces that are balanced for the horizontal plane.

   .... **(1 mark)**

   (b) Name the balanced contact forces in the vertical direction.

   .... **(1 mark)**

5 A skydiver jumps from an aeroplane. Explain which forces influence the descent of the skydiver and how the net result of the forces controls how the skydiver descends, at each stage.

   > Make sure that your answer includes the terms air resistance, terminal velocity and speed.

   ....

   ....

   ....

   ....

   ....

   .... **(4 marks)**

Gravity, weight and mass

1 The lunar roving vehicle (LRV) has a mass of 210 kg on Earth.

(a) Give the mass of the LRV on the Moon and a reason for your answer.

The mass of the LRV on the Moon is .... kg because....................

.... **(2 marks)**

(b) Draw an arrow on the LRV to show where the centre of mass would act and explain what is meant by centre of mass (in the space below).

....

.... **(2 marks)**

2 Calculate the total weight of a backpack of mass 1 kg, containing books with a mass of 2 kg and trainers with a mass of 1.5 kg. Take gravitational field strength (*g*) to be 10 N/kg.

> You will find the equation $W = m\,g$ useful.

....

....

....

....

Weight = ... N **(2 marks)**

3 A student is about to fly to Europe. The total baggage allowance is 20 kg. The student has scales that weigh only in newtons. Determine the items that she can take on holiday, as well as her clothes, to get as close to 20 kg as possible. Show your calculations. Take gravitational field strength to be 10 N/kg.

> Remember to convert the weights shown to masses before you add them up.

laptop	camera bag	walking boots	jacket	clothes
45 N	55 N	25 N	35 N	105 N

....

....

....

....

Total baggage = ... kg **(3 marks)**

Resultant forces

1 Define the term 'resultant force'.

....

.... **(1 mark)**

2 Below are diagrams of pairs of forces.

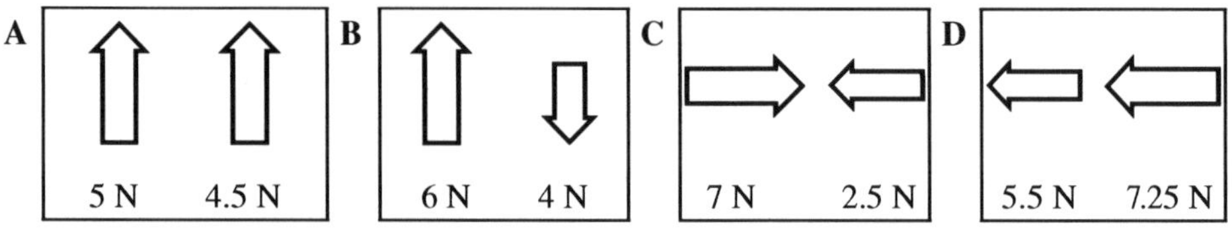

A ⇧ ⇧ 5 N 4.5 N   B ⇧ ⇩ 6 N 4 N   C ⇨ ⇦ 7 N 2.5 N   D ⇦ ⇦ 5.5 N 7.25 N

(a) Calculate the value of the resultant force for each pair.

A resultant = ... N   **B** resultant = ... N   **C** resultant = ... N   **D** resultant = ... N

(4 marks)

(b) Draw an arrow to show the direction of each resultant force.

A direction ....   **B** direction ....   **C** direction ....   **D** direction .... **(4 marks)**

3 The diagram on the right shows a pair of forces.

What is the magnitude of the resultant force?

Tick **one** box.

3 N   ☐

4 N   ☐

20 N   ☐

7 N   ☐

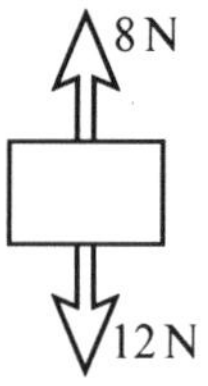

↑8 N

↓12 N   **(1 mark)**

4 A speed skater is standing on the ice waiting for the start of a race. The race begins and the skater starts to push against the ice, producing a forward thrust on the skates of 30 N. There is resistance from the air of 10 N and friction on the blades of 1 N.

Guided

(a) Calculate the resultant force.

> Add up all the forces in a straight line. Think about the direction of each force.

Resultant force = positive direction − negative direction = ...

....

Force = ... N   **(2 marks)**

(b) During the race, the resistive forces become equal to the forward thrust. Explain what happens to the velocity of the skater.

....

....

.... **(2 marks)**

Work and energy

1 Which of these is the energy equivalent to the work done when a force is moved through a vertical distance?

Tick **one** box.

gravitational potential energy ☐   latent heat ☐

kinetic energy ☐   specific heat capacity ☐   **(1 mark)**

2 (a) Explain why friction may result in wasted energy when moving an object through a distance.

Work done against friction will lead to a rise in the ....

of the object. This energy is then ....

.... **(2 marks)**

(b) Explain the consequence of friction in terms of work needed to be done in moving an object.

The greater the amount of friction ....

....

to move the body through .... **(2 marks)**

3 A suitcase is pulled along a walkway with a force of 80 N. The suitcase is pulled a distance of 60 m. Calculate the work done on the suitcase.

> You should be able to recall the equation $W = F\,s$; it won't be provided on the Physics Equation Sheet.

....

....

Work done = ... J **(2 marks)**

4 A student designs a pulley system to lift a mass of 8 kg.

The energy transferred by the force of the pulley is 320 J.

(a) Calculate the height to which the pulley system lifts the mass. Take g to be 10 N/kg.

> You should be able to recall the equation $E_p = m\,g\,h$; it won't be provided on the Physics Equation Sheet.

....

....

Height = ... m **(2 marks)**

(b) Use your answer from part (a) to calculate the force exerted by the pulley system.

....

....

Force = ... N **(3 marks)**

Forces and elasticity

1   Identify the force that would act opposite to the forward motion of a bicycle.

Tick **one** box.

upthrust   ☐

reaction force   ☐

friction   ☐

tension   ☐   **(1 mark)**

2   Give an example where each of the following may occur:

(a) tension

.... **(1 mark)**

(b) compression

.... **(1 mark)**

(c) elastic distortion

.... **(1 mark)**

(d) inelastic distortion

.... **(1 mark)**

Guided

3   A student investigates loading two aluminium beams, each with an elastic limit at 50 N.
    Beam 1 is tested to 45 N. Beam 2 is tested to 60 N.

Predict what you would expect the beams to look like after loading.

After testing, Beam 1 would return to the same size and shape as ....

.... and would be intact.

Beam 2 would ....

but would (probably) .... **(4 marks)**

Force and extension

1 Describe the difference between elastic deformation and inelastic deformation caused by stretching forces.

....

....

....

....

....

....

....

.... **(4 marks)**

2 A force is added to a spring. The extension of the spring is 0.04 m and the spring constant is 500 N/m. Calculate the force.

Tick **one** box.

0.02 N ☐   2 N ☐

0.2 N ☐   20 N ☐   **(1 mark)**

3 A spring is stretched from 0.03 m to 0.07 m, within its elastic limit. Calculate the force needed to stretch the spring. Select the correct unit from the box below.

Guided   Take the spring constant to be 80 N/m.

kg	m	N

Extension = 0.07 m – .... m = ... m

Force = ... × extension = ... × ....

Force = ... unit .... **(3 marks)**

4 (a) Calculate the spring constant (k) of a spring that is stretched 15 cm when a force of 30 N is applied.

....

....

k = ... N/m **(3 marks)**

(b) Calculate the energy transferred to the spring in part (a).

> You need to select the equation
> elastic potential energy = ½ × spring constant × extension²
> from the Physics Equation Sheet.

....

....

Energy transferred = ... J **(2 marks)**

Required practical – Force and extension

1 (a) Describe how to set up an experiment to investigate the elastic potential energy stored in a spring using a spring, a ruler, masses or weights, a clamp and a stand.

> Include a step to make sure that the spring is not damaged during the experiment.

....

....

....

....

....

.... **(4 marks)**

(b) Explain why it is important to check that the spring is not damaged during the experiment.

....

....

.... **(2 marks)**

▷ **Guided** ▷ (c) Describe how the data collected must be processed before a graph can be plotted. Assume masses are used and measurements made in mm.

Masses must be converted to ....

The extension of the spring must be ....

....

Extension measurements should be .... **(3 marks)**

(d) Describe how a graph plotted from this experiment can be used to calculate:

   (i) the elastic potential energy stored in the spring

   .... **(1 mark)**

   (ii) the spring constant k.

   .... **(1 mark)**

(e) Name the point on the graph that represents where the spring begins to permanently change shape.

.... **(1 mark)**

(f) Write the equation to calculate the energy stored by the spring.

.... **(1 mark)**

2 Explain the difference between the length of a spring and the extension of a spring.

....

.... **(1 mark)**

Distance and displacement

1 The diagram shows different points on a field.

Which of these is the correct displacement from A when a footballer warms up by running from points A to B, B to D and D to C?

Tick **one** box.

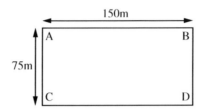

A to B to D to C = 375 m   ☐

AB × AC = 11 250 m   ☐

A to C = 75 m   ☐

AB + AC = 225 m   ☐   **(1 mark)**

> **Guided**

2 Explain why distance is described as a scalar quantity but displacement is described as a vector quantity.

Distance does not involve .... and so is a scalar quantity.

Displacement involves both ....

.... so it is a vector quantity.   **(2 marks)**

3 Two girls step into a pod on a Ferris wheel when it reaches the bottom and stops. The diameter of the Ferris wheel is 15 m. The wheel completes three cycles before the girls step off again at the bottom.

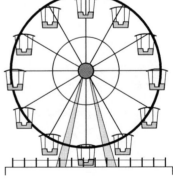

(a) Calculate the distance that the girls have travelled at the end of the ride.

> Use *2 π r* to calculate the circumference of a circle.

....

....

....   **(3 marks)**

(b) Explain the total displacement of the girls at the end of the ride.

....

....   **(2 marks)**

Speed and velocity

1 A bus travels from the bus station to the next town 10 kilometres away, passing through three villages on the way, picking up passengers at each village. The whole trip takes 40 minutes. Calculate the average speed of the bus.

> You will need to recall the equation average speed = distance / time as it's not on the Physics Equation Sheet.

....

....

Average speed = ... m/s **(2 marks)**

2 (a) The speed of runners often varies during a cross-country race. Suggest **three** factors that could affect the speed of the runners.

....

.... **(3 marks)**

(b) Give typical speeds for the following:

(i) a person walking .... **(1 mark)**

(ii) a person running .... **(1 mark)**

(iii) a person cycling .... **(1 mark)**

3 A satellite orbits the Earth with a constant speed of 3100 m/s.

> **Guided**

Explain how the speed of the satellite can be constant while the velocity is constantly changing.

The speed of the satellite is constant because the ....

...., but the velocity changes constantly because the

.... **(2 marks)**

4 A rowing team launches a boat from the boathouse and rows up the river in a north-west direction for 15 minutes at an average velocity of 4 m/s.

> You will need to recall the equation $s = v\,t$ because it's not on the Physics Equation Sheet.

(a) Calculate the distance covered by the rowing team.

....

....

Distance = ... m **(2 marks)**

(b) Explain why the term 'velocity' is used instead of 'speed' to describe the journey.

....

.... **(2 marks)**

> **Guided**

(c) Describe how the displacement of the team changes as they make their way from the boathouse to finishing the journey by boat and returning to the boathouse by bus.

At the finish of the journey by boat the displacement of the team from the boathouse

is .... m.

As they return to the boathouse by bus, the displacement .... until they

arrive back at the boathouse where the total displacement is .... m. **(3 marks)**

Distance–time graphs

1   The distance–time graph shows a runner's journey from home to the park.

(a) Give the letter on the graph that corresponds to the part of the runner's journey where he:

(i) stops ....

(ii) runs fastest. .... **(2 marks)**

Distance in m

(b) Calculate the speed of
the runner between
70 s and 110 s.

> Your answer should show ALL
> your working.

Time in s

....

....

.... m/s **(3 marks)**

(c) Explain whether the runner was running or walking for the last part of the journey.

....

....

.... **(2 marks)**

Guided   (d) Calculate the runner's speed in part A of his journey.

In part A, the runner travels .... m in .... s.

$$\text{speed} = \frac{\text{distance}}{\text{...............................}}$$

Speed = ... m/s **(3 marks)**

(e) When the runner arrives at the park his displacement from home is less than the distance he has travelled. Explain this difference.

....

....

....

.... **(2 marks)**

Velocity–time graphs

1 A cyclist takes 5 seconds to accelerate from rest to 4 m/s. The cyclist moves in a straight line.

Calculate the cyclist's acceleration.

Select the unit from the box below.

> You will need to recall and apply the equation $a = \Delta v / t$ as it's not on the Physics Equation Sheet.

| s | m/s | m/s^2 |

....

....

....

Acceleration = ... unit.............. **(3 marks)**

2 The velocity–time graph below shows how the velocity of a car changes with time.

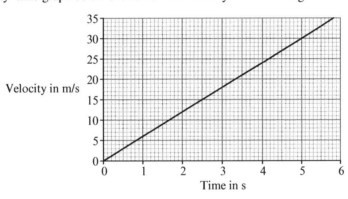

(a) This graph can be used to analyse the car's journey. Identify the statement that describes some of the information shown by the gradient of the graph.

Tick **one** box.

The velocity of the car is increasing steadily.   ☐

The velocity of the car is constant.   ☐

The car is decelerating.   ☐

The acceleration of the car is changing.   ☐   **(1 mark)**

(b) Draw on the graph to show how velocity and time taken can be used to calculate acceleration.   **(1 mark)**

(c) Calculate the acceleration of the car.

Change in velocity = ... m/s. Time taken for the change = ... s.

Acceleration = $\dfrac{\text{change in velocity}}{\text{time taken}}$ = ... m/s^2

Acceleration = ... m/s^2 **(2 marks)**

Equations of motion

1 Choose the typical acceleration of a car accelerating away from traffic lights.

Tick **one** box.

0.04 m/s² ☐

0.4 m/s² ☐

4 m/s² ☐

40 m/s² ☐   **(1 mark)**

2 (a) A racing car takes 8 seconds to speed up from 15 m/s to 25 m/s. Calculate its acceleration.

> You will need to recall the equation $a = \Delta v / t$ because it is not given on the Physics Equation Sheet.

....

....

....

Acceleration = ... m/s²   **(3 marks)**

(b) The same racing car now accelerates at the same rate for 12 seconds, from 25 m/s to a higher velocity. It travels 300 m during this time. Calculate its final velocity.

> You need to select, and rearrange, the equation $v^2 - u^2 = 2as$ from the Physics Equation Sheet.

....

....

....

....

Velocity = ... m/s   **(3 marks)**

(c) The same racing car now slows down to 5 m/s from the velocity calculated in part (b) at a rate of −2 m/s². Calculate how far the car travels when decelerating to this new final velocity.

....

....

....

Distance = ... m   **(3 marks)**

3 An object that falls near to the Earth's surface is said to be in free fall. Identify the influence that causes the object to accelerate.

Tick **one** box.

air resistance ☐   terminal velocity ☐   gravity ☐   friction ☐   **(1 mark)**

Newton's first law

1 (a) An aeroplane is waiting to take off and is stationary. Use Newton's first law to explain why it remains stationary.

....

....

.... **(2 marks)**

   (b) The aeroplane takes off and then flies at constant speed and constant height. Use Newton's first law to explain why it remains flying at a constant speed and height.

....

....

.... **(2 marks)**

2 A speed skater is standing on the ice waiting for the start of a race.

   (a) The race begins and the skater pushes against the ice producing a push force on the skates of 30 N. There is resistance from the air of 5 N and friction on the blades of 1 N. Calculate the resultant force forward.

> Consider all the forces in a straight line. Forces that act opposite to the driving force should have a negative sign.

....

....

Force = ... N **(2 marks)**

   (b) During the race, the resistive forces become equal to the push force. Explain what happens to the velocity of the skater.

....

....

.... **(2 marks)**

3 A space probe falls towards the Moon. In the Moon's gravitational field, the probe has a weight of 1700 N. After a period of free fall, the probe thrusters are fired briefly, providing an upward driving force of 1900 N.

   (a) Calculate the resultant force on the space probe when the thrusters are firing. Assume that the positive direction is downwards.

....

....

Resultant force = ... N **(2 marks)**

   (b) Describe the changes in the probe's velocity when the thrusters are firing.

....

....

.... **(2 marks)**

Newton's second law

1 In an experiment, a student pulls a force meter attached to a trolley along a bench. The trolley has frictionless wheels. The force meter gives a reading of 5 N.

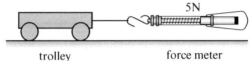

trolley   force meter

(a) Describe what happens to the trolley.

The trolley will ....

in the direction .... **(2 marks)**

(b) The student stacks some masses on the trolley and again pulls it with a force of 5 N.

Explain why the trolley takes longer to travel the length of the bench.

The acceleration is .... because .... **(2 marks)**

2 A minibus with passengers has a mass of 3000 kg and slows down with an average acceleration of -3 m/s^2.

(a) Calculate the average force acting on the minibus.

....

....

Force = ... N **(2 marks)**

(b) Give the direction in which the force acts.

.... **(1 mark)**

3 A Formula One racing car has a mass of 640 kg. A resultant force of 10 500 N acts on the car.

(a) Calculate the acceleration of the racing car. Choose the unit from the box below.

m/s^2	m/s	N

> Remember that Newton's second law refers to $F = m\,a$

....

....

Acceleration = ... unit .... **(3 marks)**

(b) Explain what will happen to the average acceleration of the car as the fuel is used, if the resultant force remains constant.

....

....

.... **(2 marks)**

Practical skills

Required practical – Force, mass and acceleration

A ramp, a trolley, masses and electronic light gates can be used to investigate the relationship between force, mass and acceleration.

1 Explain **one** advantage of using electronic measuring equipment to determine acceleration compared to using a ruler and stopwatch.

> Think about human reaction times compared with using electronic equipment.

....

....

.... **(2 marks)**

2 Describe the relationship between acceleration and mass.

.... **(1 mark)**

3 Explain why it is necessary to use two light gates when measuring acceleration in this experiment.

Guided

Acceleration is calculated by the change in speed ÷ time taken, so ....

....

.... **(2 marks)**

4 (a) Describe the conclusion that can be drawn from this experiment.

Guided

For a constant slope ....

....

.... **(2 marks)**

(b) Identify which of Newton's laws can be referred to in verifying the results of this experiment.

> The quantities of force, mass and acceleration are linked in this equation.

.... **(1 mark)**

5 Suggest **one** hazard associated with this experiment and **two** safety precautions that could be taken to minimise the risk of harm to the scientist.

> Consider the potential dangers of using accelerated masses or electrical equipment.

....

....

....

....

....

.... **(3 marks)**

Newton's third law

1 Which of these statements summarises Newton's third law?

Tick **one** box.

For every action there is a constant reaction. ☐

The action and reaction forces are different due to friction. ☐

Reaction forces may be stationary or at constant speed. ☐

For every action there is an equal and opposite reaction. ☐

(1 mark)

2 Before lift-off, a massive rocket sits on the launch pad. Use Newton's third law to explain why the rocket does not fall through the launch pad, in spite of its weight.

....

....

....

....

(2 marks)

3 The image shows a penguin standing on ice. Explain how the vertical action–reaction force pair acts on the penguin and why the forces are in equilibrium.

....

....

....

....

(2 marks)

Guided

4 Buttresses are used in architecture to strengthen walls by achieving an equilibrium of forces as they push against heavy stone walls that tend to push outwards under their own weight. Using Newton's third law, explain why buttresses are used.

Newton's third law says that the forces must be equal in ....

and .... in direction to be in equilibrium. The force exerted by

the buttresses on the .... is equal and opposite to the

force exerted on the .... by the building, resulting in no

movement occurring.

(4 marks)

Stopping distance

1 (a) Give the word equation used to calculate overall stopping distance.

.... **(1 mark)**

> **Guided**

(b) Complete the table below to summarise the factors that affect overall stopping distance.

> Separate the factors that may affect the reaction time of a driver from those that affect the vehicle.

Factors increasing overall stopping distance	
Thinking distance will increase if	**Braking distance will increase if**
	the car's speed increases
the driver is distracted	

(2 marks)

2 (a) Describe what happens when a force is applied to the brakes of a vehicle.

....

....

....

.... **(3 marks)**

(b) Explain what happens to the temperature of the brakes.

....

.... **(2 marks)**

3 Recent proposals have been made to increase the national speed limit in certain cases. Suggest how these proposals might increase the risk of damage to vehicles and their passengers.

> Remember that kinetic energy is proportional to v^2.

....

....

....

....

....

.... **(3 marks)**

Reaction time

1   The chart below includes typical thinking distances covered by vehicles at different speeds.

20 mph (32 km/h) 6 m 6 m = 12 m (40 ft) or 3 car lengths

30 mph (48 km/h) 9 m 14 m = 23 m (75 ft) or 6 car lengths

40 mph (64 km/h) 12 m 24 m = 36 m (118 ft) or 9 car lengths

50 mph (80 km/h) 15 m 38 m = 53 m (175 ft) or 13 car lengths

60 mph (96 km/h) 18 m 55 m = 73 m (240 ft) or 18 car lengths

70 mph (112 km/h) 21 m 75 m = 96 m (315 ft) or 24 car lengths

Average car length = 4 metres (13ft)

The distances shown are a general guide. The distance will depend on your attention (thinking distance), the road surface, the weather conditions and the condition of your vehicle at the time.

■ Thinking distance
▨ Braking distance

Identify the expected effect on overall stopping distance, if the driver was very tired.

Tick **one** box.

Overall stopping distance would be shorter. ☐   Only braking distance would be longer. ☐

Overall stopping distance would be longer. ☐   Only thinking distance would be longer. ☐

(1 mark)

2   Explain how human reaction time is related to the brain.

> Guided

Human reaction time is the time taken between a stimulus and ....

....

It is related to how quickly the human brain ....

....

.... **(2 marks)**

3   (a)   Explain how to measure human reaction times using a ruler.

> Human reaction time can be measured using the 'drop test'.

....

....

....

....

.... **(4 marks)**

(b)   Give the range of reaction times of an average person to an external stimulus.

.... **(1 mark)**

(c)   Explain what you would expect to find when comparing the distance measured on the ruler, during a drop test, for a person with a reaction time of 0.2 s with that of a person with a reaction time of 0.9 s.

....

....

.... **(2 marks)**

Extended response – Forces

Camera operators often use drones carrying cameras to film aerial sequences. The drones can be made to hover or move up, down, forwards or backwards to various locations.

Describe the motion of a camera drone during operation using Newton's first and second laws.

> You will be more successful in extended response questions if you plan your answer before you start writing.
>
> The question asks you to consider how Newton's first and second laws can be used to explain the motion of a drone carrying a camera. Think about:
>
> - the resultant force when a drone is hovering
> - the resultant force when a drone is moving
> - what may cause the velocity of the drone to change
> - how the resultant force may affect acceleration and how this may be calculated
> - how the mass of the drone may affect acceleration.
>
> You should try to use the information given in the question.

....

....

....

....

....

....

....

....

....

....

....

....

....

....

....

....

.... **(6 marks)**

Waves

1 Describe evidence that it is energy in a wave that travels, not the particles themselves, for ripples on the surface of water.

....

....

.... **(2 marks)**

2 Describe the difference between longitudinal and transverse waves.

....

....

.... **(2 marks)**

3 The diagram below shows a wave travelling through a medium.

Height of wave in cm

Note that both axes have units of cm.

Distance from source in cm

(a) Identify the correct amplitude of the wave in the diagram.

Tick **one** box.

0.05 m ☐   0.025 m ☐   0.12 m ☐   0.10 m ☐   **(1 mark)**

(b) Determine the wavelength of the wave in the diagram.

....

Wavelength = ... m   **(1 mark)**

(c) Sketch a second wave on the diagram to show a higher amplitude and shorter wavelength than that of the wave shown.   **(2 marks)**

Guided   (d) Determine the time period T of the first wave if the speed of the wave is 3×10^8 m/s.

> You will need to recall the equation $v = f\lambda$ as it is not on the Physics Equation Sheet.
> You will need to select the equation period = 1 / frequency from the Physics Equation Sheet.

First find the frequency of the wave ....

.... **(2 marks)**

Then find the time period of the wave ....

.... **(2 marks)**

Wave equation

1 A sound wave has a wavelength of 0.017 m and a frequency of 20 000 Hz.

Calculate the speed of the wave.

....

....

Wave speed = ... m/s   **(2 marks)**

2 Blue whales communicate over long distances by sending sound waves through the oceans.

> Guided

(a) If the speed of the sound through water is 1500 m/s, calculate the frequency of one note with a wavelength of 88 m produced by a blue whale.

Using $v = f\lambda$ rearrange the equation to give $f = $ ....

....

....

Frequency = ... Hz   **(2 marks)**

(b) If the note sent from another whale had a different frequency of 22 Hz, show that the wavelength of this note would also change from the wavelength in part (a).

....

....

Wavelength = ... m   **(2 marks)**

3 An icicle is melting into a pool of water. Drops fall every half a second, producing small waves that travel across the water at 0.05 m/s.

Calculate the wavelength of the small waves.

Select the correct unit from the box below.

seconds	hertz	metres

> Remember to write down the equation that you are using before you substitute values.

....

....

....

Wavelength = ... unit ....   **(3 marks)**

Measuring wave velocity

1 A tap is dripping into a bath. Three drops fall each second, producing small waves that are 5 cm apart.

Calculate the speed of the small waves across the water.

Select the correct unit from the box below.

m/s^2	m/s	m

The frequency of the waves (f) = ...

The wavelength of the waves (λ) = ...

....

Speed of waves = ... unit .... **(3 marks)**

2 Identify the distance between the crests of water waves with a frequency of 0.25 Hz travelling at a speed of 2 m/s.

Tick **one** box.

0.5 m   ☐

0.125 m   ☐

4 m   ☐

8 m   ☐

> You will need to recall the equation $v = f\lambda$ as it is not on the Physics Equation Sheet.

(1 mark)

3 An oscilloscope screen shows a waveform.

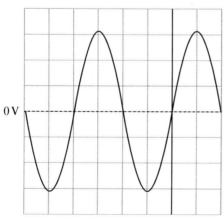

> You will find the equation period = 1 / frequency useful. You will need to select this equation from the Physics Equation Sheet.

Each division in the horizontal direction is 5 milliseconds.

Calculate the frequency of the wave.

....

....

....

Frequency = ... Hz **(3 marks)**

Required practical – Waves in fluids

1 A ripple tank is used to investigate waves.

(a) Describe how a ripple tank may be used to measure the frequency of water waves.

....

....

.... **(2 marks)**

(b) Describe how to find the wavelength of the waves in the ripple tank.

....

....

.... **(2 marks)**

(c) Give the equation you can use with the data collected in parts (a) and (b) to determine wave speed.

.... **(1 mark)**

(d) Identify the control variable when using a ripple tank to investigate wave speed.

.... **(1 mark)**

2 Describe a suitable conclusion to the method of using the ripple tank in question 1. Your conclusion should include two factors that should be moderated in this experiment.

> **Guided**

A ripple tank can be used to determine a value for ....

....

.... **(3 marks)**

3 The ripple tank experiment uses several pieces of equipment. Complete the table below to describe the hazard associated with each component and suggest a measure to minimise the risk of harm.

> Identify the hazard and describe the safety measure for each mark.

Component	Hazard	Safety measure
water		
electricity		
strobe lamp		

(3 marks)

Electromagnetic spectrum

Guided

1 Visible and infrared radiation are given out by a candle. Gamma-rays are emitted by radioactive elements such as radium.

(a) Give **two** similarities between all waves in the electromagnetic spectrum.

All waves of the electromagnetic spectrum are .... waves

and they all travel .... **(2 marks)**

(b) Give an example that shows the transfer of energy by electromagnetic waves. Include the type of electromagnetic wave in your answer.

....

.... **(1 mark)**

2 The chart, right, represents the electromagnetic spectrum. Some types of electromagnetic radiation have been labelled.

longest wavelength / lowest frequency   shortest wavelength / highest frequency

←—— radio waves ——→ ←—C—→ ←infrared→B ←→←—A—→
ultra-violet rays (UV)   ← gamma- → rays

(a) Name the three parts of the spectrum that have been replaced by letters in the diagram.

A ....

B ....

C .... **(3 marks)**

(b) Describe how frequency changes from radio waves to gamma-rays and how this is related to energy. Refer to these two types of radiation in your answer.

....

....

....

....

.... **(3 marks)**

3 The speed of electromagnetic waves in a vacuum is 300 000 000 m/s. A radio wave has a wavelength of 240 m. Calculate the frequency of the radio wave.

> You will need to remember the equation $v = f\lambda$ because it's not on the Physics Equation Sheet.

....

....

....

Frequency = ... Hz   **(2 marks)**

Required practical – Infrared radiation

1 (a) Describe an experimental method, using the apparatus in the diagram below, to investigate the radiation of thermal energy.

> The diagram shows a Leslie's cube which has four different sides – dull black, shiny black, white, silver – and can be filled with hot liquid.

....

....

....

.... **(4 marks)**

Guided

(b) Identify the independent and dependent variables in this experiment.

The dependent variable is temperature.

The independent variable is ....

.... **(2 marks)**

(c) Give **four** control variables in this experiment.

....

.... **(2 marks)**

2 (a) Identify a hazard with using Leslie's cube.

.... **(1 mark)**

(b) Explain how the hazard can be minimised.

.... **(1 mark)**

3 Conical flasks covered with different coloured foils and containing cold water may be used to investigate the absorption of thermal energy, by heating them with a radiant heater placed at a measured distance from the flasks.

(a) Suggest a reason why the conical flasks should be fitted with bungs before starting the experiment.

.... **(1 mark)**

(b) Describe the conclusion you would expect to reach at the end of the experiment for:

(i) dull and black surfaces

.... **(1 mark)**

(ii) shiny and light surfaces.

.... **(1 mark)**

Dangers and uses

1 Give **two** uses for each of the following EM waves.

(a) infrared waves:

1 .... 2 .... **(1 mark)**

(b) ultraviolet waves:

1 .... 2 .... **(1 mark)**

(c) gamma-rays:

1 .... 2 .... **(1 mark)**

(d) Give a use for microwaves other than for cooking.

.... **(1 mark)**

2 Medical X-rays are used to diagnose certain types of medical problems. The numbers of X-rays are carefully recorded.

Medical X-rays	Adult approximate effective radiation dose	Equivalent time of exposure to background radiation
radiography – chest	0.1 mSv	10 days
oral	0.005 mSv	1 day
computed tomography (CT) – lung cancer screening	1.5 mSv	6 months

(a) Using data from the table, compare the medical X-ray doses with background radiation.

....

....

....

....

....

.... **(3 marks)**

(b) Suggest why it is important to record and control the number of X-rays that a person has.

[X-rays carry high amounts of energy.]

....

....

....

.... **(2 marks)**

3 Describe the dangers of ultraviolet radiation.

....

.... **(2 marks)**

Extended response – Waves

X-rays and gamma-rays are widely used in a number of applications. Compare the characteristics and properties of these waves and give examples of how they can be used safely in medical diagnosis and in industry.

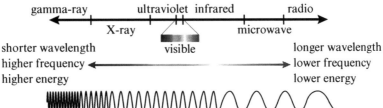

> You will be more successful in extended response questions if you plan your answer before you start writing.
>
> The question asks you to give a detailed explanation of the properties, uses and dangers of X-rays and gamma-rays. Think about:
>
> - the types of radiation and how you would describe them
>
> - the dangers of both types of radiation and the reasons why they can be dangerous
>
> - examples of how the two types of radiation are used in medicine
>
> - examples of how the two types of radiation are used in industry.
>
> You should try to use the information given in the question and in the diagram.

....

....

....

....

....

....

....

....

....

....

....

....

....

....

....

....

.... **(6 marks)**

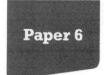
Had a go ☐   Nearly there ☐   Nailed it! ☐

Magnets and magnetic fields

1   Complete the diagram below to show the magnetic field lines for a bar magnet.

> Remember to consider the relative density of the field lines as well as their direction.
> You should show at least 10 magnetic field lines to represent the field.

N   S

(4 marks)

2   Write down **three** similarities between the magnetic field of a bar magnet and that produced by the Earth.

> Guided

A bar magnet and the Earth both have...

A bar magnet and the Earth have similar ....

The direction of both fields can be found using ....   **(3 marks)**

3   An electric doorbell uses an induced magnet to move the hammer, which then rings the bell when the switch is pressed.

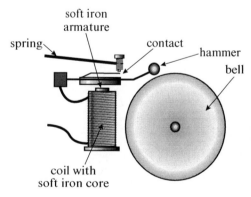

Explain why an induced magnet rather than a permanent magnet is used for this application.

....

....

....

....

....

....   **(5 marks)**

Current and magnetism

1   The diagrams below show a wire passing through a circular card. The **cross** represents the conventional current moving into the page and the **dot** represents the conventional current moving out of the page.

⊙   ⊗

(a)   (b)

(a) Draw magnetic field lines on each diagram to show the **pattern** of the magnetic field.   **(2 marks)**

(b) Draw arrows on each diagram to show the **direction** of the magnetic field.   **(2 marks)**

(c) Describe how the magnetic field around the wire can be increased.

....

....   **(1 mark)**

2 (a) Identify which of the following has a magnetic field similar in shape to that of a solenoid, as shown in the diagram below.

Tick **one** box.

ball magnet   ☐

bar magnet   ☐

circular magnet   ☐

horseshoe magnet   ☐

magnetic field

coil carrying electric current

(1 mark)

   (b) Describe how the magnetic field of the solenoid shown in the diagram in part (a) can be made stronger, without changing the circuit.

....

....   **(1 mark)**

3   Give **three** factors that affect the force acting on a current-carrying wire in a magnetic field.

The force acting on a current-carrying wire in a magnetic field depends on the

.... of the wire, the .... in the wire and the

....   **(3 marks)**

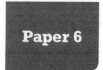
Extended response – Magnetism and electromagnetism

Describe how an experiment could show the effect and strength of a magnetic field around a long straight conductor and what would be observed when the circuit was connected.

> You will be more successful in extended response questions if you plan your answer before you start writing.
>
> The question asks you to give a detailed explanation of the magnetic field generated by a long straight conductor. Think about:
>
> - how you would safely connect the conductor to enable circuit measurements to be taken
> - the methods you could use to determine the direction of a magnetic field
> - the shape of the magnetic field that you would expect to find
> - how you would interpret the field patterns of long straight conductors
> - the variable that would influence the strength of the magnetic field around a long straight conductor
> - how the influence of the magnetic field of a long straight conductor changes.
>
> You should try to use the information given in the question.

....

....

....

....

....

....

....

....

....

....

....

....

....

....

....

....

....

....

....

.... **(6 marks)**

ANSWERS

Biology
Paper 1

1. Microscopes and magnification

1 ×50 (1)

2 The magnification of a light microscope is usually lower / less / smaller (1) than the magnification of an electron microscope. The level of detail seen with a light microscope is less than that with an electron microscope because its resolution is less / lower / smaller (1).

3 (a) 2 μm (1)

(b) 10 μm (1)

4 (a) size of the real cell = 1.5 / 750 = 0.002 mm (or 2 × 10⁻³ mm) (1)

(b) 0.002 × 1000 = 2 μm (or correct value for (a) × 1000) (1)

5 It lets scientists see more subcellular structures (than with a light microscope) (1); see more detail of these structures (1).

2. Animal and plant cells

1 ribosome (1)

2 (a) plant / alga (1)

(b) X: (permanent) vacuole (1)

Y: chloroplast (1)

(c) contains chromosomes / genes / DNA (1) which control the cell / control the cell's activities (1)

3 The cell membrane controls what enters and leaves the cell (1). However, the cell wall is made of cellulose which strengthens / supports / protects the cell (1).

4 two from: contain chlorophyll / absorb sunlight (1) for photosynthesis (1) to make glucose / food for the cell (1)

3. Eukaryotes and prokaryotes

1 1 mark for each correct row, to 4 marks maximum:

	Animal cells	Bacterial cells
Cytoplasm	✓	✓
Cell membrane	✓	✓
Cell wall		✓
Nucleus	✓	

2 The chromosomal DNA is arranged to form a loop / single loop / circle (1). Some bacterial cells also contain plasmids (1).

3 200 nm; 50 μm; 1 cm; 100 mm (1)

4 (a) 2.2 × 10⁻³ m (1)

(b) 4.5 × 10⁻⁴ m (1)

(c) 9.7 × 10⁻⁵ m (1)

5 (a) (2.5 × 10⁻⁵)/(2.0 × 10⁻⁷) (1) = 125 (1)

(b) −7 (1)

(c) 2 (1)

4. Specialised animal cells

1 acrosome – releases enzymes to aid entry to an egg cell (1)

nucleus – carries genetic information (1)

mitochondrion – releases energy for the cell (1)

tail – allows cell to move (1)

2 allows more space for haemoglobin / allows cell to contain more haemoglobin (1)

3 (a) **One mark** for each correct column:

	Part	
Function	axon	dendrite
makes a connection with another nerve cell		✓
carries impulses from one end of the cell to the other	✓	

(b) axon is long (1) to connect to distant parts of the body (1); OR many / finger-like dendrites (1) to make connections with other nerve cells (1)

4 Most types of animal cells differentiate at an early (1) stage. As a cell differentiates, it acquires different features / structures / subcellular structures (1) that allow it to carry out its function (1). Cell division in mature animals is mainly restricted to repair / replacement (1).

5. Specialised plant cells

1 (a) small volume cytoplasm and no nucleus (1)

(b) sieve plate with holes (1)

(c) companion cell with many mitochondria (1)

2 (a) Xylem tissue consists of hollow tubes formed by dead xylem cells (1). There are no end walls so that water and mineral ions can flow easily through the xylem / tissue / plant (1).

(b) It provides strength / support / it withstands the pressure of water moving through the tissue. (1)

3 (Most types of) animal cells differentiate at an early stage (1); (many types of) plant cells retain the ability to differentiate throughout life (1).

6. Required practical – Using a light microscope

1 (a) to pass light through the slide/specimen (1)

(b) to hold the slide / specimen in place (1)

(c) to move the objective lens up or down a long way (1)

2 The drawing is made with a pen rather than with a pencil (1).

any two from: the magnification is not given (1); label lines are not drawn with a ruler (1); label lines cross each other (1); cells are not drawn to scale (1); shading should not be used (except to distinguish between different structures) (1); the cell membrane cannot be seen with the light microscope (so should not be labelled) (1); outlines cross each other / are not closed for some features (1)

3 smaller field of view (1); more difficult to focus (1)

4 any three from: go back to using the low-power objective (1); find the part you need and bring it back to the centre view (1); focus on it with the coarse focus (1); return to the high-power objective (1) and use the fine focus wheel to bring the part into focus (1)

7. Mitosis

1 two genetically identical diploid daughter cells (1)

2 to produce new individuals by asexual reproduction (1); for growth (1); for repair (1)

3 (a) B (1)

(b) B – chromosomes are being copied (1); C – mitosis (1); D – cell division (1)

4 (a) A set of chromosomes is being pulled to each end of the cell (1); the nucleus is dividing (1).

(b) The cytoplasm divides (1); the cell membrane divides (1).

8. Stem cells

1 an undifferentiated cell (1)

2 (a) meristem (1)

(b) (i) tip of shoots (1)

(ii) any two from: to form root hair cells (1); xylem (1); phloem (1)

(c) Rare species can be cloned so they are saved from extinction (1).

Large numbers of identical plants with desirable features (e.g. disease resistance) can be produced (e.g. for farmers). (1)

3 (a) to become specialised (1); so they can carry out a particular function (1)

(b) any two from: the body may destroy / reject the donor cells (1); a viral infection may be transferred (1); stem cells may not stop dividing / risk of cancer (1)

(c) one disadvantage for **1 mark**, e.g. requires destruction of an embryo / some people have ethical / religious objections

9. Diffusion

1 Diffusion is the spreading out / movement (1) of particles, so that there is a net movement of particles from an area of higher concentration to an area of lower concentration (1).

2 (a) two from: difference in concentration / concentration gradient (1); surface area of the membrane (1); thickness of the membrane (1)

(b) Particles move about more quickly at higher temperatures. (1)

3 (Cytoplasm because) urea diffuses from the cells / into the plasma (1) and diffusion happens from higher to lower concentration / down a concentration gradient (1).

4 (a) left to right / to the right (1)

(b) The number / concentration of particles of substance B is the same / 10 on both sides (1), so the rate of movement is the same in each direction (1).

10. Exchange surfaces

1 one 20-mm cube (1)

2 (a) villi (1)

(b) Their shape gives them a large surface area (1). They provide a short diffusion path because their surface is a single layer of cells / is thin (1). A network of blood capillaries inside them ensures that food molecules are carried away / a high concentration gradient is maintained (1).

3 (a) $6 \times 10 \times 10 = 600 \, \mu m^2$ (1)

(b) $10 \times 10 \times 10 = 1000 \, \mu m^3$ (1)

(c) $600/1000 = 0.6$ (1) (OR correct value of (a) divided by (b))

4 (a) (flatworm because) it is thinner / wider / flatter in shape (1)

(b) Cells in the flatworm are close to its surface (1) but many cells in the earthworm are too far from its surface (for diffusion to happen easily / quickly) (1).

11. Osmosis

1 Osmosis is the diffusion of water (1) from a dilute / less concentrated (1) solution to a (more) concentrated (1) solution through a partially permeable membrane / semi-permeable membrane (1).

2 (a) The size at the start is a factor that affects the size at the end (1); it is controlled so that the procedure is valid / a fair test (1).

(b) Potato in distilled water: larger / longer (1)

Potato in strong glucose solution: smaller / shorter (1)

3 (a) allows small molecules (e.g. water) to pass through (1) but not larger molecules / ions (1)

(b) There is a net movement of water into the tubing (1) by osmosis (1).

12. Required practical – Investigating osmosis

1 (a) missing change in mass = 2.85 – 2.60 = 0.25 (1); missing percentage change = (–0.15/2.58) × 100 = –5.8 (1)

(b) points plotted ± half square (1); line of best fit (1)

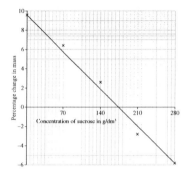

(c) answer in the range 160 g/dm³ to 190 g/dm³ (1)

(d) A balance with a resolution of ±0.1 g will give readings of 2.5 g and 2.7 g (1) so the recorded change in mass would be 0.2 g (1), giving a different percentage change in mass / 8% / less accurate value (1).

13. Active transport

1 active transport (1)

2 One mark for each correct row to 4 marks:

Feature	Diffusion	Active transport
involves the movement of particles	✓	✓
requires energy		✓
can happen across a partially permeable membrane	✓	✓
net movement down a concentration gradient	✓	

3 (a) Osmosis is the movement of water (not ions). (1)

(b) Diffusion is the net movement of particles from a higher concentration to a lower concentration (1); from the information given, nitrate ions are moved in the opposite direction / from lower to higher concentration (1).

(c) The nitrate ions are being moved by active transport (1). This process requires energy (1) from respiration (1).

4 Absorption of glucose will stop / slow down (1) because energy is needed for active transport (1) and the toxins will stop energy being released (1).

14. Extended response – Cell biology

The answer should include some of the following points: (6)

Similarities – both have:

- cell membrane, which controls what enters and leaves the cell
- cell wall, which strengthens the cell
- cytoplasm, in which cell reactions happen
- ribosomes, where protein synthesis happens.

Differences:

- Plant cells have mitochondria, where respiration happens, but bacterial cells do not.

- Plant cells have chloroplasts, where photosynthesis happens, but bacterial cells do not.

- DNA, which contains genetic information, is contained in a nucleus in plant cells, but is found in a single chromosome / loop and in plasmids in bacterial cells.

- Cell wall in plant cells is made from cellulose but from different substances in bacterial cells.

- Plant cells have a permanent vacuole filled with cell sap, which helps to keep the cell rigid, but bacterial cells do not.

15. The digestive system

1 A, liver (1); B, stomach (1); C, pancreas (1); D, large intestine (1); E, small intestine (1)

2 (a) A tissue is a group of cells with a similar structure (1) and function (1) (structure and function can be given in the opposite order).

(b) aggregations / combinations of tissues (1) with specific functions (1)

(c) two from the following: nervous system (1); circulatory system (1); respiratory system (1); excretory system (1); endocrine system (1); reproductive system (1); immune system (1); muscular / skeletal system (1); exocrine system (1)

3 (a) 1 mark for each correct box:

Type of enzyme	Substrate	Product(s)
carbohydrase	carbohydrates (1)	simple sugars
protease	proteins	amino acids (1)
lipase	lipids / fats (1)	fatty acids *and* glycerol (1)

(b) starch (1)

16. Required practical – Food testing

1 (a) pestle and mortar (1)

(b) a red-stained layer floating on a layer of water (1)

2 Put some egg white in a test tube. Add an equal volume of Biuret reagent / solution (1) and shake to mix. If protein is present, the mixture turns pink / purple / mauve (1).

3 (a) Heat water in a kettle (1); pour hot water into a beaker and place the test tubes in the water (1).

(b) Both food samples contain reducing sugars (1) but the one that gives the red colour contains more / a higher concentration (1).

4 Add iodine solution (1); turns black / blue–black if starch is present (1).

17. Enzymes

1 The surface area of the fat is increased (1).

2 The active site in proteases matches the shape of proteins (1) but the active site in lipases does not match the shape of proteins / is the wrong shape / fits fats / lipids instead (1).

3 (a) answer in the range 60–65 °C (1)

(b) At high temperatures the shape of the active site changes (so that the substrate can no longer fit into it) **(1)** and the enzyme is denatured **(1)**.

4   (a) answer in the range 6.6–7.0 **(1)**

(b) pepsin because its optimum pH is about 2 / it works best in acidic conditions **(1)**

18. Required practical – Investigating enzymes

1   (a) Values for rate calculated:

pH	6	8	10
Time	3.6	1.2	8.3
Rate	0.28	0.83	0.12

1 mark for all 3 correct values, **1 mark** for 2 significant figures

(b) pH on horizontal axis, scale 1 pH unit per cm **(1)**; all points plotted ±½ square **(1)**; curve of best fit through all points **(1)**

(c) two from the following: use a thermostatically controlled water bath **(1)**; repeat at each pH and calculate mean values **(1)**; repeat at pH values close to pH 8 **(1)**; record times in seconds **(1)**

19. The blood

1   plasma – carries other blood components **(1)**; platelet – involved in forming blood clots **(1)**; red blood cell – carries oxygen **(1)**; white blood cell – part of the body's immune system **(1)**

2   (a) nucleus **(1)**

(b) haemoglobin **(1)**

(c) Their biconcave shape gives them a large surface area **(1)** for diffusion to happen efficiently. They are also flexible, which lets them fit through narrow blood vessels / capillaries **(1)**.

3   urea **(1)**; carbon dioxide **(1)**

4   Phagocyte: engulfs and destroys pathogens **(1)**

Lymphocyte: produces antibodies **(1)** which bind to pathogens **(1)**

5   two from: platelets respond to a wound by triggering clotting **(1)**; platelets are trapped in a meshwork of fibrin / protein **(1)**; clot prevents pathogens from entering **(1)**

20. Blood vessels

1   vein **(1)**

2   (a) Blood can flow easily at low pressure / a lot of blood can flow / blood can flow with less resistance. **(1)**

(b) to withstand high blood pressure / to stretch as blood flows through **(1)**; to regain shape afterwards **(1)**, which smooths the flow of blood **(1)**

3   The capillaries are about as wide as one red blood cell, so the distance oxygen must travel to the capillary wall is small / short **(1)**. The walls are only one cell thick, so the diffusion distance is small / short **(1)**.

4   two from: muscles (in the body) contract and press on veins **(1)**; veins have valves **(1)**; to keep blood flowing in the same direction / prevent back-flow **(1)**

21. The heart

1   **1 mark** for each correct row:

Blood vessel	Carries blood from	Carries blood to	Carries oxygenated blood (✓ or ✗)
aorta	heart	body	✓
pulmonary artery	heart	lungs	✗
pulmonary vein	lungs	heart	✓
vena cava	body	heart	✗

2   (a) It acts as a pump **(1)**; muscles contract to pump the blood **(1)**.

(b) vena cava → right atrium → right ventricle → pulmonary artery **(1)**, lungs **(1)**; pulmonary vein → left atrium → left ventricle → aorta **(1)**

3   (a) It closes when ventricle relaxes **(1)**; prevents back-flow **(1)**.

(b) right ventricle **(1)**; pumps blood to the lungs / pulmonary artery **(1)**

(c) has to pump harder / produce more pressure **(1)** to get blood all round body **(1)**, not just to lungs **(1)**

22. The lungs

1   A, trachea **(1)**; B, bronchus / bronchi **(1)**

2   (a) diffusion **(1)**

(b) There is a net movement of carbon dioxide from the blood / plasma to air in the alveoli / lungs **(1)**, and a net movement of oxygen from the air in the alveoli / lungs to the red blood cells **(1)**.

(c) two from the following:
*   Millions of alveoli create a large surface area **(1)** for the diffusion of gases **(1)**.
*   Each alveolus is closely associated with a network of capillaries **(1)** to minimise diffusion distance **(1)**.
*   Wall of alveolus is one cell thick **(1)** to minimise diffusion distance **(1)**.

3   smaller surface area for gas exchange **(1)** so less oxygen absorbed **(1)**

23. Cardiovascular disease

1   (a) The coronary arteries supply blood to the heart muscle **(1)**; the fatty deposits reduce the blood flow in these arteries **(1)**, which reduces the amount of oxygen available to the heart muscle **(1)**.

(b) (i) A stent is a wire frame inserted into the artery **(1)**; it is expanded and allows blood to flow more easily **(1)**.

(ii) Statins are drugs / medicines that reduce blood cholesterol levels **(1)**; this slows down the rate at which fatty material is deposited **(1)**.

2   (a) may not open fully **(1)**; may develop a leak / not close fully **(1)**

(b) biological / human / animal valves **(1)**; mechanical / artificial / metal / polymer valves **(1)**

(c) tiredness / breathlessness / death **(1)**

3   **1 mark** for each box, e.g. lifestyle changes benefit: no side effects, may reduce risk of other health problems **(1)**; lifestyle changes drawback: may take a long time to work, may not work effectively **(1)**; medication benefit: easier than changing lifestyle / starts working immediately / cheaper and less risky than surgery **(1)**; medication drawback: may have side effects / needs to be taken long term / may interfere with other medication **(1)**; surgery benefit: usually a long-term solution **(1)**; surgery drawback: risk of infection / risk of complications / expensive / more difficult than medication **(1)**

24. Health and disease

1   diet / stress / life situation **(1)**

2   (a) communicable disease **(1)**

(b) (i) example of a communicable disease, e.g. colds / flu / measles / food poisoning **(1)**

(ii) example of a non-communicable disease, e.g. cardiovascular disease / cancer / diabetes **(1)**

(c) **1 mark** for each correct row:

	Communicable disease	Non-communicable disease
Number of cases	rapid variation over time	changes gradually over time
Distribution of cases	often localised	may be widespread

3   (a) Scabies is caused by a mite / arthropod **(1)**, which can be passed from person to person **(1)**.

(b) The itchy skin is an allergic immune response **(1)**, which cannot be passed from person to person **(1)**.

25. Lifestyle and disease

1   He is obese **(1)**, and needs to lose mass **(1)**.

2   (a) (Scientists can show that): it is a cause of the disease **(1)**; know / understand how this works **(1)**

(b) cells that have changed **(1)**, so they have uncontrolled growth / division **(1)**

3   (a) The risk of diabetes increases as a person's mass increases **(1)**; there is a large / largest increase in risk going from overweight to obese **(1)**.

(b) (i) Total percentage of people with diabetes = 0.7 + 0.9 + 1.2 + 2.1 = 4.9% **(1)**

(ii) Number of people with diabetes = 4.9 ÷ 100 × 19 500 000 **(1)** = 955 500 **(1)** (allow 0.955 million / 0.96 million / 960 000) *Correct calculation using an incorrect answer to part (a) gains full marks.*

26. Alcohol and smoking

1   (a) (i) × 4 / four times **(1)**

(ii) 114 mg per 100 cm³ of blood **(1)**

(b) As the concentration of alcohol in the blood rises, the risk of having a car accident increases / rises (1). The change in the risk increases as the concentration of alcohol in the blood rises (1).

(c) Alcohol causes slower reactions / blurred vision / increased risk taking. (1)

2 (a) total number of deaths = 123 800 + 86 800 + 90 600 + 84 600 + 17 400 + 34 700 = 437 900; percentage of deaths from lung cancer = (123 800/437 900) × 100 (1) = 28.3% (1)

(b) to reduce the risk of having a baby with low birth weight / abnormal facial features / behavioural and learning problems (1)

27. The leaf

1 organ (1)

2 anchors the plant in the soil (1); absorbs water / ions from the soil water (1)

3 (a) (i) chloroplasts (1)

(ii) They pack closely together / there are few cell walls for light to pass through (1).

(b) (i) guard cells (1)

(ii) stoma / stomata (1)

(c) (i) This is so that light can pass through easily (1).

(ii) one from: reduces water loss (1); protects the leaf (e.g. from water or microorganisms entering it) (1); helps to keep the upper surface clean (1)

(d) The cells are packed loosely / irregularly together (1).

28. Transpiration

1 Mineral ions enter by active transport and water by osmosis (1).

2 Water evaporates (1) from the leaves, mostly through the stomata (1). This causes a pull so that water moves through the plant / xylem (1) and is replaced by water entering the roots.

3 (a) Lower surface: (22 + 18 + 23 + 19) / 4 = 20.5 (1)

Upper surface: (0 + 2 + 3 + 1) / 4 = 1.5 (1)

(b) It has the most / more stomata (1), and most water is lost through stomata (1).

(c) (i) It will reduce water loss / reduce wilting (1).

(ii) one from: carbon dioxide for photosynthesis is needed (1); oxygen for respiration is needed (1); gas exchange is needed (1); minerals are transported in the xylem by transpiration when the stomata are open (1)

29. Investigating transpiration

1 (a) 3.2 cm (1)

(b) (i) radius of tube = 0.5 / 2 = 0.25 mm

volume travelled = $\pi \times 0.25^2 \times 90$ = 17.7 mm³ (1)

rate of transpiration = 17.7 / 5 = 3.5 mm³/min (1) (to 1 decimal place)

(ii) The rate of transpiration was higher when the fan was on (1).

2 (a) second box ticked (1)

(b) The stomata are more open (for gas exchange) (1).

30. Translocation

1 phloem (1)

2 movement of dissolved food / sucrose molecules (1) from leaves / storage organs to the rest of the plant (1)

3 1 mark for each correct row:

Structure or mechanism	Transpiration	Translocation
xylem	✓	
phloem		✓
pulled by evaporation from the leaf	✓	
energy needed		✓

4 distance = 0.40 × 1000 = 400 mm *and* time = 67 × 60 = 4020 s (1); rate = 400 / 4020 = 0.1 mm/s (1)

5 can differentiate (1), to form specialised cells / any type of plant cell (1)

31. Extended response – Organisation

The answer should include some of the following points: (6)

Outline of route:

- right atrium → right ventricle
- right ventricle → pulmonary artery
- pulmonary artery → (capillaries in) lungs
- (capillaries in) lungs → pulmonary vein
- pulmonary vein → left atrium
- left atrium → left ventricle
- left ventricle → aorta
- aorta → rest of the body / capillaries in the body
- rest of the body / capillaries in the body → vena cava
- vena cava → right atrium

Answer might also include:

- Valves in heart / veins prevent backflow of blood.
- Deoxygenated blood enters / leaves right side.
- Oxygenated blood enters / leaves left side.
- Walls of left side of heart are thicker than those of right side.

32. Viral diseases

1 influenza (1)

2 (a) 1 mark for each correct row:

Feature	Incorrect (✗)
Viruses are about the same size as cells.	✗
Viruses can infect plants or animals.	
Viruses reproduce outside cells.	✗
Viruses are spread by direct contact, air or water.	

(b) Viruses are much smaller than cells (1). Viruses reproduce inside cells (1).

3 (a) Chloroplasts contain chlorophyll (1). Lighter-coloured areas appear where there is less chlorophyll / fewer chloroplasts (1).

(b) less photosynthesis (1), so less glucose made (1), and less respiration / release of energy / synthesis of other substances (1)

4 (a) red skin rash (1)

(b) Measles can be fatal if complications occur. (1)

(c) inhaling droplets from sneezes / coughs (1)

33. Bacterial diseases

1 cholera (1)

2 one from: fever (1); abdominal cramps (1); vomiting (1); diarrhoea (1)

3 (a) one from: bacteria more easily enter the body during surgery (1); contaminated hands (1); contaminated equipment (1)

(b) Fewer patients died (1); one from: reduced from 45 per 100 to 15 per 100 (1); reduced from 45% to 15% (1); reduced by two-thirds (1); reduced to a third (1); reduced by 67% (1)

4 (a) one from: thick yellow / green discharge from vagina / penis (1); pain on urinating (1)

(b) Resistant strains of bacteria have appeared. (1)

5 Bacteria get into the body, where they reproduce rapidly (1). The bacteria produce toxins which damage cells / tissues (1).

34. Fungal and protist diseases

1 fungus, protist (1)

2 (a) fungicide (1)

(b) Fungus / fungal spores from an infected person could get on the towel (1), and pass to you when you use the towel (1).

3 If the leaves are damaged or there are fewer leaves, photosynthesis (1) is reduced. The plant cannot make enough glucose / food for healthy growth (1).

4 (a) one from: recurring fever (1); nausea (1); anaemia (1)

(b) It is a vector (1). It carries the pathogen / *Plasmodium* from person to person (1).

(c) Mosquito net prevents mosquitoes biting / reaching people (1), so mosquitoes cannot transfer the pathogen / *Plasmodium* (1) from an infected person to an uninfected person (1).

35. Human defence systems

1 (a) (i) Hairs trap bacteria / pathogens / harmful particles (1).

(ii) Hydrochloric acid kills bacteria / pathogens in food / drink (1).

(b) two from: physical barrier to pathogens (1); secretes antimicrobial substances / substances that kill bacteria / substances that inhibit bacterial growth (1); scabs form over damaged skin (1)

(c) It kills bacteria (1), by digesting their cell walls (1).

2 (a) mucus (1)

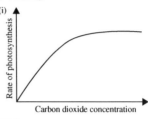

(b) It is sticky (**1**), so it traps bacteria / pathogens (**1**).

(c) (i) cilia / cilium (**1**)

(ii) The structures on the surface of the cells move in waves (**1**), which move mucus / substance A out of the lungs (**1**) towards the throat where it is swallowed (**1**).

36. The immune system

1 (a) Antibodies are proteins (**1**). They attach to antigens (**1**) produced by the pathogen, which leads to its destruction.

(b) Cells / phagocytes ingest pathogens (phagocytosis) (**1**) and destroy / digest the pathogens (**1**). White blood cells produce antitoxins (**1**) which attach to toxins / poisonous substances and make them inactive (**1**).

2 (a) The concentration of antibodies rises then falls (**1**); it reaches a maximum about 2 weeks after infection (**1**).

(b) In either order: the concentration of antibodies rises faster in the second infection (**1**); the maximum concentration of antibodies is greater in the second infection (**1**).

(c) The antibodies destroyed the measles virus (**1**) before it could cause illness / symptoms / disease (**1**).

37. Vaccination

1 (a) an inactive form of a pathogen (**1**)

(b) side effect, e.g. soreness / swelling / mild symptoms of disease (**1**); may give only partial protection if there are different strains of the pathogen (**1**)

(c) The vaccine causes white blood cells to make antibodies (**1**) against the pathogen. If the same pathogen enters the body again, white blood cells respond quickly / rapidly (**1**) to produce the correct antibodies / antibodies against the pathogen to prevent illness (**1**).

2 (a) 2003 (**1**)

(b) Fewer babies were immunised so they were not protected from infection (**1**).

(c) One from: the pathogen can be transmitted only from an infected individual (**1**); if most people are immune, the chances of an unvaccinated person meeting an infected person are very small (**1**).

38. Antibiotics and painkillers

1 (a) Antibiotics kill bacteria / prevent bacteria reproducing (**1**).

(b) The pharmacist's advice would be not to take (**1**) penicillin. This is because antibiotics do not kill / are not effective against viruses (**1**).

2 (a) Number of deaths increased between 2000 and 2005 (then levelled off) (**1**), then declined after 2006 (**1**).

(b) (i) one from: the number of MRSA bacteria increased (**1**); MRSA bacteria spread into more places (**1**)

(ii) one from: new antibiotics were invented (**1**); hygiene in hospitals

improved (**1**); steps were taken to reduce the spread of MRSA bacteria (**1**)

3 (a) inside living cells (**1**)

(b) Substances that kill viruses may also harm the body (**1**).

39. New medicines

1 aspirin (**1**)

2 (a) 3, 1, 5, 2, 4 (all correct = **2 marks**, 3 correct = **1 mark**)

(b) two from: check that substance is not toxic (**1**); check its efficacy / how well it works at treating the disease (**1**); determine the dose / how much is needed for the drug to work (**1**)

(c) one from: testing in cells / tissues (to see if it has a desired effect) (**1**); testing on animals (to see how it works in a whole body / has no harmful side effects) (**1**)

3 (a) dummy drug / looks like the drug but does not contain any of it (**1**)

(b) Fewer people had high blood pressure at the end of the trial (**1**), but far fewer had high blood pressure when given the medicine (compared with the placebo) (**1**).

40. Extended response – Infection and response

The answer should include some of the following points: (**6**)

Differences:

• Vaccines stimulate the body's immune system but antibiotics kill bacteria / inhibit their cell processes / stop them growing.

• Vaccines must be given before infection but antibiotics can be given after infection with a pathogen.

• Vaccinated people become immune to a disease without getting it but the pathogen must already be present for antibiotics to work.

• Vaccines can protect against viruses as well as bacteria but antibiotics are effective only against bacteria.

• Herd immunity means not everyone in a population needs to be vaccinated but all infected people need to be given an antibiotic against a particular pathogen.

• Vaccines prevent reinfection by the same pathogen but antibiotics do not.

Similarities:

• Some vaccines and antibiotics may give only partial protection (e.g. if there are different strains of the pathogen).

• Some people develop side effects, e.g. soreness and mild symptoms of disease with a vaccine, diarrhoea with antibiotics.

• Vaccines may fail to protect against different strains of a pathogen.

41. Photosynthesis

1 an endothermic process in which energy is transferred to the chloroplasts by light (**1**)

2 carbon dioxide + water → glucose + oxygen (**1**)

3 (a) starch / fat / oil / lipid (**1**)

(b) cellulose (**1**) to strengthen the cell wall (**1**)

OR amino acids (**1**) to make proteins (**1**)

4 (a) light intensity (**1**); amount / mass of chlorophyll (**1**)

(b) For each graph, correct axis labels (**1**); correct shape of line (**1**) (to a maximum of **4 marks**):

(i)
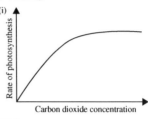

(ii)
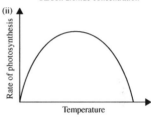

42. Required practical – Investigating photosynthesis

1 (a) 5 points correctly plotted (**2**) *but* 4 points correctly plotted (**1**); line of best fit (**1**)

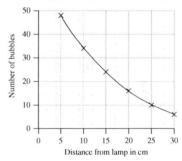

(b) answer in the range 22–24 cm (**1**)

(c) The greater the distance from the lamp, the lower the number of bubbles (**1**).

(d) (i) Avoid touching the lamp (**1**) to reduce the chance of being burnt (**1**).

(ii) The rate of photosynthesis also depends upon the temperature (**1**); the results would not depend only on the light intensity if the plant were heated (**1**).

43. Respiration

1 glucose + oxygen → carbon dioxide + water (**1**)

2 (a) keeping warm (**1**); two from: movement (**1**); chemical reactions to build larger molecules (**1**); active transport (**1**)

(b) It is an exothermic reaction because energy is transferred to the surroundings (**1**), and energy is transferred from the surroundings in an endothermic reaction (**1**).

3 two from: plants cannot use energy from sunlight directly for metabolic processes (**1**) so they need energy from respiration for this purpose (**1**) during the day as well as at night (**1**)

4 (a) fermentation (1)

(b) making bread (1); making alcoholic drinks (e.g. wine, beer) (1)

5 (a) In order, missing words are: absence (1); ethanol (1); lactic acid (1)

(b) one from: both release energy (1); both use glucose (1)

44. Responding to exercise

1 third box ticked (1)

2 (a) 100 – 80 = 20 beats/min (1)

percentage increase = (20 / 80) × 100 = 25% (1)

(b) Respiring cells need oxygen (1); increased exercise increases the demand for oxygen (1); pulse / heart rate increases to supply the muscles with more oxygen / oxygenated blood (1).

3 (a) one from: more oxygen is used in aerobic respiration (1); more oxygen is used by respiring muscles (1)

(b) one from: no more oxygen can be delivered for aerobic respiration (1); increased energy needed comes from anaerobic respiration (1); there is a limit to breathing rate / breath volume (1)

45. Metabolism

1 the sum of all the reactions in a cell or the body (1)

2 1 excess glucose into glycogen (1) for storage in the liver

2 excess amino acids into ammonia (then into urea) (1)

3 (a) nitrate (1)

(b) protein / polypeptide (1)

(c) starch (1); cellulose (1)

4 (a) glycerol (1); fatty acids (1)

(b) one glycerol molecule *and* three fatty acid molecules (1)

5 carbohydrase / amylase – carbohydrates / starch (1); lipase – lipids / fats / oils (1); protease – proteins (1)

46. Extended response – Bioenergetics

The answer should include some of the following points: (6)

Similarities – both processes:

- take place in cells / subcellular structures
- involve the transfer of energy
- involve chemical reactions
- involve glucose / oxygen / carbon dioxide / water
- require diffusion / gas exchange to obtain / release gases.

Differences:

- photosynthesis: carbon dioxide + water → glucose + oxygen / $6CO_2 + 6H_2O \rightarrow C_6H_{12}O_6 + 6O_2$
- aerobic respiration: glucose + oxygen → carbon dioxide + water / $C_6H_{12}O_6 + 6O_2 \rightarrow 6CO_2 + 6H_2O$
- Carbon dioxide and water are the reactants for photosynthesis, but the products of aerobic respiration.

- Glucose and oxygen are the products of photosynthesis, but the reactants for aerobic respiration.
- Photosynthesis is endothermic / takes in energy from the surroundings, but aerobic respiration is exothermic / gives out energy to the surroundings.
- Energy is transferred as light for photosynthesis, but (for example) by heating for aerobic respiration.
- Photosynthesis takes place in chloroplasts, but aerobic respiration takes place in mitochondria.

Paper 2

47. Homeostasis

1 Homeostasis is the regulation of the internal conditions (1) of a cell or organism to maintain optimum conditions (1) in response to internal and external (1) changes.

2 (a) detect stimuli (1), which are changes in the environment (1)

(b) one from: brain (1); spinal cord (1)

(c) (i) muscles (1); glands (1)

(ii) bring about responses (1), which restore optimum levels (1)

3 (a) blood glucose concentration (1); water level (1)

(b) In order, missing words are: receptors (1); coordination (1); increases (1).

48. Neurones

1 (a) one from: carry electrical / nerve impulses from one part of the CNS to another (1); carry impulses from sensory neurones to motor neurones (1)

(b) carry electrical / nerve impulses from the CNS to effectors / muscles / glands (1)

2 (a) The myelin sheath speeds up impulses / increases the impulse speed (1).

(b) Their movement would be impaired / made difficult (1).

3 The axon and dendron are long so the neurone can transmit impulses over long distances (1); there are several axon terminals which can pass impulses to other neurones (1); dendrites collect impulses from receptor cells (1); myelin sheath insulates the neurone so the impulse cannot cross from adjacent neurones / impulse speed is increased (1).

49. Reflex actions

1 (a) neurone Y, because it carries impulses to an effector / muscle (1)

(b) Neurone X releases a neurotransmitter (1) which diffuses across the synapse / gap (1), causing neurone Y to generate an electrical impulse (1).

2 innate (1); in either order: rapid (1); automatic (1)

3 (a) a change in the environment (1)

(b) In order: stimulus is detected by receptors (1); nerve impulse travels through a sensory neurone (1); through a relay neurone (in the CNS) (1); then through a motor neurone to the effector (which produces a response) (1).

50. Required practical – Investigating reaction times

1 (a) mean = (193 + 186 + 190 + 184 + 181 + 176) / 6 = 1110 / 6 = 185 mm (1)

(b) (i) 176 mm (1) because this was the shortest distance / the ruler fell for the shortest time (1)

(ii) distance = 193/10 = 19.3 cm reaction time = $\sqrt{19.3/491}$ (1) = 0.198 (1) = 0.20 s (1) (to 2 significant figures)

(c) The drop distance decreased between the first and last drop (1), showing that the drop time decreased (1).

51. Hormones

1 (a) In order, missing words are: glands (1); target (1)

(b)

Endocrine system	Nervous system
slow, long-lasting	fast, short-lasting

(1)

2 A – pituitary (1); B – thyroid (1); C – pancreas (1); D – adrenal (1); E – testis / testes (1); F – ovary / ovaries (1)

3 1 mark for each correct row:

Hormone	Produced in	Target organ
adrenaline	adrenal gland	heart / muscles
FSH and LH	pituitary gland	ovaries
insulin	pancreas	liver / muscle
oestrogen	ovary / ovaries	ovaries / uterus / pituitary gland
progesterone	ovary / ovaries	uterus
testosterone	testis / testes	male reproductive organs

52. Blood glucose regulation

1 (a) glycogen (1)

(b) 3, 5, 1, 4, 2 (all 5 correct = **3 marks**, 3 correct = **2 marks**, 1 correct = **1 mark**)

2 (a) 1.3 g/dm³ (1)

(b) three from: blood sugar level increases then decreases (1); increases from 0.7 g/dm³ to 1.15 g/dm³ (1); reaches a maximum at about 10.15 am / after about 2 hours (1); decreases from 1.15 g/dm³ to 0.97 g/dm³ (1).

(c) Blood glucose concentration lowers more rapidly (1) because muscles use more glucose for respiration during exercise (1).

53. Diabetes

1 (a) Total percentage with Type 2 diabetes = 3.2 + 7 + 12.6 = 22.8% (1)

Number of people = 22.8 × 1 864 035 / 100 = 425 000 (1)

(b) one from: the sample size may be small **(1)**; the sample may not accurately represent the whole population **(1)**; the percentages are rounded values / not precise **(1)**

(c) As the BMI increases the percentage of people with Type 2 diabetes increases **(1)**; more than half the people with Type 2 diabetes are obese **(1)**.

2 (a) Type 1 diabetes: the pancreas fails to produce sufficient insulin / pancreatic cells are destroyed by the body's immune system **(1)**. Type 2 diabetes: liver and muscle cells no longer respond to insulin **(1)**.

(b) injections of insulin **(1)** to reduce the levels of blood glucose **(1)**

(c) one from: carbohydrate-controlled diet **(1)**; exercise **(1)**

54. Reproductive hormones

1 (a) testosterone **(1)**

(b) one from: increases growth / size of testes **(1)**; stimulates sperm production **(1)**

(c) two from: growth spurt **(1)**; underarm / pubic hair begins to grow **(1)**; external genitals grow **(1)**; voice deepens **(1)**; brain matures **(1)**

2 (a) menstruation **(1)**

(b) (i) luteinising hormone **(1)**; stimulates the release of an egg **(1)**

(ii) follicle-stimulating hormone **(1)**; causes maturation of an egg in an ovary **(1)**

(c) ovulation **(1)**

(d) oestrogen **(1)**; progesterone **(1)**

55. Contraception

1 (a) vasectomy **(1)**

(b) (i) condom **(1)**; diaphragm **(1)**

(ii) Spermicidal agents kill / disable sperm. **(1)**

2 (a) The chance of a non-smoker getting a clot increases 5 times when on the pill (last box ticked). **(1)**

(b) one from: smoker, on 'the pill' **(1)**; non-smoker, pregnant **(1)**

3 (a) FSH causes an egg to mature **(1)** and LH causes an egg to be released **(1)**. A missed pill causes the level of progesterone to decrease **(1)**, so (FSH and LH are not inhibited and) a mature egg is released **(1)**.

(b) more likely to be effective **(1)** because a daily dose cannot be missed **(1)** OR longer-lasting contraception **(1)** because progesterone is released slowly **(1)**

56. Extended response – Homeostasis and response

The answer should include some of the following points: **(6)**

Control of blood glucose concentration:

- Pancreas monitors and controls blood glucose concentration.

- If the blood glucose concentration is too high, the pancreas produces insulin.

- This causes glucose to move from the blood into the cells / to be converted into glycogen for storage.

Causes and treatments of diabetes:

- In Type 1 diabetes the pancreas fails to produce enough insulin but in Type 2 the body cells no longer respond to insulin.

- In both types the blood glucose concentration becomes too high.

- Type 1 diabetes is normally treated with insulin injections but Type 2 diabetes is commonly treated with a controlled diet / exercise regime.

- Insulin injections reduce the blood glucose concentration.

- Controlled diet reduces the amount of glucose entering the bloodstream / exercise reduces blood glucose concentration.

- Obesity is a risk factor for Type 2 diabetes but not for Type 1 diabetes.

57. Sexual and asexual reproduction

1 **1 mark** for each correct row:

	Sexual reproduction	Asexual reproduction
Mixing of genetic information	mixes genetic information from each parent	no mixing of genetic information
Characteristics of offspring	show variety	same characteristics as parent / each other

2 Chromosomes are copied / DNA is replicated. **(1)**

3 four daughter cells drawn **(1)**; each cell with a different combination of large / small and black / white chromosomes **(1)**, e.g.

4 (a) 10 chromosomes **(1)**

(b) Each daughter cell has a copy of one chromosome from each pair of different chromosomes **(1)**; different daughter cells have different combinations of these chromosomes **(1)**.

58. DNA and the genome

1 genome (first box) **(1)**

2 (a) chromosome **(1)**

(b) two **(1)**

(c) double helix **(1)**

(d) A gene is a small section of DNA **(1)** that codes for a specific protein **(1)**.

3 improves our understanding and treatment of inherited disorders **(1)**; can be used in tracing human migration patterns from the past **(1)**

4 One benefit from: she could have earlier / more frequent screening for breast cancer **(1)**; she could consider surgery to remove the breast / mastectomy as a precaution **(1)**; her doctor may be able to prescribe drugs to reduce the risk of developing cancer **(1)**

One drawback from: it might make her more worried / anxious **(1)**; just because she has the mutation doesn't mean she will develop breast cancer **(1)**; could have unnecessary surgery / medication **(1)**

59. Genetic terms

1 (a) a sex cell **(1)** produced by meiosis **(1)**

(b) different forms **(1)** of a gene **(1)**

2 The genotype of an organism is the alleles of a particular gene present **(1)**. However, an organism's phenotype is its observed characteristics / traits **(1)** produced by these alleles (working at a molecular level) **(1)**.

3 (a) (i) Bb **(1)**

(ii) The B allele is dominant **(1)**, so only one copy is needed for it to be expressed **(1)**.

(b) bb **(1)**; to have blue eyes she must have two recessive alleles **(1)**

60. Genetic crosses

1 (a) dd **(1)**; the d allele is recessive so two copies are needed for poorly formed wings **(1)**

(b) Completed diagram:

Parent 1

		D	d
Parent 2	D	DD	Dd
	d	Dd	dd

parent gametes correct **(1)**; offspring genotypes correct **(1)**; dd circled in the diagram **(1)**; probability = 0.25 / 25% / ¼ / 1 in 4 / 1:3 **(1)**

2 (a) Completed Punnett square diagram:

Parent genotype

		G	g
Parent gametes			
Parent genotype	g	Gg	gg
	g	Gg	gg

parent gametes correct **(1)**; offspring genotypes correct **(1)**

(b) 20 **(1)**

(c) Gg **(1)**

61. Family trees

1 Both parents are heterozygous for the sickle cell allele. **(1)**

2 (a) two / 2 **(1)**

(b) one / 1 / individual 5 only **(1)**

(c) Person 4 doesn't have cystic fibrosis but she must have inherited an f **(1)** allele from her mother. So she must have inherited an F **(1)** allele from her father. This means that person 4's genotype is Ff **(1)**.

(d) Two healthy parents (person 3 and person 4) **(1)** produce a child (person 8) with CF **(1)**.

62. Inheritance

1 (a) 23 **(1)**

(b) completed Punnett square diagram:

	Father		
		X	Y
Mother	X	XX	XY
	X	**XX**	XY

parent gametes correct **(1)**; offspring genotypes correct **(1)**

(c) female **(1)**

2 The graph shows that the chance of a woman having a child with Down's syndrome increases as the woman's age increases **(1)**. So pregnant women over the age of 40 are more **(1)** likely to be offered embryo screening.

3 (a) Punnett square diagram:

	Father		
		P	p
Mother	P	PP	Pp
	p	Pp	pp

offspring genotypes correct **(1)**

(b) PP **(1)**

(c) pp (bottom right offspring) circled only **(1)**

(d) probability = 0.75 / 75% / ¾ / 3 in 4 / 3:1 **(1)**

63. Variation and evolution

1 (a) Most **(1)**

(b) Few **(1)**

2 (a) environmental **(1)**

(b) environmental **(1)**

(c) combination / genetic and environmental **(1)**

3 There is variation / differences in the characteristics of individuals in a population **(1)**; individuals who are better suited to their environment are more likely to survive **(1)**.

4 In order, missing words are: populations **(1)**; different **(1)**; fertile **(1)**

5 (a) They will be able to get more food **(1)**.

(b) They are likely to have long necks as well **(1)** because they inherit the alleles / genes for long necks **(1)** from their parents.

64. Selective breeding

1 It is the process by which humans breed plants / animals **(1)** for particular genetic characteristics / traits **(1)**.

2 one from: high milk yield **(1)**; high / low in milk fat **(1)**; high in calcium **(1)**

3 (a) one from: gentle nature / not aggressive **(1)**; 'cute' appearance or similar **(1)**

(b) large / unusual / colourful flowers **(1)**

4 (a) one from: to obtain more light for photosynthesis **(1)**; to avoid shading from other plants **(1)**

(b) one from: short-stemmed plants are less likely to fall over **(1)**; greater proportion of growth goes into the seeds **(1)**

5 Select the pigs in the group that have the least body fat **(1)**; breed from these pigs **(1)**; choose pigs with the least body fat from the offspring and breed from them **(1)**; repeat this process over many generations **(1)**.

65. Genetic engineering

1 changed their genome and their phenotype **(1)**

2 The gene from a jellyfish **(1)** is cut out using enzymes **(1)**. This gene is transferred to a mouse **(1)** embryo cell, and inserted into a chromosome. The embryo is then allowed to develop as normal.

3 two from: human insulin will be more effective / is the right form of insulin / is less likely to cause adverse reactions **(1)**; can be produced in large quantities by the bacteria **(1)**; can be produced at low cost **(1)**; no ethical / religious objections **(1)**

4 (a) Eating golden rice can increase vitamin A production / levels **(1)**, which reduces the chance of vitamin A deficiency / poor immune response / illness from infection / difficulty seeing at night **(1)**.

(b) The gene that is modified might transfer from the GM crop into wild rice / non-GM strains of rice **(1)** where it could have unknown effects **(1)**.

OR

Eating GM crops might have an effect on human health **(1)**, although this possibility has not been researched enough / risks are not known **(1)**.

66. Fossils

1 (a) 1 low temperatures **(1)**

2 absence of oxygen / water **(1)**

(b) remains / traces of organisms from millions of years ago **(1)**, which are found in rocks **(1)**

2 Black rats carried a parasite **(1)**, to which they were immune, but the native rats were not **(1)**.

3 (a) two from: new disease **(1)**; new competitors **(1)**; new predators **(1)**; changes to the environment, e.g. climate **(1)**

(b) Mammoths and humans existed at the same time **(1)**. Mammoths became extinct but humans did not **(1)**.

4 two from: early forms of life had soft bodies and left few traces **(1)**; traces / fossils destroyed by geological changes **(1)**; conditions not present for fossils to form **(1)**; fossils of small / delicate organisms less likely to survive or be discovered **(1)**

67. Resistant bacteria

1 No, because evolution can also produce new strains / breeds / varieties **(1)**.

2 (a) an antibiotic **(1)**, because it is used to treat bacterial infections / penicillin is an antibiotic **(1)**

(b) (i) MRSA already resistant to meticillin / other antibiotics **(1)**, so no / few / fewer antibiotics are left to treat vancomycin-resistant MRSA **(1)**

(ii) Mutations produce bacteria in the population that are resistant to vancomycin **(1)**; these bacteria are not killed in the presence of vancomycin **(1)**; they reproduce / divide **(1)**; remaining non-resistant bacteria in the population are killed **(1)**.

3 one from: doctors should not prescribe antibiotics inappropriately **(1)**, patients should complete their course of antibiotics **(1)**

68. Classification

1 (a) Completed table:

Classification group	Humans	Wolf	Panther
kingdom **(1)**	Animalia	Animalia	Animalia
phylum **(1)**	Chordata	Chordata	Chordata
class	Mammalia	Mammalia	Mammalia
order	Primate	Carnivora	Carnivora
family **(1)**	Hominidae	Canidae	Felidae
genus	Homo	Canis	Panthera
species **(1)**	sapiens	lupus	pardus
binomial name	Homo sapiens	*Canis lupus* **(1)**	*Panthera pardus* **(1)**

(b) panther and wolf **(1)**, because they both belong to the same order **(1)**

2 (a) *Melogale* **(1)**

(b) All the badgers belong to a different genus / species **(1)**; they are not closely related despite all being called badgers **(1)**.

(c) any two from: no confusion about which organisms being referred to / no two species have the same binomial name **(1)**; correct organism is easily identified from a similar species **(1)**; it can help scientists to study / conserve species **(1)**

69. Evolutionary trees

1 one from: amoebae have a nucleus (1) but bacteria do not (1); bacteria have a cell wall (1) but amoebae do not (1); amoebae have mitochondria (1) but bacteria do not (1)

2 Completed table:

Domain	Type(s) of organism in domain
archaea	primitive bacteria (that usually live in extreme environments) (1)
bacteria	true bacteria and cyanobacteria (1)
eukaryota	protists (1), plants (1), animals (1), fungi (1)

3 (a) toad (1)

(b) mouse, rat (1)

70. Extended response – Inheritance, variation and evolution

The answer should include some of the following points: (6)

Using the graph:

* The numbers of dark-form moths decreased over time.

Explaining the change:

* The population of peppered moths contains two different forms / colours / variants / kinds.
* dark form and light form
* In 1959 / mid-twentieth century most / 95% were the dark form.
* The two forms are controlled by genes / alleles
* which individual moths inherit.
* The trunks of trees where moths rest in the day are part of their environment.
* When these trunks are covered in soot the dark moths are less likely to be seen and eaten by birds.
* Dark moths are more likely to survive and reproduce than the light moths.
* When soot emissions stopped tree trunks became light-coloured again, so dark moths were now more likely to be seen and eaten by birds.
* Dark moths became less likely to survive and reproduce.

71. Ecosystems

1 (a) two from: water (1); mineral ions (1); space (1)

(b) territory and (1) food / mates (1)

2 community – all the different populations in a habitat (1)

organism – a single living individual (1)

population – all the organisms of the same species in a habitat (1)

ecosystem – all the living organisms and non-living parts in an area (1)

3 (a) two from: more lichens grow on the tree than on the concrete post (1); more lichens grow on the sides facing the Sun than away from / side-on to the Sun (1); the most lichens are found on the tree facing the Sun (1); the fewest lichens are found on the post facing away from the Sun (1)

(b) Lichens on the trees can obtain more nutrients from the trees (1) but less from the concrete (1). Lichens on the sides facing the Sun receive the most light (1) for photosynthesis (1).

72. Interdependence

1 All the species and environmental factors (1) are in balance so that the population sizes stay fairly constant (1).

2 (a) owl (1)

(b) two from: grasshoppers (1); mice (1); rabbits (1)

(c) The number of snakes would decrease (1) because snakes eat only mice / there would be less food for the snakes (1).

(d) The number of mice will decrease (1) because the numbers of stoats and snakes increase (1), and because stoats and snakes are not being eaten (by owls) so more mice are eaten (by stoats and snakes) (1).

73. Adaptation

1 (a) extremophiles (1)

(b) Bacteria provide food (1) to allow other organisms to survive there (1).

2 (a) Roses produce flowers to attract insects. These flowers have very bright colours / petals (1) and they also give off a strong scent / smell (1).

(b) They have a light, feathery structure (1), so can easily be blown away / distributed by the wind (1).

3 Animal A: any three from: A has a thick(er) coat for insulation (1); A has dark skin in order to absorb as much energy from the Sun as possible (1); A has wide feet in order not to sink through the snow / spread its mass on ice (1); A has small(er) ears so as to preserve heat / not radiate heat (1).

74. Food chains

1 (a) (i) grasshopper / mouse / rabbit (1)

(ii) owl (1)

(b) grass → mouse → snake → owl (1)

(c) one from: It is the producer (1); it makes glucose / food by photosynthesis (1).

2 (a) There is plenty of food for the ladybirds (1), so more ladybirds survive to reproduce (1).

(b) There are many ladybirds (1), so they eat more aphids (1).

75. Fieldwork techniques

1 (a) mean = (11 + 12 + 7 + 12 + 8 + 8 + 12) / 7 = 70 / 7 = 10 (1)

(b) median = 11 (1)

(c) Quadrats have a known area (1); slugs are slow moving (so easily counted in the quadrat) (1).

2 Set up a transect line (e.g. string / tape) between the path and the woodland (1); place quadrats at regular intervals along the transect (1); count the number of these plants in each quadrat (1).

3 area of the football pitch = 100 × 65 = 6500 m^2 (1)

number of clover plants = 7 × 6500 = 45 500 (1)

76. Required practical – Field investigations

1 (He is correct) because the percentage cover is greater on the south side (1), and this is the side with the higher light intensity (1).

OR

(He is not correct) because although the percentage cover is greater on the side with the higher light intensity (1), other factors may be responsible for the difference (1).

2 (a) (13 + 8) / 2 = 10.5 (1)

(b) As the distance from the sea increases, the number of limpets decreases (1); this decrease is linear with the distance / it decreases by 4 limpets every 0.5 m (1); limpets are more likely to survive if they live closer to the sea (1).

77. Cycling materials

1 (a) photosynthesis (1)

(b) respiration (1)

(c) combustion (1)

(d) decomposition (1)

2 Water vapour escapes from plants by transpiration (1) and from rivers and soil by evaporation (1). If the water is not replaced by rainfall, the rivers will dry up / there will not be enough water for plants / animals / water must be conserved by restricting water use (1).

3 one from: They are decomposers (1); they release carbon dioxide into the atmosphere (from respiration) (1).

4 Fish and plants respire (1); respiration releases carbon dioxide into the water (1); plants absorb carbon dioxide (1), which they use in photosynthesis (1).

78. Waste management

1 (a) Pollution is the release or presence in the environment of a harmful / toxic substance. (1)

(b) The lichen grows in unpolluted and polluted air (1); more bricks are covered by the lichen in unpolluted air than in polluted air / the lichen grows better in unpolluted air (1).

2 (a) increase in living standards (1)

(b) two from: land is used for building (1); land is used for quarrying (1); land is used for farming (1); land is used for dumping waste / landfill sites (1)

3 (a) Decomposers decompose the dead plants (1) and use up oxygen in the water (faster than it can be replaced) (1).

(b) one from: less oxygen (1) so fish cannot get enough for respiration (1); water plants die (1) so less food for the fish (1).

79. Deforestation

1 permanent destruction of forests to make land available for other uses (1)

2 (a) 32 + 34 + 3 = 69% (1)

(b) one from: fuel (1); timber for buildings / furniture (1)

(c) Planting trees increases (**1**) the rate at which carbon dioxide is taken from the atmosphere. The carbon dioxide is 'locked up' as wood (**1**).

3 (a) the variety of all the different species in an ecosystem / area / on Earth (**1**)

(b) two from: some species are destroyed in the deforestation (**1**); some species have their habitat destroyed (**1**); some species have their food sources destroyed (**1**)

80. Global warming

1 (a) As carbon dioxide levels increase, the average world temperature increases (**1**); as carbon dioxide levels decrease, the average world temperature decreases (**1**); high temperatures occur at about the same times as high carbon dioxide levels (**1**).

(b) a very large increase in average temperatures (**1**)

2 (a) methane (**1**)

(b) an increase in the Earth's average temperature (**1**) due to rising levels of greenhouse gases (**1**)

3 one biological effect of global warming, e.g. change in the migration patterns of birds (**1**); change in the distribution of species (**1**); change in biodiversity (**1**); spread of tropical diseases into new areas (**1**)

81. Maintaining biodiversity

1 two from: moral / ethical reasons (**1**); aesthetic reasons, e.g. enjoyment of seeing animals and plants (**1**); value / usefulness of different species to humans (**1**)

2 (a) one from: to increase the area of the fields (**1**); to make it easier for large machinery to move around (**1**); to reduce weeds / pests that might live in hedgerows (**1**); farm animals more likely to be kept indoors now (so hedgerows not needed) (**1**)

(b) two from: fewer plant species (**1**); fewer animal species (**1**); food / shelter has been removed (**1**)

(c) (i) one from: provides shelter for farm animals (**1**); provides windbreak for crops (**1**); provides habitat for predators that prey on crop pests (**1**); may be paid to replant hedgerows (**1**)

(ii) one from: provides shelter / nesting places for wild animals (**1**); provides food for wild animals (**1**); reduces soil erosion (**1**); provides a safe pathway for animals to move from place to place (**1**)

3 two from: restores habitat for endangered species (**1**); reduces the effects of soil erosion because tree roots bind soil together (**1**); helps to reduce the overall release of carbon dioxide because of photosynthesis by the trees (**1**)

4 Hedgehogs may be run over by traffic if they cross the road looking for food (**1**); a tunnel allows hedgehogs to move under the road safely (**1**), so more survive to reproduce (**1**).

82. Extended response – Ecology

The answer should include some of the following points: (**6**)

Using the graph:

- The rate of deforestation has changed over time
- but does not fall to zero,
- so the deforested area increased over time.

Use of land:

- May be used for farming.
- Farm animals, e.g. cattle, release methane.
- Methane is a greenhouse gas.

Use of wood:

- Trees may be burned / used as fuel.
- This releases carbon dioxide.
- Carbon dioxide is a greenhouse gas.

Carbon cycle:

- Fewer trees to absorb carbon dioxide for photosynthesis.
- Dead trees decompose.
- Decomposers release carbon dioxide because of respiration.

Link with climate change:

- Greenhouse gases are a cause of global warming.
- Global warming leads to climate change.

Chemistry
Paper 3

83. Elements, mixtures and compounds

1 copper (1)

2 (a) C (1)   (b) A (1)

3 a substance made up of two or more elements chemically joined together (1)

4 (a) Na (1)

(b) NH_3 (1)

(c) NaOH (1)

5 (a) iron sulfide (1)

(b) An element contains one type of atom only. (1) A compound contains two or more different types of atom. (1)

84. Required practical – Filtration, crystallisation and chromatography

1 (a) A, crystallisation; B, filtration; C, chromatography (3)

(b) (i) B   (ii) A   (iii) B   (iv) C (4)

2 *step 1*   addition of water

reason   to dissolve the sodium chloride (1)

step 2   heating and stirring

reason   to speed up dissolving / ensure the salt fully dissolves (1)

step 3   filtration

reason   to separate the insoluble solids from the solution (1)

step 4   crystallisation / evaporation

reason   to remove most of the water (1)

(1 mark for correct order of steps)

85. Distillation

1 distillation (1)

2 (a) 100 °C (1)

(b) fractional distillation (1)

3 (a) distillation (1)

(b) to condense the vapour (1)

(c) evaporation (1)

(d) C fractionating column (1)
   D water in (1)   E thermometer (1)

(e) Use an electrical heating mantle (1).

86. Historical models of the atom

1 (a) positive (1)

(b) electron (1)

(c) The atom has a nucleus which contains protons / positive charge (1) with electrons in the shells (1).

2 (a) nucleus (1)

(b) positive (1)

(c) proton (1)

(d) electron (1)

3 Chadwick (1)

87. Particles in an atom

1 (a) Ca (1)

(b) 20 (1)

2 (a) The sum of the protons and neutrons in an atom is its mass number (1).

(b) There is an equal number of protons and electrons so the total number of positive

charges cancels the total number of negative charges (1).

(c) 11 protons, 12 neutrons, 11 electrons (3)

(d) protons and neutrons (both needed) (1)

3 (a)

Atom	Atomic number	Mass number	Number of electrons	Number of neutrons	Number of protons
A	27	59	27	59 – 27 = 32	27
B	28	59	28	31	28
C	13	27	13	14	13
D	19	39	19	20	19

(4) (1 mark for each correct line)

(b) A is cobalt, B is nickel, C is aluminium, D is potassium (4)

88. Atomic structure and isotopes

1 (a)

Particle	Relative mass	Relative charge
electron	very small	–1
neutron	1	0
proton	1	+1

(3) (1 mark for each correct line)

(b) protons, 19; neutrons, 20; electrons, 19 (3)

(c) 1×10^{-10} m (1)

(d) They have the same number of protons (atomic number) (1), but different numbers of neutrons (mass number) (1).

2 (a) They are atoms with the same atomic number and a different number of neutrons (1).

(b) $= \dfrac{12 \times 99 + 13 \times 1}{99+1}$ (1) = 12.01 = 12.0 (1)
   (to one decimal place)

89. Electronic structure

1 nitrogen (1)

2 2,8,3 drawn (1) 2,8,7 drawn (1) 2,8,8,2 drawn (1)

3 (a) silicon (1) 14 (1)

(b) 14 of each (1)

(c) mass number (1)

4 (a) 2,8,8,1 (1)

(b) 2,8,5 (1)

(c) 2,8,8,2 (1)

90. Development of the periodic table

1 (a) 7 (1)

(b) noble gases / Group 0 (1)

(c) two elements in one position / copper present / silver present (1)

(d) any two from: Mendeleev's table has gaps (1)

has fewer elements (1)

has no noble gases (1)

is arranged in order of atomic weight not atomic number (1)

(e) germanium (1)

(f) isotopes (1) weight (1)

2 atomic weight (1)

91. The modern periodic table

1 (a) metal (1) metal (1) non-metal (1)

(b) mercury (1)

(c) 2 (1) 2 (1)
   7 (1) 7 (1)

2 by increasing atomic number (1)

3 (a) A and F (1)   (b) D (1)   (c) E (1)

4 (a) They have the same number of electrons in the outer shell of their atoms (1).

(b) The element with the smallest atomic number is boron. The atomic number gives the number of protons, so the element with the lowest number of protons is boron (1).

92. Group 0

1 (a) 2,8 (1)

(b) It has a full outer shell and is stable (1).

2 2 (1)

3 (a) Group 0 (1)

(b) approximately –160 (°C) (1)

(c) Boiling point increases with increasing relative atomic mass (1).

(d) approximately 2.5 (g/dm³) (1)

(e) He, 2 (1) Ne, 2,8 (1)

4 They have a full outer shell and are stable (1).

93. Group 1

1 (a) rubidium (1)

(b) potassium (1)

(c) sodium (1)

2 (a) Their atoms have one electron in the outer shell (1).

(b) (i) Similarities – any two from: metal floats, moves, disappears, bubbles (2)

Differences – any two from: potassium: reacts faster / bubbles faster, moves faster (on the surface), melts, produces (lilac / purple) flame (2)

(ii) potassium hydroxide and hydrogen gas (2)

3 (a) sodium chloride (1)
   sodium oxide (1)

(b) (i) $2Na + 2H_2O \rightarrow 2NaOH + H_2$ (1)

(ii) hydroxide ion (1)

94. Group 7

1 halogens (1)

2 (a) sodium + bromine → sodium bromide (1)

(b) 7 (1)

(c) $2K + Cl_2 \rightarrow 2KCl$ (1)

(d) potassium chloride (1)

3 (a) Reactivity decreases down the group and so bromine is less reactive than chlorine (**1**). It will not displace the more reactive chlorine from the sodium chloride solution (**1**).

(b) sodium chloride + iodine (**1**)

(c) displacement (**1**)

(d) Reactivity decreases as you go down the group (**1**).

95. Chemical equations

1 (a) potassium + chlorine → potassium chloride (**1**)

(b) magnesium + oxygen → magnesium oxide (**1**)

(c) hydrogen + bromine → hydrogen bromide (**1**)

(d) copper + oxygen → copper oxide (**1**)

2 (a) One molecule of methane reacts with two molecules of oxygen (**1**) to produce one molecule of carbon dioxide and two molecules of water (**1**).

(b) 16 g (**1**)

3 (a) $2Mg + O_2 \rightarrow 2MgO$ (**1**)

(b) $2HCl + Ca \rightarrow CaCl_2 + H_2$ (**1**)

(c) $N_2 + 3H_2 \rightarrow 2NH_3$ (**1**)

(d) $2SO_2 + O_2 \rightarrow 2SO_3$ (**1**)

(e) $H_2 + F_2 \rightarrow 2HF$ (**1**)

4 (a) $4Na + O_2 \rightarrow 2Na_2O$ (**1**)

(b) $4K + O_2 \rightarrow 2K_2O$ (**2**) *(1 mark for symbols, 1 mark for balancing)*

5 3 (**1**)

96. Extended response – Periodic table

The answer should include some of the following points: (**6**)

- Group 7 reactivity decreases down the group.
- Group 7 atoms have 7 electrons in outer shell.
- Group 7 atoms need to gain one electron to gain a noble gas structure.
- Further down the group the outer electron is further from the nucleus due to more shells of electrons.
- An electron is less easily gained because the outer electron is further from the nucleus, so there is less attraction between the outer electron and the nucleus due to more shielding.
- Group 1 reactivity increases down the group.
- Group 1 atoms have 1 electron in outer shell.
- Group 1 atoms need to lose one electron to gain a noble gas structure.
- Further down the group the outer electron is further from the nucleus due to more shells of electrons.
- An electron is more easily lost because the outer electron is further from the nucleus and so there is less attraction between the outer electron and the nucleus due to more shielding.

This answer is not exhaustive; other creditworthy responses will be awarded marks too.

97. Forming bonds

1 electrostatic forces (**1**)

2 (a) metal: calcium, magnesium (**1**)

non-metal: chlorine, oxygen, hydrogen, sulfur, nitrogen (**1**)

(b) ionic: calcium oxide (**1**), magnesium chloride (**1**)

covalent: hydrogen chloride (**1**), hydrogen sulfide (**1**)

3 (a) NH_3 (**1**)

(b) covalent (**1**) sharing of electrons between atoms (**1**)

(c) metallic (**1**)

4 nitrogen and hydrogen (**1**)

98. Ionic bonding

1 2– (**1**)

2 (a) 2,8,1 (**1**)

(b) 2,8 (**1**)

3 Each chlorine atom gains one electron (**1**).

4 Two sodium atoms each lose one electron (**1**), forming Na^+ ions (**1**). The electrons are transferred from sodium to oxygen (**1**). Each oxygen atom gains 2 electrons (**1**), forming O^{2-} ions (**1**).

99. Giant ionic lattices

1 usually dissolve in water (**1**)

high melting point (**1**)

2 six chloride ions (**1**)

3 (a) ionic (**1**)

(b) giant ionic lattice (**1**)

(c) It shows there are gaps between the ions but in the crystal the ions are touching (**1**).

(d) electrostatic attraction (**1**) between oppositely charged ions (**1**)

(e) The ions are held tightly in the lattice (**1**) and cannot move and carry charge (**1**).

100. Covalent bonding

1 (a) B (**1**)

(b) A (**1**)

(c) C (**1**)

(d) water (**1**)

2

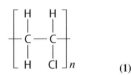

(**2**)

(1 mark for dot and cross in shared area; 1 mark for 3 pairs of crosses for Cl)

3 (a) (i) The lone pair is 'XX' (**1**).

(ii) The covalent bond is any 'OX' (**1**).

(b) PH_3 (**1**)

(c) compound (**1**)

(d) shared pair of electrons (**1**)

101. Small molecules

1 (a) covalent (**1**)

(b) It does not conduct electricity (**1**) as the molecules do not have an overall electric charge / there are no charged particles free to move (**1**).

2 (a) (i) CCl_4 (**1**) (ii) HCl (**1**)

(b)

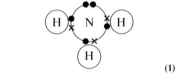

(**1**)

3

(**1**)

4 The forces between the molecules are weak (**1**).

102. Polymer molecules

1 (a) a large molecule made of repeating units, linked by covalent bonds (**1**)

(b) carbon (**1**) fluorine (**1**)

(c) covalent (**1**)

2

$$\begin{bmatrix} \begin{array}{cc} H & H \\ | & | \\ C & C \\ | & | \\ H & Cl \end{array} \end{bmatrix}_n$$ (**1**)

3 large; atoms; strong; strong (**4**)

4 (a) a large number (**1**)

(b) covalent bond (**1**)

(c) solid (**1**)

103. Diamond and graphite

1 carbon (**1**)

2 It has no free electrons or ions (**1**).

3 simple molecular, simple molecular, giant covalent, giant covalent, simple molecular (**5**)

4 A: carbon atom, B: covalent bond, C: intermolecular force (**3**)

104. Graphene and fullerenes

1 Graphene is a single layer of graphite (**1**).

Graphene has hexagonal rings of carbon (**1**).

2 graphene (**1**)

3 (a) any two from: 5 (**1**) 6 (**1**) 7 (**1**)

(b) carbon nanotubes and buckminsterfullerene (**2**)

4 (a) carbon nanotubes (**1**)

(b) good, high (**2**)

105. Metallic bonding

1 (a) in layers (**1**)

(b) delocalised (**1**)

2 (a) It has layers of positive ions (**1**) with delocalised electrons (**1**).

(b) The outer shell electrons are delocalised (**1**) and the sharing of delocalised electrons forms the bond (**1**).

3 (a) (i) metallic (**1**) (ii) ionic (**1**)

(b) good thermal conductor / shiny when freshly cut (**1**)

106. Giant metallic structures and alloys

1 (a) (i) can be hammered into shape (**1**)

(ii) It contains delocalised electrons. (**1**)

(iii) protons 79 (**1**) neutrons 118 (**1**)

(b) In an alloy there are different sizes of atoms present (**1**). This makes it difficult for the layers of atoms to slide over each other (**1**).

2 Percentage = 9/37 (**1**) × 100 = 24% (**1**)

107. The three states of matter

1 W gas (**1**)

X solid (**1**)

Y solid (**1**)

Z liquid (**1**)

2 (a) A melting (**1**)

B evaporation (**1**)

C condensation (**1**)

D freezing (**1**)

(b) The particles gain energy and vibrate faster (**1**). They overcome the forces between them and move apart and form a liquid (**1**).

108. Extended response – Bonding and structure

*The answer should include some of the following points: (**6**)

- Metals have giant structures with strong metallic bonds,
- which take much energy to break so they have high melting points.
- They are good conductors of electricity because the delocalised electrons in the metal move and carry electrical charge.
- They are good conductors of heat because the thermal energy is carried by the delocalised electrons.
- The layers of ions are able to slide over each other,
- but they are held in the structure by the attraction of the electrons and ions. Hence copper is soft and malleable.

This content is not exhaustive; other creditworthy responses will be awarded marks too.

109. Relative formula mass

1 Cl_2: 2 × 35.5 = 71 (**1**)

HF: 1 + 19 = 20 (**1**)

NaOH: 23 + 16 + 1 = 40 (**1**)

K_2O: (39 × 2) + 16 = 94 (**1**)

2 (a) 62 (**1**) (b) 342 (**1**) (c) 88 (**1**) (d) 98 (**1**)
(e) 164 (**1**) (f) 342 (**1**)

110. Balanced equations and masses

1 (a) (i) sodium hydrogen carbonate + citric acid → sodium citrate + carbon dioxide + water (**1**)

(ii) carbon dioxide gas (**1**)

(b) (i)

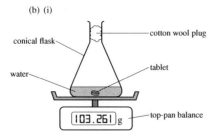

conical flask — cotton wool plug

water — tablet

103.261 g — top-pan balance

(**3** marks if all correct, **2** marks if one label missing, **1** mark if two labels missing)

(ii) A gas was lost from the flask (**1**).

2

Reactant	Relative formula mass	Product	Relative formula mass
$CuCO_3$	123.5	$CuCl_2$	134.5
HCl	36.5	H_2O	18
		CO_2	44

(**5**)

total formula mass of reactants
= 123.5 + (2 × 36.5) = 196.5 (**1**)

total formula mass of products
= 134.5 + 18 + 44 = 196.5 (**1**)

111. Concentration of a solution

1 D (**1**)

2 (a) volume = 2500 / 1000 = 2.5 dm^3 (**1**)

(b) 0.5 dm^3 (**1**)

(c) 0.025 dm^3 (**1**)

3 (a) 25 g/dm^3 (**1**)

(b) 36.5 g/dm^3 (**1**)

(c) 5 g/dm^3 (**1**)

4 concentration = (10 / 250) × 1000 = 40 g/dm^3 (**1**)

5 16 g/dm^3 (**1**)

6 (a) mixture of a solute and water / solution in which the solvent is water (**1**)

(b) 100 g (**1**)

112. Extended response – Quantitative chemistry

*The answer should include some of the following points: (**6**)

- Put a crucible on a balance.
- Use a spatula to add 0.62 g of copper carbonate.
- Place crucible on a pipeclay triangle and heat for several minutes with a Bunsen burner.
- Allow the crucible to cool.
- Weigh the crucible and contents.
- Re-heat the crucible.
- Allow to cool again and re-weigh.
- Keep heating and weighing until the mass does not change.
- Subtract the final mass of contents from the original mass (0.62 g).
- The mass should have gone down by 0.22 g because the carbon dioxide formed has been released into the air.

113. Reactivity series

1 (a) zinc, iron, copper (**1**)

(b) Blue colour fades (**1**) OR red–brown solid is produced (**1**).

2 (a) magnesium hydroxide + hydrogen (**1**)

(b) calcium nitrate + hydrogen (**1**)

(c) zinc chloride + hydrogen (**1**)

3 (a) hydrogen (**1**) (b) potassium hydroxide (**1**)
(c) any two from: heat, potassium disappears, lilac flame, bubbles, moves on surface (**2**)

4 calcium, magnesium, zinc, copper (**1**)

114. Oxidation, reduction and the extraction of metals

1 gain of oxygen (**1**)

2 (a) silver or gold (**1**)

(b) aluminium, calcium (**2**)

(c) carbon (**1**)

(d) any one from: calcium, aluminium (**1**)

3 (a) They are very unreactive (**1**).

(b) (i) $2Fe_2O_3 + 3C → 4Fe + 3CO_2$ (**1**)

(ii) Fe_2O_3 (**1**)

(iii) C has been oxidised because it has gained oxygen (**1**) and formed CO_2 (**1**).

115. Reactions of acids

1 neutralisation (**1**)

2 (a) base (**1**)

(b) magnesium chloride, aluminium chloride (**2**)

3

Acid	Base	Salt
hydrochloric acid	lithium hydroxide	lithium chloride
nitric acid	calcium oxide	calcium nitrate
sulfuric acid	sodium hydroxide	sodium sulfate
hydrochloric acid	magnesium oxide	magnesium chloride

(**4**)

4 (a) magnesium (**1**)

(b) potassium sulfate (**1**)

(c) carbon dioxide (**1**)

(d) copper sulfate (**1**)

116. Required practical – Salt preparation

1 (a) blue (**1**)

(b) from top: filter funnel, filter paper, residue / copper carbonate, filtrate / copper sulfate solution (all four correct for **2 marks**, any 3 correct for **1 mark**, 2 or less correct **0 marks**)

(c) Heat the filtrate to evaporate some of the water, and crystals start to form (**1**). Leave to cool and crystallise (**1**).

2 (a) sodium sulfate (**1**)

(b) Sodium is too reactive (**1**) and the reaction would be too violent (**1**).

3 Measure out some dilute hydrochloric acid into a beaker. Add a spatula measure of cobalt oxide, with stirring (**1**). Filter (to remove excess cobalt oxide) (**1**). Heat the filtrate to evaporate some of the water, and crystals start to form (**1**). Leave to cool and crystallise (**1**).

117. The pH scale

1 (a) Add some universal indicator (**1**); compare against colour chart (**1**) OR use a pH meter (**1**); record to 1 decimal place (**1**)

(b) C (**1**)

(c) A and B (**1**)

(d) E **(1)**

(e) An aqueous solution is one in which the solute is dissolved in water **(1)**.

(f) hydrogen ion **(1)**, hydroxide ion **(1)**

2 (a) sulfuric acid + potassium hydroxide → potassium sulfate + water **(1)**

(b) a reaction between hydrogen ions and hydroxide ions to produce water **(1)**

(c) green **(1)**

118. Electrolysis

1 (a) Lamp would light **(1)**.

(b) Solid lead bromide does not conduct as the ions cannot move and carry charge **(1)**. When molten the ions can move and carry charge **(1)**.

(c) anode: bromine **(1)**, cathode: lead **(1)**

(d) good conductor of electricity **(1)**, inert / does not react **(1)**

2 (a) anode: chlorine **(1)**, cathode: sodium **(1)**

(b) It does not decompose / no products form **(1)** as the ions cannot move and it does not conduct **(1)**.

(c) Metal ions are positive **(1)** and move to the negative cathode **(1)**.

119. Aluminium extraction

1 (a) Aluminium ion moves to cathode **(1)**.

Oxide ion moves to anode **(1)**.

(b) Al_2O_3 **(1)**

2 (a) The ions can move when molten **(1)** and carry a charge **(1)**.

(b) to lower the melting point, and so it is more economical **(1)**

(c) Aluminium ions are positive and they move to the negative electrode **(1)**, where they discharge and gain electrons and are reduced, forming aluminium **(1)**.

(d) oxygen **(1)**, carbon dioxide **(1)**

(e) cathode **(1)**

(f) Oxygen is formed at the anode **(1)** and it reacts with the carbon **(1)** anode to produce carbon dioxide **(1)**.

120. Electrolysis of solutions

1 It contains ions that can move **(1)**.

2 hydrogen bromine **(1)**

3 (a) (i) hydrogen **(1)** (ii) oxygen **(1)**

(b)

Electrolyte solution	Anode	Cathode
copper chloride	chlorine	copper
potassium bromide	bromine	hydrogen
sodium iodide	iodine	hydrogen
sodium sulfate	oxygen	hydrogen

(4) (1 mark per row)

121. Required practical – Electrolysis

1 (a) A, cathode **(1)**, B, anode **(1)**, graphite **(1)**

(b) solute: potassium chloride **(1)** solvent: water **(1)**

(c) potassium chloride: cathode, hydrogen **(1)** anode, chlorine **(1)**

calcium nitrate: test, relights a glowing splint **(1)**; cathode, hydrogen **(1)**; anode, oxygen **(1)**

sulfuric acid: cathode, hydrogen **(1)** anode, oxygen **(1)**

zinc bromide: anode, bromine **(1)**

silver nitrate: anode, oxygen **(1)**

(d) Carry out in a fume cupboard **(1)** – chlorine is toxic **(1)**.

122. Extended response – Chemical changes

The answer should include some of the following points: **(6)**

- calcium chloride formed in both
- Water is other product in reaction of calcium hydroxide with hydrochloric acid.
- Hydrogen is other product in reaction of calcium with hydrochloric acid.
- observations for calcium hydroxide and hydrochloric acid – solution remains colourless
- observations for calcium and hydrochloric acid
- bubbles/effervescence
- Solid disappears.
- colourless solution formed
- $Ca(OH)_2 + 2HCl \rightarrow CaCl_2 + H_2O$
- $Ca + 2HCl \rightarrow CaCl_2 + H_2$

This content is not exhaustive; other creditworthy responses will be awarded marks too.

123. Exothermic reactions

1

Initial temperature in °C	Final temperature in °C	Temperature change in °C
21	26	increased by 5
21	−5	decreased by 26
21	36	increased by 15

(6)

2 (a) The amount of energy in the Universe at the end of a chemical reaction is the same **(1)** as before the reaction takes place **(1)**.

(b) If a reaction transfers energy to the surroundings the products must have less energy than the reactants, by the amount transferred **(1)**.

3 (a) An exothermic reaction is one that transfers energy to the surroundings **(1)** so the temperature of the surroundings increases **(1)**.

(b) handwarmers **(1)** and self-heating cans **(1)**

4 (a) $CH_4 + 2O_2 \rightarrow CO_2 + 2H_2O$ **(1)**

(b) increases **(1)**

124. Endothermic reactions

1 (a) gives out **(1)**, takes in **(1)**

(b) Place a thermometer in **(1)**; temperature drops **(1)**.

(c) any one from: thermal decomposition **(1)**, citric acid and sodium hydrogen carbonate **(1)**, photosynthesis **(1)**

2 The equation states that energy is given out in the reaction of glucose with oxygen **(1)**. Hence energy is taken in in the reverse reaction (photosynthesis) meaning it is endothermic **(1)**.

3 (a) A – exothermic **(1)** B – endothermic **(1)** C – exothermic **(1)** D – endothermic **(1)**

(b) +29 **(1)**, −11 **(1)**

125. Required practical – Energy changes

1 (a) sodium hydroxide + hydrochloric acid → sodium chloride + water **(1)**

(b) Polystyrene cup is a poor conductor of heat and so no energy is lost to the surroundings **(1)**.

(c) to ensure the two solutions mix completely and fully react **(1)**

(d) Add a lid **(1)** to reduce heat loss **(1)**.

(e) (i) exothermic **(1)** because the temperature increased **(1)**

(ii) type of acid **(1)**

(iii) one from: volume of acid **(1)**, volume of sodium hydroxide **(1)**

126. Activation energy

1 y (vertical) axis – Energy **(1)**; x (horizontal) axis – Progress of reaction **(1)**

(b) A **(1)**

(c) C **(1)**

(d) exothermic **(1)**

2 reaction 1, endothermic **(1)**; reaction 2, exothermic **(1)**; reaction 3, exothermic **(1)**

3 (a) It is the energy needed for a reaction to occur **(1)**.

(b) collide with sufficient energy (to overcome the activation energy) **(1)**

127. Extended response – Energy changes

The answer should include some of the following points: **(6)**

- Combustion is exothermic.
- An exothermic reaction transfers heat energy to the surroundings.
- The temperature of the surroundings increases.
- Thermal decomposition is endothermic.
- An endothermic reaction takes in energy from the surroundings.
- The temperature of the surroundings decreases.

Paper 4

128. Rate of reaction

1 time taken = 2 × 60 = 120 seconds

rate = change / time = 1.2/120 **(1)**

mean rate of reaction = 0.01 g/s **(1)**

2 (a) (i) rate = change / time =
(0.36 – 0.22) / (4 – 2) = 0.14/2 **(1)**
rate of reaction = 0.07 g/min **(1)**

(ii) rate = change / time =
(0.42 – 0.36) / (6 – 4) = 0.06/2 **(1)**
rate of reaction = 0.03 g/min **(1)**

(b) conical flask on balance **(1)** acid
and calcium carbonate in flask **(1)**
cotton wool **(1)**

129. Rate of reaction on a graph

1 (a) magnesium + hydrochloric acid →
magnesium chloride + hydrogen **(1)**

(b) axes labelled with sensible scales **(1)**, all
points from table plotted taking up more
than half the grid **(1)** and a smooth curve
drawn **(1)**

2 (a) experiment A, 30 cm³ **(1)**, experiment B,
16 cm³ **(1)**

(b) 58 **(1)**, 29 **(1)**, 58 – 29 = 28 cm³ **(1)**

(c) (i) 24 **(1)**

(ii) 24/40 **(1)** = 0.6 **(1)**

130. Collision theory

1 when particles collide with sufficient
energy **(1)**

2 (a) any two from:

Rate is fast at start **(1)**.

Rate slows down **(1)**.

When graph is horizontal rate is zero **(1)**.

(b) The particles have more energy **(1)**.
The particles move faster **(1)**.

(c) The rate of reaction would have increased.
The acid was more concentrated so there
were more particles **(1)** in the same
volume **(1)** so there were more frequent
collisions / more collisions per second **(1)**
and a faster rate of reaction **(1)**.

131. Rate: pressure, surface area

1 There are more particles in the same volume
and there are more collisions **(1)**.

2 calcium carbonate powder reacting with
concentrated nitric acid **(1)**

3 (a) 70 s **(1)**

(b) A **(1)**; it has a steeper slope because it is
a faster reaction (due to a larger surface
area of metal) but the same volume of gas
is produced **(1)**.

(c)

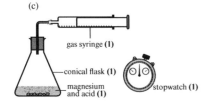

gas syringe **(1)**

conical flask **(1)**

magnesium
and acid **(1)**

stopwatch **(1)**

132. Rate: temperature

1 (a) (i) flask A **(1)**

(ii) least reactive metal **(1)**
lowest temperature **(1)**

(b) (i) A and B or C and D **(1)**

(ii) any two from: same concentration **(1)**,
same volume of acid **(1)**, same mass
of magnesium **(1)**, same surface area /
volume ratio **(1)**

2 (a) faster **(1)**

(b) There are more frequent **(1)** collisions **(1)**
as the particles have more energy **(1)**.

133. Required practical – Rate of reaction

1 (a) stopwatch **(1)**

(b) bubbles **(1)**, magnesium disappears **(1)**

(c) The temperature **(1)** and the volume **(1)**
of the hydrochloric acid must be kept the
same in all the experiments.

(d) A **(1)**

(e) A **(1)**

(f) the result at 8 minutes for C **(1)**

(g) Place magnesium and acid on balance
and record mass **(1)**. Record mass every
minute until reaction stops **(1)**. Plot
a graph of mass lost against time and
gradient is rate **(1)**.

134. Catalysts

1

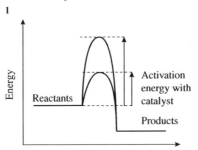

Energy

Reactants

Activation
energy with
catalyst

Products

Progress of reaction

(4) (1 mark for each correct label)

2 (a) gas syringe **(1)**

(b) (i) 48 cm³ **(1)**

(ii) zinc oxide **(1)**; reaction takes most
time **(1)**

(iii) The line should start at (0,0) and
remain steeper and above the graph
line, but level off earlier and to the
same volume **(1)**.

135. Reversible reactions

1 a reaction in which the products of the
reaction can react to produce the original
reactants **(1)**

2 (a) $N_2 + 3H_2 \rightleftharpoons 2NH_3$ **(2)** (1 mark for
symbols and 1 mark for balancing)

(b) ⇌ / double arrow **(1)**

3 (a) This means the reaction goes in both
directions **(1)**.

(b) carbon monoxide, hydrogen, methane,
water **(2)** (1 mark for any three)

4 (a) reverse (right to left) direction **(1)**

(b) white **(1)** to blue **(1)**

(c) contains water **(1)**

136. Equilibrium

1 (a) Equilibrium is reached when the forward
and reverse reactions **(1)** occur at exactly
the same rate **(1)**.

(b) The apparatus must be sealed / prevent
the escape of reactants and products / a
closed system must be used **(1)**.

2 (a) Increasing the pressure increases the
yield **(1)**.

(b) Increasing the temperature decreases the
yield **(1)**.

(c) 40% **(1)**

(d) reversible **(1)**

137. Extended response – Rates of reaction

*The answer should include some of the
following points:* **(6)**

- Add magnesium to acid.

- Time reaction until magnesium disappears or
measure volume of gas, per minute.

- Change concentration and repeat at several
different concentrations.

- Repeat experiment for reliability.

- same mass of magnesium

- same surface area of magnesium

- same volume acid

- same temperature

This content is not exhaustive; other creditworthy
responses will be awarded marks too.

138. Crude oil

1 mixture **(1)**

2 (a) $C_{11} – C_{13}$ **(1)**

(b) (i) residue **(1)**

(ii) petrol **(1)**

(c) fractional distillation **(1)**

(d) The higher the number of carbon atoms,
the higher the boiling point range **(1)**.

(e) (i) any two from: fuel oil **(1)**,
kerosene **(1)**, diesel oil **(1)**,
gasoline **(1)** fuel gases **(1)**

(ii) any three from: solvents **(1)**,
lubricants **(1)**, polymers **(1)**,
detergents **(1)**

139. Alkanes

1 (a) a compound made up of hydrogen and
carbon atoms **(1)** only **(1)**

(b) (i) methane **(1)**

(ii) e.g. –45 (a negative number greater
than –89) **(1)**

(iii) C_3H_8 **(1)**

2 (a)

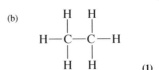

(1)

(b)

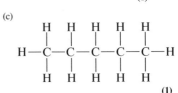

(1)

(c)

H   H   H   H   H
| | | | |
H—C—C—C—C—C—H
| | | | |
H   H   H   H   H

(1)

3 C_4H_8 **(1)**

140. Properties of hydrocarbons

1 (a) $C_3H_8 + 5O_2 \rightarrow 3CO_2 + 4H_2O$ **(1)**

  (b) propane **(1)**

2 (a) In tube A a colourless liquid **(1)** is formed. In tube B, the limewater changes from colourless **(1)** to cloudy **(1)**.

  (b) Anhydrous copper sulfate **(1)** turns from white **(1)** to blue **(1)**.

  (c) carbon dioxide **(1)** + water **(1)**

3 (a) octane **(1)**; it has a larger molecular size **(1)**

  (b) pentane **(1)**

  (c) It flows easily **(1)** and catches fire easily **(1)**.

141. Cracking

1 thermal decomposition **(1)**

2 (a) breaking up a large molecule **(1)** to produce a smaller, more useful molecule **(1)**

  (b) $C_8H_{18} \rightarrow C_6H_{14} + C_2H_4$ **(1)**

  (c) catalytic **(1)**, steam **(1)**

  (d) Smaller hydrocarbons make better fuels than larger ones **(1)**. Alkenes can be used to make polymers **(1)**.

3 (a) bitumen and residue **(1)**

  (b) B **(1)**

142. Alkenes

1

(1)

2 (a) B and D **(1)**

  (b) C: propane **(1)**

  (c) All contain hydrogen and carbon **(1)** only **(1)**.

  (d) $CH_4 + 2O_2 \rightarrow CO_2 + 2H_2O$ **(2)** *(1 mark for symbols and 1 mark for balancing)*

  (e) C_nH_{2n} **(1)**

3 (a) $x = 3$ **(1)** $y = 8$ **(1)**

  (b) propane **(1)**

  (c) one from:

(1)

143. Extended response – Organic chemistry

The answer should include some of the following points: **(6)**

- Heat the crude oil.
- Crude oil evaporates.
- The vaporised crude oil condenses in the fractionating tower.
- Different hydrocarbons condense at different heights because they have different boiling points.
- Cracking is breaking down large molecules into smaller molecules.
- Cracking produces alkanes and alkenes.
- Cracking produces more useful molecules.

- Fractional distillation does not involve a chemical reaction but cracking does.
- Cracking may involve a catalyst or adding a reactant (steam); fractional distillation just requires heating.

This answer is not exhaustive; other creditworthy responses will be awarded marks too.

144. Pure substances and formulations

1 A pure substance in chemistry is a single element or compound **(1)**. A pure substance in everyday life is one that has had nothing added to it **(1)**.

2 Determine its melting point **(1)**.

3 steel **(1)**

4 (a) A solid **(1)**; B solid **(1)**; C liquid **(1)**

  (b) A, element – sharp melting point and boiling point **(1)**

   B, formulation – melting and boiling points are not sharp but have a range **(1)**

   C, element – sharp melting point and boiling point **(1)**

5 Compare with the measured melting point in a data book **(1)**.

145. Required practical – Chromatography

1 (a) A, purple food dye **(1)**; B, filter paper / chromatography paper **(1)**; C, beaker **(1)**; D, solvent **(1)**

  (b) The paper is not touching the solvent **(1)**, so the solvent cannot move up the paper and over the dye to separate it **(1)**.

2 (a) 1 **(1)**

  (b) Graphite in pencil does not dissolve in the solvent **(1)**.

  (c) No, it has more than one spot on chromatogram **(1)**.

  (d) distance moved by dye X = 2.25 cm **(1)**

   distance moved by solvent = 4.5 cm **(1)**

   $R_f = 2.25/4.5$ **(1)** $= 0.5$ **(1)** *(your actual measurements may be different from this but the ratio should still be the same, to give you the same answer 0.5)*

146. Tests for gases

1 Put a piece of damp litmus paper into the gas. **(1)**

2 oxygen **(1)**

3 (a) calcium carbonate + hydrochloric acid $\rightarrow$ calcium chloride + water + carbon dioxide **(1)**

  (b) colourless solution **(1)** to milky **(1)**

  (c) calcium hydroxide solution **(1)**; $Ca(OH)_2$ **(1)**

147. Extended response – Chemical analysis

The answer should include some of the following points: **(6)**

- Add a burning splint – hydrogen pops.
- Add a glowing splint – relights – oxygen is present.
- Add a piece of damp litmus paper – it turns red – possibly chlorine.
- Then bleaches white, confirms chlorine.
- Bubble into limewater – colourless to milky – carbon dioxide.

- Helium – no reaction with any of above.

This answer is not exhaustive; other creditworthy responses will be awarded marks too.

148. The early atmosphere and today's atmosphere

1 nitrogen **(1)**

2 (a) oxygen 20 **(1)**; nitrogen 78 **(1)**

  (b) argon **(1)**

  (c) methane **(1)**; ammonia **(1)**

3 (a) $2Mg + O_2$ **(1)** $\rightarrow 2MgO$ **(1)**

  (b) volume of oxygen = 28 cm³ **(1)**

  (c) $28 / 200 \times 100$ **(1)** $= 14\%$ **(1)**

149. Evolution of the atmosphere

1 (a) any three from:

- The early atmosphere contained no oxygen but today's atmosphere contains 20% oxygen **(1)**.
- The early atmosphere was mainly carbon dioxide (95.5%) but today's only has 0.04% carbon dioxide **(1)**.
- The early atmosphere had only 3.1% nitrogen but today's has 78% **(1)**.
- The earth's atmosphere today has slightly less argon (0.9%) compared to 1.2% **(1)**.

  (b) We have accurate methods of measuring including instrumental methods **(1)**.

  (c) Algae and plants decreased the percentage of carbon dioxide in the atmosphere by photosynthesis **(1)** and oxygen increased **(1)**.

2 (a) $CO_2(g)$ **(1)**

  (b) (i) shells **(1)**

   (ii) limestone **(1)**

  (c) $6CO_2 + 6H_2O \rightarrow C_6H_{12}O_6 + 6O_2$ **(1)**

150. Greenhouse gases

1 oxygen **(1)**

2 (a) 40% **(1)**

  (b) water vapour **(1)**, which has formula H_2O **(1)**, and methane **(1)**, which has formula CH_4 **(1)**

  (c) any two from: The percentage of carbon dioxide decreased rapidly from 4500 to 3500 million years ago **(1)**.

   The percentage of carbon dioxide decreased more gradually from 2500 years ago **(1)**.

   The percentage of carbon dioxide levels off / stays constant **(1)**.

  (d) combustion of fossil fuels **(1)** deforestation **(1)**

151. Global climate change

1 (a) During photosynthesis plants take in carbon dioxide **(1)** and give out oxygen **(1)**.

  (b) Burning fossil fuels **(1)** releases carbon dioxide **(1)** into the atmosphere.

  (c) any two from:

- sea level rise, which may cause flooding and increased coastal erosion **(1)**
- more frequent and severe storms **(1)**
- changes in the amount, timing and distribution of rainfall **(1)**

- temperature and water stress for humans and wildlife (1)
- changes in the food-producing capacity of some regions (1)
- changes to the distribution of wildlife species (1).

2 (a) When the carbon dioxide concentration increased (1) the temperature change increased (1).

(b) ice caps melting (1)

(c) an increase in the average global temperature (1)

152. Carbon footprint

1 the total amount of all greenhouse gases emitted over the full life cycle of a substance (1)

2 (a) 12% approx. (1)

(b) 28 + 12 + 3 = 43% approx. (1)

(c) any two from: use a bike (1), car share (1), use public transport (1), holiday locally (1)

(d) any two from: solar power (1), hydroelectric (1), geothermal (1), wind power (1)

(e) carbon dioxide (1), methane (1)

153. Atmospheric pollution

1 (a) 66 + 18 + 10 = 94 (1)

100 − 94 = 6% (1)

(b) sulfur dioxide (1)

2 (a) carbon monoxide and soot (1)

(b) carbon – global dimming (1)

carbon monoxide – prevents the blood from taking up oxygen (1)

carbon dioxide – global warming (1)

3 (a)

Name of pollutant	Formula	Effect of pollutant
sulfur dioxide	SO_2	acid rain / respiratory problems
carbon monoxide	CO	toxic – can cause suffocation
soot / carbon particles / particulates	C	global dimming / health problems
nitrogen oxides	NO_x	acid rain / respiratory problems

(5)

(b) Sulfur in the fuel reacts with oxygen when it burns (1).

(c) Carbon monoxide is produced by incomplete combustion of the fuel (1).

154. Extended response – The atmosphere

The answer should include some of the following points: (6)

- The concentration of carbon dioxide changed little up until about 1800.
- The concentration of carbon dioxide increased dramatically from 1800 to 2000.
- This increase could be due to increased human activity such as

- increased combustion of fossil fuels
- and deforestation.
- Many scientists believe that increased carbon dioxide will cause the temperature of the Earth's atmosphere to increase at the surface.
- This will result in global climate change
- which may cause sea levels to rise and ice caps to melt – flooding.

This content is not exhaustive; other creditworthy responses will be awarded marks too.

155. The Earth's resources

1 renewable (1)

2 oil (1)

3 renewable (1), finite (1), renewable (1), renewable (1), finite (1)

4 Wool is natural (1).

Plastic is synthetic (1).

Cotton is natural (1).

Wood is natural (1).

156. Water

1 (a) It contains dissolved minerals (1).

(b) step 1: passing through a filter bed (1) to remove any solids (1)

step 2: sterilising using chlorine or ozone (1) to kill microbes (1)

(c) (i) removal of salt from water (1)

(ii) distillation (1); reverse osmosis (1)

(iii) It requires large amounts of energy (1).

2 (a) 1, screening and grit removal
2, sedimentation
3, anaerobic digestion of sewage sludge (1)

(b) It removes large solids and grit from the waste water (1).

157. Required practical – Analysis and purification of water

1 (a) in the conical flask (1)

(b) in the test tube (1)

(c) to cool the vapour and cause condensation (1)

(d) A, conical flask; B, delivery tube (1)

(e) Liebig condenser (1)

(f) Measure its boiling point (1); it should be 100 °C (1).

(g) It needs large amounts of energy and often this uses up finite resources (e.g. crude oil) (1); using fossil fuels to provide energy causes carbon dioxide and other pollutants to be released, which can lead to global warming or acid rain (1).

158. Life cycle assessment

1 An LCA can be carried out to assess the total impact on the environment of a product (1) over its whole life, from extracting the raw materials to its disposal (1).

2 (a) 7 520 000 (J) (1)

(b) any three from:

- extracting and processing raw materials (1)
- manufacturing and packaging (1)

- use and operation during its lifetime (1)
- disposal at the end of its useful life, including transport and distribution at each stage (1)

(c) To manufacture once, and fill the glass bottle four times, the energy is 7 520 000 + (2 000 000 × 4) = 15 520 000 joules (2)

To manufacture four plastic bottles the energy is (4 × manufacture) + (4 × filling) = (4 × 2 200 000) + (4 × 4 500 000) = 26 800 000 J (2)

Energy saving = 26 800 000 − 15 520 000 = 11 280 000 J (1)

(d) any two from:

- increased use of alternative energy supplies to manufacture the bottle (1)
- energy conservation (1)
- carbon capture and storage (1)
- carbon off-setting, including through tree planting (1)

159. Conserving resources

1 (a) lead and aluminium (1)

(b) Its ore might be scarce (1).

It might be expensive to extract the metal (1).

(c) 72% of lead is recycled.

72 / 100 × 4.6 (1) = 3.312 = 3.3 million tonnes (1)

(d) reduces the use of limited resources (1)

reduces energy consumption (1)

reduces waste (1)

2 (a) (2 × 27) + (3 × 16) = 102 (1)

(b) (27 × 2) / 102 × 100 = 52.9% (2)

(c) any two from: reduces the use of resources of bauxite (1); causes much less energy consumption (1); reduces waste and the associated environmental impacts (1)

160. Extended response – Using resources

The answer should include some of the following points: (6)

- Cardboard cartons are made from a renewable resource – wood.
- Plastic cartons are made from a finite resource – crude oil.
- Higher temperature used to produce plastic,
- hence more energy needed to manufacture plastic.
- Cardboard cartons produce more carbon dioxide during manufacture.
- Growing wood uses carbon dioxide by photosynthesis so this may offset the carbon dioxide produced.
- Cardboard cartons require more water to produce.
- Cardboard cartons are biodegradable.
- Agree or disagree or inconclusive based on information given.

This answer is not exhaustive; other creditworthy responses will be awarded marks too.

Physics
Paper 5

161. Energy stores and systems

1 elastic potential (1)

2 A – gravitational, C – chemical, D – kinetic (1) (all three needed for mark)

3 (a) store of chemical energy (1)

(b) energy transfer by electrical current (1)

(c) energy transfer to the surroundings by sound waves and by heating (1) (both needed for mark)

4 The total energy available initially in this closed system, in the gravitational potential store, is 250 J (1). As the basket reaches the ground, the gravitational potential store will become 0 J (1), because it has been transferred to useful kinetic energy (1) and wasted sound and thermal energy, which total 250 J (1). (Accept 'thermal' as the only identified wasted energy).

162. Changes in energy

1 $E_p = m\,g\,h$ (1)

2 Kinetic energy $E_k = \frac{1}{2}mv^2 = 0.5 \times (70$ m/s $\times (6$ m/s$)^2)$ (1) so $E_k = 1260$ (1) J (1).

3 Convert units: 15 cm = 0.15 m (1)

Energy transferred $E_e = \frac{1}{2}k\,e^2 = \frac{1}{2} \times 200$ N/m $\times (0.15$ m$)^2$ (1) = 2.25 (1) J

4 Gravitational potential energy $E_p = m\,g\,h = 60$ kg $\times 10$ N/kg $\times 0.7$ m (1) = 420 (1) J

163. Energy changes in systems

1 specific heat capacity = change in thermal energy / (mass × change in temperature) or $c = \Delta E / (m \times \Delta T)$ (1)

2 $\Delta E = m\,c\,\Delta\theta$ (1) = 0.8 kg $\times$ 4200 J / kg °C $\times$ 50 °C (1) = 168 000 (1) J

3 $\Delta\theta = \Delta E / (m\,c)$ so $\Delta\theta = 20\,000$ J / (1.2 kg $\times$ 385 J/kg °C) (1) = 43 (1) so

Change in temperature of the copper = 43 °C (1)

4 $\Delta E = m\,c\,\Delta\theta$ (1) so

Specific heat capacity $c = 16\,200$ J / (0.8 kg $\times$ 25 °C) (1) = 16 200/20 = 810 (1) J / kg °C

164. Required practical – Specific heat capacity

1 (a) the amount of energy required to raise the temperature of 1 kg of material by 1 °C (1)

(b) energy supplied, mass and change in temperature (1)

2 (a) Place a beaker on a balance, zero the balance and add a measured mass of water (1). Take a start reading of the temperature (1). Place the electrical heater into the water and switch on for a measured amount of time (1). Switch off the heater (1) and then take a final temperature reading once the thermometer stops rising. (1)

(b) Measure the current supplied, the potential difference across the heater and the time for which the current is switched on (1). Use these values to calculate the thermal energy supplied using the equation $E = VIt$ (1).

(c) Add insulation around the beaker (1) so less thermal energy is transferred to the surroundings and a more accurate value for the specific heat capacity of the water may be obtained (1).

3 Plot a graph of temperature against time (1). The changes of state are shown when the line on the graph is horizontal (the temperature is not increasing) (1).

165. Power

1 2500 W (1)

2 Energy transferred = 15 000 J, time taken = 20 s

$P = E / t$ so power $P = 15\,000$ J / 20 s (1) = 750 (1) W

3 (a) $E_p = m\,g\,h$ so $E_p = 60 \times 10 \times (0.08 \times 20)$ (1) = 960 (1) joules / J (1)

(b) $P = E / t$ so $P = 960 / 12 = 80$ watts / W (1) (allow value for energy calculated in part (a))

4 (a) for 3 W motor: $t = 360$ J / 3 W (1) = 180 (1) s

(b) for 5 W motor: $t = 360$ J / 5 W (1) = 72 (1) s

166. Energy transfers and efficiency

1 (a) concrete (1)

(b) Low relative thermal conductivity means that a material will have a slow (1) rate of transfer of thermal energy (1).

2 (a) Thicker walls provide more material for thermal energy (1) to travel through from the inside to outside, so the rate of thermal energy loss (1) is less, keeping the houses warmer.

(b) Thicker walls provide more material for thermal energy (1) to travel through from the outside to inside, so the rate of thermal energy transfer (1) is less, keeping the houses cool.

3 rate of data collection (1)

4 The useful energy transferred to the box = 100 J; total energy transferred by the motor = 400 J; efficiency = 100 J / 400 J (1) = 0.25 (1) (accept × 100% = 25%)

167. Energy resources

1 coal, oil and gas (any order) (1) (all three needed for mark)

2 (a) A hydroelectric power station is a reliable producer of electricity because it uses the gravitational potential energy of water, which can be stored until it is needed (1). As long as there is no prolonged drought / lack of rain, the supply should be constant (1).

(b) Hydroelectric power stations need to be in mountainous / high enough areas (1). The UK has very few mountainous/very high (accept 'Only possible in areas such as North Wales / Scottish Highlands'). (1)

3 (a) When carbon dioxide is released into the atmosphere it contributes to the greenhouse effect / build-up of CO_2 (1),

which is believed to contribute to global warming (1).

(b) Sulfur dioxide and nitrogen oxides have been found to dissolve in the water droplets in rainclouds, increasing their acidity (1); this can kill plants and forests / lakes or dissolve the surfaces of historical limestone buildings (1).

(c) Any two from: Coal mines / oil / gas wells create environmental scars on the landscape (1). Vehicles used to transport fossil fuels add to environmental pollution (1). Alternative answers may include: Accidents in the extraction of oil from deep sea reserves can result in sea pollution (1). New methods of extraction may have an impact on previously unused areas of the environment, e.g. fracking (1). Large transport networks may be needed to transport fuels (1).

168. Patterns of energy use

1 (a) 1 After 1900, the world's energy demand rose / increased (1) as the population grew.

2 There was development in industry / demand in energy supply (1).

3 The rise of power stations using fossil fuels added to demand (1).

(b) (i) coal, oil and natural gas (1) (all three needed)

(ii) Any two from: population has increased so domestic energy use has increased (1); industry has grown, requiring more energy (1); vehicle use and travel have grown, requiring more energy (1) (and any other valid reason)

(iii) Nuclear research only began from the 1940s onwards (1).

(iv) hydroelectric (1)

2 As the population continues to rise the demand for energy will also continue to rise (1). Current trends show that the use of fossil fuels is the major contributor to the world's energy resources (1). These are running out and no other energy resource has, so far, taken their place (1). This could lead to a large gap between demand and supply (1). (any other valid reason)

169. Extended response – Energy

The answer should include some of the following points: (6)

- Refer to the change in gravitational potential energy (E_p) as the swing seat is pulled back / raised higher.
- Before release, the E_p is at maximum / kinetic energy (E_k) of the swing is at a minimum.
- When the swing is released, the E_p store falls and the E_k store increases.
- E_k is at a maximum at the mid-point, E_p is at a minimum.
- The system is not 100% efficient; some energy is dissipated to the environment.
- Friction due to air resistance and / or at the pivot results in the transfer of thermal energy to the surroundings / environment.

- Damping, due to friction, will result in the E_k being transferred to the thermal energy store of the swing and hence to the environment.
- Eventually all the E_p will have been dissipated to the surroundings / environment (so is no longer useful).

170. Circuit symbols

1 LDR **(1)**

2 (a) 1 resistor **(1)**

   2 fuse **(1)**

   3 variable resistor **(1)**

   (b) fuse **(1)**

3

Component	Symbol	Purpose
ammeter	(A)	measures electric current
fixed resistor		provides a fixed resistance to the flow of current
diode		allows the current to flow one way only
switch	or	allows the current to be switched on / off

(Each correctly completed row gains **1 mark**.)

4 Diagram showing series circuit diagram with cell / battery / power supply **(1)**. Resistor **(1)** with ammeter in series **(1)**. Voltmeter connected in parallel across the resistor **(1)**.

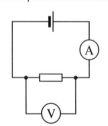

171. Electrical charge and current

1 (a) An electric current is the rate **(1)** of flow of charge (electrons in a metal) **(1)**.

   (b) Charge $Q = I\,t = 4\text{ A} \times 8\text{ s}$ **(1)** = 32 **(1)** coulombs / C **(1)**

2 (a) (i) The current is the same in all parts of a series circuit so the readings on ammeter 1 and ammeter 3 will be the same as that shown for ammeter 2 **(1)**.

      (ii) Add another cell / increase the energy supplied **(1)**.

   (b) cell **(1)**

3 (a) any series circuit diagram with a component (e.g. lamp) **(1)** and an ammeter **(1)**

   (b) stopwatch / timer **(1)**

172. Current, resistance and pd

1 resistance **(1)**

2 The current flowing through a resistor **(1)** at constant temperature is directly proportional **(1)** to the potential difference across the resistor.

---

3 (a) Potential difference = $I\,R$ = 0.20 A × 60 Ω **(1)** = 12 **(1)** V

   (b) Current $I = V / R$ = 22 V / 55 Ω **(1)** = 0.40 **(1)** A

4 (a) line A – straight line through origin **(1)**

      line B – straight line through origin – different gradient **(1)**

   (b) line with smaller gradient **(1)**

173. Required practical – Investigating resistance

1 Ammeter is connected in series but voltmeter is connected in parallel across the component **(1)**.

2 $R = V / I$ so R = 90 V / 1.5 **(1)** A = 60 **(1)** Ω

3 All circuit symbols correct (2 cells, 2 lamps, 1 ammeter, 1 voltmeter, wire) **(1)**. Ammeter connected in series **(1)**. Voltmeter connected in parallel with one lamp **(1)**.

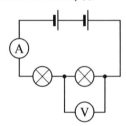

4 (a) fixed resistor **(1)**

   (b) filament lamp **(1)**

   (c) diode **(1)**

174. Resistors

1 (a) As the potential difference increases, the current increases **(1)** in a linear / proportional relationship **(1)**.

   (b) As the potential difference increases the current increases **(1)** but the increase in current becomes smaller as the potential difference continues to increase **(1)**.

2 (a) Fixed resistor: as graph A in Q1 **(1)**

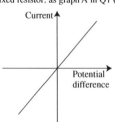

      Filament lamp: as graph B in Q1 **(1)**

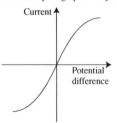

   (b) The different shaped graphs are because the fixed resistor is ohmic so the current and potential difference have a proportional relationship **(1)**; the filament lamp is not ohmic so the

---

relationship between current and potential difference is not proportional / current begins to level off as potential difference increases **(1)**.

3 Data can be collected using an ammeter to measure current **(1)** and a voltmeter to measure potential difference **(1)**. A wire should be included and a fixed resistor **(1)** to prevent overheating. A range of potential difference **(1)** measurements should be made so that resistance can be calculated using the equation $R = V / I$ **(1)**.

175. LDRs and thermistors

1 light **(1)**

2

light-dependent resistor (LDR)	thermistor
(1)	**(1)**

3 (a) The resistance goes down as the light becomes more intense (brighter) (more current flows) **(1)**.

   (b) The resistance goes down as the temperature goes up (more current flows) **(1)**.

4 The thermistor reacts to rise in temperature **(1)** in the engine. Above a certain temperature, it allows current **(1)** in the circuit to flow to a fan, which cools **(1)** the engine.

176. Required practical – Investigating I–V characteristics

1 (a) ammeter connected in series **(1)** voltmeter connected in parallel across the component to be tested **(1)**

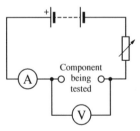

   (b) (i) Potential difference (V) **(1)**

      (ii) Current (I) **(1)** (can be in reverse order)

   (c) The terminal connections should be reversed to obtain negative values **(1)**.

   (d) y-axis: current (I), x- axis: potential difference (V) **(1)** (both needed)

2 (a) V (in V or volts) = I (in A or amps / amperes) × R (in Ω or ohms)

   (b) A conductor where current through the conductor **(1)** is directly proportional to the potential difference across the conductor **(1)**

3 Resistors can become hot and cause burns or fire **(1)**.

177. Series and parallel circuits

1 (a) In a series circuit the current flowing through each component is the same **(1)**.

In a parallel circuit, the current is shared between the components **(1)**.

(b) Series: $A_2 = 3$ A, $A_3 = 3$ A **(1)** (both needed)

Parallel: $A_2 = 1$ A, $A_3 = 1$ A, $A_4 = 1$ A **(1)** (all three needed)

2 (a) In a series circuit, the total potential difference supplied is shared between the components **(1)**. In a parallel circuit, the potential difference across each component is the same as the potential difference supplied **(1)**.

(b) Series: $V_2 = 3$ V, $V_3 = 3$ V, $V_4 = 3$ V **(1)** (all three needed)

Parallel: $V_2 = 9$ V, $V_3 = 9$ V, $V_4 = 9$ V **(1)** (all three needed)

3 The total resistance of two or more resistors arranged in series is equal to **(1)** the sum of the resistance of each component **(1)**. The total resistance of two or more resistors arranged in parallel is less than **(1)** the resistance of the smallest individual resistor **(1)**.

178. ac and dc

1 (a) Direct potential difference is constant **(1)** and the current flows in the same direction **(1)**.

(b) Alternating potential difference is changeable **(1)** and the current constantly changes direction **(1)**.

2 230 V and 50 Hz **(1)**

3 (a) The current is a direct current **(1)** because the electrons all flow in the same direction **(1)**.

(b) There should be one horizontal line anywhere on the screen **(1)**.

179. Mains electricity

1 (a) earth wire (yellow and green) **(1)**, live wire (brown) **(1)**, neutral wire (blue) **(1)**, fuse **(1)**

(b) live wire **(1)** because it carries the current into the appliance **(1)**

2 (a) alternating current **(1)**

(b) about 230 V **(1)**

(c) The earth wire is at 0 V **(1)** and only carries a current if there is a fault **(1)**.

(d) 50 Hz **(1)**

3 When a large current enters the live wire **(1)**, this produces thermal energy **(1)**, which melts the wire in the fuse **(1)** and the circuit is then broken **(1)**.

4 The earth wire is connected to the metal casing **(1)**. If the live wire becomes loose and touches anything metallic, the user is protected because the current passes out through the earth wire **(1)** rather than through the user **(1)**.

180. Electrical power

1 $P = I\,V = 5$ A $\times$ 230 V **(1)**

Power = 1150 **(1)** W

2 (a) $P = I\,V$ so $I = P / V$ **(1)** = 3 W / 6 V **(1)**

Current = 0.5 **(1)** A

(b) $P = I^2\,R$ **(1)** = $(0.5$ A$)^2 \times 240\ \Omega$ **(1)**

Power = 60 **(1)** W

3 Power = 6×230 (W) **(1)**

4 (a) $I = V / R = 80$ V / 8 Ω **(1)** = 10 **(1)** A

(b) Power $P = I\,V$ so $P = 10$ A $\times$ 80 V **(1)** = 800 **(1)** W or

$P = I^2\,R$ so $P = 100$ A $\times$ 8 Ω **(1)** = 800 **(1)** W

181. Electrical energy

1 force **(1)**

2 $E = Q\,V = 30$ C $\times$ 9 V **(1)** = 270 **(1)** J

3 (a) $Q = I\,t = 0.2$ A $\times$ 4 V **(1)** = 0.8 **(1)** C

(b) $E = Q\,V = 0.8$ C $\times$ 30 s **(1)** = 24 **(1)** J **(1)**

4 (a) The power of a circuit device is a measure of the rate of energy transfer / how fast the energy is transferred by the device **(1)**.

(b) Energy transferred is the amount of power over a given time **(1)** and the power of a device is the product of the current passing through it and the potential difference across it **(1)**.

182. The National Grid

1 (a) When a current flows through a wire, the resistance of a wire **(1)** causes energy to be transferred to the wire and heats it **(1)**.

(b) As the voltage is increased so the current goes down **(1)**, so this reduces the heating effect due to resistance **(1)** and means that less energy is wasted in transmission **(1)**.

(c) Wasting less energy in transmission means that more energy is transferred to where it is needed **(1)**, making the National Grid an efficient way to transmit energy **(1)**.

(d) The voltages are high enough to kill you if you touch or come into contact with a transmission line **(1)**.

2 any two from: step-up transformers increase voltage and so lower the current, reducing the heating losses **(1)**; wires are thermally insulated **(1)**; wires of low resistance are used **(1)**

3 Step-up transformers are used to increase the potential difference **(1)** from the power station to the National Grid, **(1)** then step-down transformers are used to decrease **(1)** the potential difference **(1)** for domestic use.

183. Extended response – Electricity

The answer should include some of the following points: **(6)**

- The thermistor can be connected in series with an ammeter to measure current with a voltmeter connected in parallel across it to measure potential difference.
- $V = I\,R$ can be referred to in calculating the resistance.
- When the temperature is low the resistance of the thermistor will be high, allowing only a small current to flow.
- When the temperature is high the resistance of the thermistor will be low, allowing a larger current to flow.
- The light-dependent resistor can be connected in series with an ammeter to measure current with a voltmeter connected in parallel across it to measure potential difference.
- When light levels are low (dark) the resistance of the light-dependent resistor will be high, allowing only a small current to flow.

- When light levels are high (bright) the resistance of the light-dependent resistor will be low, allowing a larger current to flow.
- Thermistors can be used in fire alarms as a temperature sensor to switch on an alarm.
- Light-dependent resistors can be used in security systems as a light sensor to switch on a light.

184. Density

1 (a) 1 solid
    2 liquid
    3 gas **(1)**

(b) In a solid, mass per unit volume is higher than for a liquid or a gas because the particles are very close together **(1)**. In a liquid, mass per unit volume is lower than that for a solid, because the particles are further apart, but higher than that for a gas because the particles are closer together **(1)**. In a gas, mass per unit volume is low because the particles are furthest apart **(1)**.

2 Density is calculated by dividing mass by volume **(1)**.

3 (a) Density = $m / V = 1650$ kg / 3 m^3 **(1)** = 550 **(1)** kg/m^3

(b) Density = $m / V = 4000$ kg / 5 m^3 **(1)** = 800 **(1)** kg/m^3

185. Required practical – Investigating density

1 (a) mass **(1)**

(b) electronic balance **(1)**

2 (a) For regularly shaped solids: any one of the following methods:

1 Volume can be directly measured using Vernier callipers / ruler to measure the length, width and height of the object **(1)**. The measurements are then multiplied together to find the volume, e.g. 3 cm $\times$ 3 cm $\times$ 3 cm to give the volume of a 3-cm cube **(1)**.

2 If the object is a regular shape, e.g. cube, cylinder, sphere, prism, the appropriate mathematical expression can be used **(1)**, e.g. use $4 / 3\ \pi\ r^3$ to find the volume of a sphere **(1)**.

3 If the density and mass are already known the volume can be calculated by using the equation **(1)**, i.e. volume = mass / density **(1)**.

(b) For an irregular solid: any one of the following methods:

1 Pour water into a measuring cylinder to a specific level and record the level **(1)**. Add the object to the water and record the new water level. The difference between the new water level and the original level will be the object's volume **(1)**.

2 Use a Eureka can by filling it with water until the water runs out from the spout **(1)**. When no more water runs out, carefully place the irregular solid into the can and measure the volume of water displaced through the spout by collecting the water in a measuring cylinder **(1)**.

3 (a) Place a measuring cylinder on a balance and then zero the scales with no liquid in the measuring cylinder **(1)**. Add the liquid and measure the level **(1)**. Record the mass of the liquid (in g) from the balance and the volume (in cm³) by reading from the level in the measuring cylinder **(1)**.

(b) Take the value at the bottom of the meniscus **(1)** making sure that the reading is made at 'eye level', to avoid a 'parallax error' **(1)**.

(c) Density = mass / volume so ρ = 121 g / 205 cm³ **(1)** = 0.59 **(1)** g/cm³

186. Changes of state

1 In a liquid there are some intermolecular forces between particles as they move round each other **(1)**. In a gas there are no intermolecular forces as the particles are far apart **(1)**.

2 physical change **(1)**

3 melts; boils; evaporates; condenses; freezes; 1 or 2 correct: **1 mark**; 3 or 4 correct: **2 marks**; all 5 correct: **3 marks**

4 Energy is transferred to the ice → energy is transferred to surroundings. **(1)**

5 At boiling point, the liquid changes state **(1)** so the energy applied after boiling point is reached goes into breaking bonds **(1)** between the liquid particles. The particles gain more energy and become a gas **(1)**.

187. Internal energy

1 the total sum of the kinetic and potential energies of the particles inside the system **(1)**

2 At boiling point / latent heat of vaporisation there will be a change / increase in the potential energy of the particles **(1)** but the kinetic energy of the particles will not change **(1)**.

3 (a) When temperature rises due to heating, internal energy increases **(1)** because the kinetic energy of the particles increases **(1)**.

(b) When temperature does not rise due to heating, internal energy increases **(1)** because the potential energy of the particles increases **(1)**.

4 When the water vapour condenses into a liquid there will be no change in the kinetic energy **(1)** of the water particles so the temperature does not change **(1)** but there will be a change in the potential energy **(1)** of the water particles as they move from a gas state to a liquid state.

188. Specific latent heat

1 Specific latent heat is the energy that must be transferred to change 1 kg of a material from one state of matter to another **(1)**.

2 temperature of the mass **(1)**

3 $E = m L = 25$ kg × 336 000 J/kg **(1)** = 8400 000 **(1)** J

4 (a) Melting – B **(1)**

(b) Evaporating – D **(1)**

(c) Specific latent heat of fusion – B **(1)**

(d) Specific latent heat of vaporisation – D **(1)**

(e) The energy being transferred to the material is breaking bonds **(1)**; as a result, the material undergoes a phase change **(1)**.

5 $E = m L = 36$ kg × 2260 kJ/kg **(1)** = 81 360 **(1)** kJ

189. Particle motion in gases

1 Temperature is a measurement of the average kinetic energy of the particles in a material **(1)**.

2 At a constant volume, the pressure and temperature of a gas are directly proportional **(1)**.

3 (a) As the temperature increases the particles will move faster **(1)** because they gain more energy **(1)**.

(b) As the particles are moving faster they will collide with the container walls more often **(1)**, therefore increasing the pressure **(1)**.

(c) The average kinetic energy of the particles increases **(1)**.

190. Extended response – Particle model

The answer should include some of the following points: **(6)**

- Solid, liquid and gas states of matter have increasing kinetic energy of particles.
- Thermal energy input or output will result in changes to the thermal energy store of the system and will result in changes of state or a change in temperature.
- Changes in states of matter are reversible because the material recovers its original properties if the change is reversed.
- Thermal energy input does not always result in a temperature rise if the energy is used to make or break bonds between particles / result in a change of state.
- Latent heat is the amount of heat / thermal energy required by a substance to undergo a change of state.
- The thermal energy required to change from solid / ice to water (accept converse) is called the latent heat of fusion and is calculated using $E = m L$.
- The thermal energy required to change from liquid to gas / water to steam (accept converse) is called the latent heat of vaporisation and is calculated using $E = m L$.

191. The structure of the atom

1 (a) Protons – labelled in the nucleus (+ charge) **(1)**

(b) Neutrons – labelled in nucleus (0 charge) **(1)**

(c) Electrons – labelled as orbiting (– charge) **(1)**

2 (a) The number of positively charged protons **(1)** in the nucleus is equal to the number of negatively charged electrons **(1)** orbiting the nucleus.

(b) The atom will become a positively charged ion / charge of +1 **(1)**.

3 Size of an atom: 10^{-10} m **(1)**

Size of a nucleus: 10^{-15} m **(1)**

4 When an electron absorbs electromagnetic radiation **(1)** it will move to a higher

energy level **(1)**. When the electron moves back from a higher energy level to a lower energy level **(1)** it will emit electromagnetic radiation **(1)**.

192. Atoms, isotopes and ions

1 (a) the name given to particles in the nucleus **(1)**

(b) the number of protons in the nucleus **(1)**

(c) the total number of protons and neutrons in the nucleus **(1)**

2 The number of neutrons is different **(1)**.

3 Isotopes will be neutral because the number of positively charged protons **(1)** still equals the number of negatively charged electrons **(1)**.

4 atoms: Cu, B; ions: F⁻, Na⁺, K⁺ (4 or 5 correct, **2 marks**; 2 or 3 correct, **1 mark**; 1 correct, **0 marks**)

5 Any two of the following explanations:

1 An atom can lose one or more electrons by friction **(1)** where contact forces rub electrons away **(1)** from the atom.

2 An atom can lose one or more electrons by ionising radiation **(1)**, where electrons are removed from the atom by an alpha or beta particle colliding **(1)** with an electron.

3 An atom or molecule can lose one or more electrons by electrolysis **(1)** when it was previously bonded in an ionic compound and is separated in solution in an electrolytic cell **(1)**.

193. Models of the atom

1 the electron **(1)**

2 The plum pudding model showed the atom as a 'solid', positively charged **(1)** particle containing a distribution of negatively charged electrons **(1)**, whereas the nuclear model showed the atom as having a tiny, dense, positively charged nucleus **(1)** surrounded by orbiting, negatively charged electrons **(1)**.

3 Rutherford fired positively charged alpha particles at atoms of gold foil and most went through, showing that most of the atom was space / a void **(1)**. Some were repelled or deflected **(1)**, showing that the nucleus was positively charged **(1)**.

4 (a) The particle Chadwick had found was electrically neutral **(1)** and so could not be a proton / must be a new particle **(1)**.

(b) neutron **(1)**

194. Radioactive decay

1 (a) Activity is the rate **(1)** at which the unstable / radioactive nuclei decay per second.

(b) The unit of activity is the becquerel (Bq) **(1)**.

(c) Count rate is the number of counts of radioactive decay **(1)** per unit of time / second / minute **(1)**.

2 The number of neutrons decreases by 1 **(1)**.

3 electromagnetic radiation **(1)**

4 (a) alpha radiation / particle: **(1)** the alpha particle consists of 4 nucleons / 2 protons and 2 neutrons / a 'helium' nucleus **(1)**

(b) beta radiation / particle: **(1)** a neutron changes to a proton increasing the positive charge by 1 **(1)**

195. Nuclear radiation

1 helium nucleus with charge +2 **(1)**

2 alpha – very low, stopped by 10 cm of air

beta minus – low, stopped by thin aluminium

gamma – very high, stopped by very thick lead

all correct **(2)**, 2 correct **(1)**

3 (a) no change in relative atomic mass **(1)**

(b) high-energy electron emitted from the nucleus **(1)**

(c) moderately ionising **(1)**

4 Compared with other types of ionising radiation, the chance of collision with air particles at close range is high **(1)** because the alpha particles are large / massive **(1)** compared with other types of radiation. As an alpha particle collides with other particles it loses its ionising energy **(1)**.

196. Uses of nuclear radiation

1 (a) Beta **(1)** radiation is used because alpha radiation / particles would not pass through **(1)** and gamma radiation / waves / rays would pass too easily **(1)**.

(b) (i) The paper has become too thick **(1)**.

(ii) The pressure on the rollers would be increased to make the paper thinner **(1)**.

2 They have high frequency / they carry large amounts of energy **(1)**.

3 (a) Alpha particles cannot pass through to the outside of the smoke alarm **(1)** and they are contained in a metal box / stopped by about 10 cm of air / are situated away from normal traffic of people **(1)**.

(b) The smoke particles absorb the energy of the alpha particles **(1)** so the air is less ionised **(1)** causing a fall in the current **(1)** and this triggers the bell to ring **(1)**.

4 Beta particles are less ionising than alpha particles **(1)** so they are much less likely to cause damage to body cells **(1)**.

197. Nuclear equations

1 (a) α **(1)**

(b) β **(1)**

2 The mass number is reduced by 4 **(1)**.

3 (a) (for nitrogen) 7 **(1)**

(b) (for phosphorus) 15 **(1)**

4 (a) beta-plus (positron) **(1)**

(b) alpha particle **(1)**

(c) neutron **(1)**

5 (a) add 208 to Po **(1)**; type of decay = alpha **(1)**

(b) add 86 to Rn **(1)**; type of decay = alpha **(1)**

(c) add 42 to Ca **(1)**; type of decay = beta-minus **(1)**

(d) add 9 to Be **(1)**; type of decay = neutron **(1)**

198. Half-life

1 random **(1)**

2 Half-life is the time taken for half the nuclei in a radioactive isotope to decay **(1)**.

3 (a) 8 million nuclei **(1)**

(b) 9.3 minutes = 3 half-lives **(1)** so, after 1 half-life, 8 million nuclei left, after 2 half-lives, 4 million nuclei left and, after 3 half-lives, 2 million nuclei left **(1)**

4 starting activity = 480 Bq at 0 minutes **(1)**. Half this activity = 240 Bq, at 5.3 **(1)** minutes (between 5.0 and 5.5 is allowed), so the half-life is 5.3 min **(1)**. (Answers between 5.0 and 5.5 min are allowed.) *(If you used other points on your graph and got an answer of around 5 min you would get full marks. For this question your working can just be pairs of lines drawn on the graph.)*

199. Contamination and irradiation

1 irradiation **(1)**

2 (a) External contamination: radioactive particles come into contact with skin, hair or clothing **(1)**.

(b) Internal contamination: a radioactive source is eaten, drunk or inhaled **(1)**.

(c) Irradiation: a person becomes exposed to an external source of ionising radiation **(1)**.

3 (a) Any suitable example, e.g. contaminated soil may get on to hands **(1)**.

(b) Any suitable example, e.g. contaminated dust or radon gas may be inhaled **(1)**.

4 Internal contamination means that the alpha particles come into contact with the body through inhalation or ingestion **(1)**, where they are likely to cause internal tissue damage **(1)**. Alpha particles that are irradiated are less likely to cause damage because they have to travel through air **(1)** and are therefore less likely to ionise body cells **(1)** (at distances of over 10 cm).

200. Hazards of radiation

1 alpha particles **(1)**

2 1 Limit the time of exposure / keep the time that a person needs to be in contact with the ionising source as low as possible **(1)**.

2 Wear protective clothing / wearing a lead apron will absorb much of the ionising radiation **(1)**.

3 Increase the distance from the radioactive source / the further a person is from the ionising radiation, the less damage it will do **(1)**.

3 A source of alpha particles with high activity inside the body will ionise body cells **(1)** because they are highly ionising / massive / undergo many collisions **(1)** before transferring all of their ionising energy. Gamma-rays can pass out of the body fairly easily **(1)** without causing much damage to cells **(1)**.

4 Radioactive tongs allow the source to be kept as far as possible away from a person's

hand **(1)** and allow it to be pointed away from people at all times **(1)**.

5 Those who use X-rays on a regular basis, such as medical workers, would have a high exposure / dose of radiation, which would cause damage if the dose were too high **(1)**. They leave the room so that they are not exposed to high levels of cumulative radiation / high dose **(1)**. The number of X-rays that a patient has is carefully monitored to minimise risk of high dose / exposure to high levels of radiation **(1)**.

201. Extended response – Radioactivity

The answer should include some of the following points: **(6)**

- All three types of radiation can pass into / penetrate different materials.
- Alpha particles have high relative mass and so transfer a lot of energy when they collide, so they are good at ionising.
- Alpha particles produce a lot of ions in a short distance, losing energy each time.
- Alpha particles have a short penetration distance so are absorbed by low density / thin materials such as a few centimetres of air and a sheet of paper.
- Beta particles have a low relative mass and can pass into / through more materials than alpha particles.
- Beta particles are less ionising than alpha particles and can be absorbed by 3-mm-thick aluminium.
- Gamma-rays are high-frequency EM waves and can travel a few kilometres in air.
- Gamma-rays are weakly ionising and need thick lead or several metres of concrete to absorb them.

Paper 6

202. Scalars and vectors

1 (a) Scalars: speed, energy, temperature, mass, distance **(1)**

Vectors: acceleration, displacement, force, velocity, momentum **(1)**

(b) Any correct choice and explanation, e.g. mass **(1)** is a scalar because it has a size / magnitude **(1)** but no direction **(1)**.

2 (a) weight **(1)**

(b) Weight has size / magnitude and direction but the other quantities just have a magnitude **(1)**.

3 (a) (i) Velocity is used because both a size and a direction are given **(1)**.

(ii) The students are jogging in opposite directions so the negative sign for one student indicates this **(1)**.

(b) The length of the arrow is proportional to the magnitude of the vector (in this case velocity) **(1)**. An increase in velocity to 3 m/s would mean an arrow 1½ times longer than that for 2 m/s **(1)**.

203. Interacting forces

1 gravitational **(1)**, magnetic **(1)**, electrostatic **(1)**

2 Like poles and charges repel **(1)**.

3 Weight and normal contact force are both vectors because they have a direction **(1)**.

Weight is measured downwards **(1)** whereas normal contact force is measured upwards / opposite to weight **(1)**.

4 (a) pull (by the student on the bag) and friction / drag of the bag against the floor **(1)**

(b) weight and normal contact / reaction force **(1)**

5 As the skydiver leaves the plane, weight acting downwards is greater than air resistance acting upwards so he accelerates **(1)**. As speed increases, air resistance increases to become equal to weight, so there is no net force / terminal velocity reached **(1)**. When the skydiver opens the parachute, air resistance upwards is greater than weight downwards so he decelerates **(1)**. The skydiver decelerates until air resistance upwards equals weight downwards – there is no net force (so a new terminal velocity is reached) **(1)**. (or similar wording)

204. Gravity, weight and mass

1 (a) The mass of the LRV on the Moon is 210 kg **(1)** because the mass of an object does not change if nothing is added or removed **(1)**.

(b)

Arrow points vertically downwards / top of arrow estimated around the seat area of the LRV **(1)**. (both points needed for mark) The centre of mass is where the weight of a body can be assumed to act downwards through a single point **(1)**.

2 $W = m\,g$ so $(1 + 2 + 1.5)$ kg × 10 N/kg **(1)** = 4.5 kg × 10 N/kg = 45 **(1)** N

3 calculating correct masses for all items (laptop 4.5 kg; camera bag 5.5 kg; walking boots 2.5 kg; jacket 3.5 kg; clothes 10.5 kg) **(1)**; selecting and adding up correct items **(1)** (clothes 10.5 kg + camera bag 5.5 kg + jacket 3.5 kg) = 19.5 kg **(1)**

205. Resultant forces

1 Resultant force is the net force after adding together all the forces acting on an object / is the single force that has the same effect on an object as all the forces acting on it **(1)**.

2 (a) A: 9.5 N **(1)**; B: 2 N **(1)**; C: 4.5 N **(1)**; D: 12.75 N **(1)**

(b) A – arrow pointing up **(1)**; B – arrow pointing up **(1)**; C – arrow pointing to the right **(1)**; D – arrow pointing to the left **(1)**

3 4 N **(1)**

4 (a) resultant force = positive direction – negative direction = 30 N – 10 N – 1 N **(1)** = 19 N **(1)**

(b) The resultant force is zero / 0 N **(1)** so the velocity is constant / stays the same **(1)**.

206. Work and energy

1 gravitational potential energy **(1)**

2 (a) Work done against friction will lead to a rise in the thermal energy store of the object **(1)**. This energy is then dissipated to the environment **(1)**.

(b) The greater the amount of friction, the more work that has to be done **(1)** to move the body through the same distance **(1)**.

3 $W = F\,s = 80$ N × 60 m **(1)** = 4800 **(1)** J

4 (a) $h = E_p / (m\,g)$ so $h = 320 / (8 × 10)$ **(1)** (remember to convert the grams to kilograms) = 4 **(1)** m

(b) Use $W = F\,s$ so $F = W / s$ **(1)** and $F = 320 / 4$ **(1)** = 80 **(1)** N

207. Forces and elasticity

1 friction **(1)**

2 (a) tension: washing line (or any valid example) **(1)**

(b) compression: G-clamp, pliers (or any valid example) **(1)**

(c) elastic distortion: fishing rod (with a fish on the line) (or any valid example) **(1)**

(d) inelastic distortion: dented can or deformed spring (or any valid example) **(1)**

3 After testing, Beam 1 would return to the same size and shape as before the test **(1)** and would be intact **(1)**. Beam 2 would distort and change shape **(1)** but would (probably) still be intact **(1)**.

208. Force and extension

1 Elastic deformation means that the object will change shape in direct proportion to the force(s) exerted, up to the limit of proportionality **(1)**, and the change in shape is not permanent **(1)**. Inelastic deformation means that the object will change shape beyond the limit of proportionality / the limit of proportionality is exceeded **(1)** and the change in shape will be permanent **(1)**.

2 20 N **(1)**

3 Extension = 0.07 m – 0.03 m = 0.04 m

Force = (spring constant / k) × extension = 80 N × 0.04 m **(1)**

Force = 3.2 **(1)** N **(1)**

4 (a) $F = k\,e$ so $k = F / e$ **(1)** = 30 N / 0.15 m **(1)** = 200 **(1)** N/m

(b) $E_e = ½\,k\,e^2 = ½ × 200$ N/m × $(0.15$ m$)^2$ **(1)** = 2.25 **(1)** J

209. Required practical – Force and extension

1 (a) Hang a spring from a clamp attached to a retort stand and measure the length before any masses or weights are added using a half-metre ruler, marked in mm **(1)**. Carefully add the first mass or weight and measure the total length of the extended spring **(1)**. Unload the mass or weight and re-measure the spring to make sure that the original length has not changed **(1)**. Add at least five masses or weights and repeat the measurements each time **(1)**.

(b) to check that the spring is not damaged during the experiment to identify when the spring permanently changes shape **(1)**

and so can no longer be used to recover all the energy transferred / energy is no longer stored as elastic potential energy **(1)**

(c) Masses must be converted to force (N) by using $W = m × g$ **(1)**. The extension of the spring must be calculated for each force by taking away the original length of the spring from each reading **(1)**. Extension measurements should be converted to metres **(1)**.

(d) (i) The area under the graph equals the work done / the energy stored in the spring as elastic potential energy **(1)**.

(ii) The gradient of the linear part of the force–extension graph gives the spring constant k **(1)**.

(e) limit of proportionality **(1)**

(f) elastic potential energy = 0.5 × spring constant × extension^2 or $E_e = ½\,k\,e^2$ **(1)**

2 The length of a spring is measured with no force applied to the spring whereas the extension of a spring is the length of the spring measured under load / force less the original length **(1)**.

210. Distance and displacement

1 A to C = 75 m **(1)**

2 Distance does not involve a direction and so is a scalar quantity **(1)**. Displacement involves both the distance an object moves and the direction that it has moved in from its starting point so it is a vector quantity **(1)**.

3 (a) The circumference of the Ferris wheel is $2\,\pi × (15 / 2) = 47.1$ m **(1)**. The wheel completed three cycles so the total distance travelled was $3 × 47.1$ **(1)** = 141.3 m **(1)**. (accept 141 m)

(b) The total displacement was 0 m **(1)** as the girls returned to the starting point at the end of the ride **(1)**.

211. Speed and velocity

1 Average speed = 10 000 m / 2400 s **(1)** = 4.17 **(1)** m/s

2 (a) Any **three** of the following: age **(1)**, terrain **(1)**, fitness **(1)**, distance travelled **(1)**

(b) (i) walking: 1.5 m/s **(1)**

(ii) running: 3 m/s **(1)**

(iii) cycling: 6 m/s **(1)**

3 The speed of the satellite is constant because the distance being covered each second is constant **(1)**, but the velocity changes constantly because the direction of motion is constantly changing **(1)**.

4 (a) $s = v\,t$, so distance = $4 × (15 × 60)$ **(1)** = 3600 **(1)** m

(b) The term 'velocity' is used because the boat has both speed **(1)** and direction **(1)**.

(c) At the finish of the journey by boat, the displacement of the team from the boathouse is 3600 m **(1)**. As they return to the boathouse by bus, the displacement decreases **(1)** until they arrive back at the boathouse where the total displacement is 0 m **(1)**.

212. Distance–time graphs

1 (a) (i) B **(1)**

   (ii) C **(1)**

   (b) Evidence of attempt to calculate the gradient of the slope to find speed / use of change in distance divided by the change in time / speed = distance / time, **(1)** so s = 20 / 40 **(1)** = 0.5 **(1)** m/s.

   (c) walking (slowly) **(1)** as the average walking speed is 1.5 m/s **(1)**

   (d) In part A, the runner travels 60 m in 40 s. Speed = distance / time **(1)** = 60 m / 40 s **(1)** = 1.5 **(1)** m/s. (You can use any part A of the graph to read off the distance and the time as the line is straight; you should always get the same speed.)

   (e) Displacement is the length and direction of a straight line between the runner's home and the park **(1)**, but the distance the runner ran may have included bends and corners on the path that the runner took **(1)**.

213. Velocity–time graphs

1 (a) $a = \Delta v / t = 4 / 5$ **(1)** = 0.8 **(1)** m/s^2 **(1)**

2 (a) The velocity of the car is increasing steadily **(1)**.

   (b) a right-angled triangle with a horizontal side and a vertical side that covers as much of the line as possible for precision **(1)**

   (c) Change in velocity = 30 – 0 m/s. Time taken for change = 5 – 0 s. Acceleration = $\dfrac{\text{change in velocity}}{\text{time taken}}$ or $a = \Delta v / t = 30$ m/s / 5 s **(1)** (or any calculation that gives the same answer) = 6 **(1)** m/s^2. (The triangle drawn may be different, and so give different numbers in the calculation, but the answer should be the same.)

214. Equations of motion

1 4 m/s^2 **(1)**

2 (a) $a = \Delta v / t$ **(1)** = (25 m/s – 15 m/s) / 8 s **(1)** = 1.25 **(1)** m/s^2

   (b) $v^2 = u^2 + 2\,a\,s$ = (25 m/s)^2 + 2(1.25 m/s^2 × 300 m) **(1)** = 1375 m/s^2 **(1)**
   $v = \sqrt{1375}$ m/s = 37 **(1)** m/s (allow rounding error – answers between 37.00 m/s and 37.10 m/s)

   (c) $v^2 - u^2 = 2\,a\,s$, so $s = (v^2 - u^2) / (2\,a)$ **(1)** = ((5 m/s)^2 – 1375 m/s^2) / (2 × –2 m/s^2) **(1)** = –1350 m/s^2 / –4 m/s^2
   Distance = 337.5 m **(1)**

3 gravity **(1)**

215. Newton's first law

1 (a) The forces on the plane are balanced and there is no net force in any direction **(1)**. Newton's first law says that, when there is no net force on an object and it is stationary, it will remain stationary **(1)**.

   (b) The forces on the plane are balanced and there is no net force in any direction **(1)**. Newton's first law says that, when there is no net force on an object and it is moving at a constant speed, it will continue to move at a constant speed **(1)**.

2 (a) Resultant force = 30 N + (–5 N) + (–1 N) **(1)** = 24 **(1)** N

   (b) The resultant force is zero / 0 N **(1)** so the velocity is constant / stays the same **(1)**.

3 (a) Assume downwards is positive, so resultant downward force is positive = 1700 N – 1900 N **(1)** = –200 **(1)** N. (You should state which direction you are using as the positive direction.)

   (b) The velocity of the probe towards the Moon will decrease **(1)** because the force produces an upward acceleration / negative acceleration **(1)**.

216. Newton's second law

1 (a) The trolley will accelerate **(1)** in the direction of the pull / force **(1)**.

   (b) The acceleration is smaller / lower **(1)** because the mass is larger **(1)**.

2 (a) $F = m\,a$ = 3000 kg × –3 m/s^2 **(1)** = –9000 **(1)** N

   (b) backwards / in the opposite direction to the motion of the minibus **(1)**

3 (a) $a = F / m$ = 10 500 N / 640 kg **(1)** = 16.4 **(1)** m/s^2 **(1)**

   (b) The mass of the car decreases **(1)** so the acceleration will increase **(1)**.

217. Required practical – Force, mass and acceleration

1 Electronic equipment is much more accurate **(1)** than using a ruler and a manual stopwatch to obtain values for distance and time to calculate velocity and acceleration. **(1)** (Reference should be made to distance, time and velocity.)

2 Acceleration is inversely proportional to mass **(1)**.

3 Acceleration is calculated by the change in speed ÷ time taken, so two velocity values are needed **(1)**; the time difference between these readings **(1)** is used to obtain a value for the acceleration of the trolley.

4 (a) For a constant slope, as the mass increases, the acceleration will decrease **(1)** due to greater inertial mass **(1)**.

   (b) Newton's second law, $a = F / m$ **(1)**

5 An accelerating mass of greater than a few hundred grams can be dangerous and may hurt somebody if it hits them at speed **(1)**. Any two of the following precautions: do not use masses greater than a few hundred grams **(1)**, wear eye protection **(1)**, use electrically tested electronic equipment **(1)**, avoid trailing electrical leads **(1)**.

218. Newton's third law

1 For every action there is an equal and opposite reaction **(1)**.

2 As the rocket sits on the launch pad, its weight downwards is equal and opposite to **(1)** the reaction force upwards of the launch pad **(1)**, so the rocket does not fall through.

3 The weight of the penguin is pushing down on the ice and the reaction force of the ice is pushing back on the penguin **(1)**, so the penguin is supported by the ice and does not fall through **(1)**.

4 Newton's third law says that the forces must be equal in size / magnitude **(1)** and opposite **(1)** in direction to be in equilibrium. The force exerted by the buttresses on the building **(1)** is equal and opposite to the force exerted on the buttresses by the building **(1)**, resulting in no movement occurring.

219. Stopping distance

1 (a) thinking distance + braking distance = overall stopping distance **(1)**

   (b) Thinking distance will increase if: the car's speed increases, the driver is distracted, the driver is tired, or the driver has taken alcohol or drugs **(1)**. (All four points needed for mark.)
   Braking distance will increase if: the car's speed increases, the road is icy or wet, the brakes or tyres are worn, or the mass of the car is bigger **(1)**. (All four points needed for mark.)

2 (a) Work done **(1)** by the friction force between the brakes and the wheel **(1)** reduces the kinetic energy of the vehicle **(1)**.

   (b) The temperature of the brakes increases because kinetic energy of the vehicle **(1)** is transferred to thermal energy by the brakes **(1)**.

3 Driving faster will increase thinking distance **(1)** and braking distance **(1)**. If drivers do not increase their normal distance behind the vehicle in front accordingly, there is an increased risk of an accident / collision **(1)**.

220. Reaction time

1 Overall stopping distance would be longer **(1)**.

2 Human reaction time is the time taken between a stimulus and a response **(1)**. It is related to how quickly the human brain can process information and react to it **(1)**.

3 (a) A person waits with his index finger and thumb opened to a gap of about 8 cm **(1)**. A metre ruler is held, by a partner, so that it is vertical and exactly level with the person's finger and thumb / with the lowest numbers on the ruler by the person's thumb **(1)**. The ruler is dropped and then grasped by the other person as quickly as possible **(1)**. A reading of distance can then be taken from the ruler. **(1)**

   (b) 0.2 s to 0.9 s **(1)**

   (c) The distance measured on the ruler would be short for the person with a reaction time of 0.2 s **(1)** and longer for the person with a reaction time of 0.9 s **(1)**.

221. Extended response – Forces

The answer should include some of the following points: **(6)**

Newton's first law:

• When the drone is hovering / stationary, the resultant force acting on it is zero.

- If the drone is hovering / stationary, it will remain stationary unless acted on by another force.
- If the drone is moving at a constant / steady speed, it will continue to move at the same speed and in the same direction, so velocity will remain constant, unless acted on by another force (both points needed).
- When the drone moves at a constant / steady speed (through the air) the resistive forces / air resistance balance the driving force of the motors.
- The velocity (speed and / or direction) of the drone will change only if a resultant force acts on the drone.
- If the speed and / or direction of the drone changes, its velocity will change.

Newton's second law:

- The acceleration of the drone is proportional to the resultant force acting on the drone.
- The acceleration of the drone is inversely proportional to the mass of the drone.
- As the drone accelerates
  - the resultant force acting on the drone can be calculated using $F = m\,a$.

222. Waves

1 When energy travels through water, we can see evidence that the water particles themselves do not travel. This is because an object on the surface will 'bob' up and down / vertically **(1)** as the wave passes horizontally **(1)**.

2 The vibrations in a longitudinal wave are in the same direction as the wave is travelling / energy transfer **(1)**. The vibrations in a transverse wave are at right angles to the direction the wave is travelling / energy transfer **(1)**.

3 (a) 0.025 m **(1)**

(b) 12 cm / 2 (as there are 2 waves shown) so wavelength = 6 cm = 0.06 **(1)** m

(c) any correct wave with higher amplitude (height) **(1)** and shorter wavelength **(1)**

(d) To find frequency use $v = f\lambda$, so $f = 3 \times 10^8$ m/s / 0.06 m **(1)** = 5×10^9 Hz **(1)** (or 5 × 10⁶ kHz / 5000 MHz / 5 GHz)

To find time period use period = 1 / frequency so period = $1 / 5 \times 10^9$ **(1)** (allow error carried forward from finding frequency) = 2×10^{-9} seconds / s **(1)**

223. Wave equation

1 Wave speed = 0.017 m × 20000 Hz **(1)** = 340 **(1)** m/s

2 (a) $v = f\lambda$ rearranged is $f = v / \lambda$, so $f =$ 1500 m/s / 88 m **(1)** = 17 **(1)** Hz

(b) $\lambda = v / f$ so $\lambda =$ 1500 m/s / 22 Hz **(1)** = 68.2 m **(1)**

3 $\lambda = v / f =$ 0.05 m/s / 2 Hz **(1)** = 0.025 **(1)** m **(1)**

224. Measuring wave velocity

1 The frequency of the waves (f) = 3 Hz. The wavelength of the waves (λ) = 0.05 m, so speed of waves = 3 Hz × 0.05 m **(1)** = 0.15 **(1)** m/s **(1)**

2 8 m **(1)**

3 T = 4 divisions × 0.005 ms = 0.02 s **(1)**

period = 1 / frequency so period = 1 / 0.02 s **(1)** = 50 **(1)** Hz

225. Required practical – Waves in fluids

1 (a) Count the number of waves that pass a point each second and do this for one minute (or any suitable time interval) **(1)**; divide the total by 60 to get a more accurate value for the frequency of the water waves **(1)**.

(b) Use a stroboscope to 'freeze' the waves **(1)** and find their wavelength by using a ruler in the tank / on a projection **(1)**.

(c) wave speed = frequency × wavelength or $v = f\lambda$ **(1)**

(d) the depth of the water **(1)**

2 A ripple tank can be used to determine a value for the wavelength, frequency and wave speed of water waves **(1)** as long as small wavelengths **(1)** and small frequencies **(1)** are used.

3 water: hazard – spills may cause slippages; safety measure – report and wipe up immediately **(1)**; electricity: hazard – may cause shock or trailing cables; safety measure – do not touch plugs / wires / switches with wet hands OR keep cables tidy **(1)**; strobe lamp: hazard – flashing lights may cause dizziness or fits; safety measure – check that those present are not affected by flashing lights **(1)**

226. Electromagnetic spectrum

1 (a) All waves of the electromagnetic spectrum are transverse waves **(1)** and they all travel at 3×10^8 m/s / the same speed in a vacuum **(1)**.

(b) Any suitable example, e.g. transmission of radio and TV signals using radio waves, use of microwaves to transfer information to and from mobile phones **(1)**

2 (a) A: X-rays **(1)**

B: visible light **(1)**

C: microwaves **(1)**

(b) Frequency increases from radio waves to gamma-rays **(1)**. The energy of the radiation increases with frequency **(1)**, so gamma-rays have the most energy and radio waves the least **(1)**.

3 $v = f\lambda$, so $f = v / \lambda = 3 \times 10^8$ m/s / 240 m **(1)** = 1.25×10^6 **(1)** Hz

227. Required practical – Infrared radiation

1 (a) any four from: Fill Leslie's cube with hot water at a known temperature (e.g. wait until it falls to 80 °C before taking temperature measurements) **(1)**. Measure the temperature at a distance (e.g. 10 cm) **(1)** from one of the four sides of Leslie's cube for a period of time (e.g. 5 minutes) **(1)**. Take regular readings (e.g. every 30 seconds) **(1)**. Repeat method for the other three sides **(1)**.

(b) The dependent variable is temperature **(1)**. The independent variable is the sides of the Leslie's cube **(1)**.

(c) Any four from: starting temperature of the water, distance of heat sensor / thermometer from the cube, length of time, same number of readings taken, same intervals of time for each temperature reading, use the same thermometer or temperature sensor. All four correct for **2 marks**; three correct for **1 mark**; two or fewer correct for **0 marks**.

2 (a) and (b) Any one hazard and method of minimising it from: Hot water in eyes can cause damage **(1)** – always wear eye protection **(1)**. Boiling water can cause scalds **(1)** – place the kettle close to cube and fill the cube in its place **(1)**. The cube can cause burns **(1)** – do not touch the cube until the temperature reading is low **(1)**. Water and electricity can result in a shock **(1)** – when using an electrical temperature sensor, keep well away from water **(1)**. Trailing wires can be a trip hazard **(1)** – avoid trailing leads / tuck leads out of the way **(1)**.

3 (a) The bungs would minimise thermal energy transferred from the flasks through evaporation **(1)**.

(b) (i) Dull and black surfaces are the best emitters and best absorbers **(1)**.

(ii) Shiny and light surfaces are the worst emitters and worst absorbers **(1)**.

228. Dangers and uses

1 (a) infrared waves: (any **two** from) night vision goggles / security sensor / TV remote control / cooking / thermal imaging camera **(1)**

(b) ultraviolet waves: (any **two** from) disinfecting water / sterilising surgical / scientific instruments / entertainment lighting / security marking **(1)**

(c) gamma-rays: (any **two** from) sterilising food / treating cancer / detection of cracks (pipes / aircraft, etc.) **(1)**

(d) Communication / mobile phones / satellites **(1)**

2 (a) The oral X-ray delivers the least amount of radiation, 0.005 mSv, which is the same as 1 day's normal exposure to background radiation. The next highest dose is for a chest X-ray which delivers 0.1 mSv, equivalent to 10 days of background radiation, and the highest dose is for the lung cancer screening, which delivers 1.5 mSv, equivalent to 6 months' exposure to background radiation. (X-rays in the right order **(1)**, dose related to equivalent background radiation for all three **(1)**, data quoted from table for all three **(1)**)

(b) If a person has too many X-rays in a certain time, particularly higher-dose X-rays, they may be more at risk of damage to body cells **(1)** if the X-rays are not carefully controlled to allow the body to recover from the high-energy doses **(1)**.

3 Any two of the following:

Ultraviolet radiation can cause eye damage **(1)**. Ultraviolet radiation can increase the risk of skin cancer **(1)**. Ultraviolet radiation can cause skin to age prematurely **(1)**.

229. Extended response – Waves

The answer should include some of the following points: (6)

- X-rays and gamma-rays are both transverse waves.
- X-rays and gamma-rays have a high frequency and therefore carry high amounts of energy.
- X-rays and gamma-rays cause ionisation in atoms and exposure can be dangerous / cause cells to become cancerous.
- People who work regularly with X-rays and gamma-rays should limit their exposure by using shields or leaving the room during use.
- X-rays are transmitted by normal body tissue but are absorbed by bones and other dense materials such as metals.
- X-rays and gamma-rays mostly pass through body tissue but can be absorbed by some types of cells such as bone.
- X-rays and gamma-rays can be used to investigate / treat medical problems.
- X-rays and gamma-rays are used in industry to examine / 'see' into objects to examine for cracks / failures.

230. Magnets and magnetic fields

1 field lines **out** (arrows) of N (1), field lines **in** (arrows) at S (1), field line close at poles (1), further apart at sides (1)

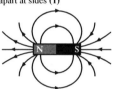

2 A bar magnet and the Earth both have north and south poles (1). A bar magnet and the Earth have similar magnetic field patterns (1). The direction of both fields can be found using a plotting compass (1).

3 An induced magnet is used for an electric doorbell because it can be magnetised when the current is switched on (1), which attracts the soft iron armature to ring the bell (1), and is de-magnetised when the current is switched off (1) (moving the armature away from the bell). An induced magnet is used as the 'switching' off and on of the magnet allows the arm to be moved and the bell rung (1). Also, the default 'rest' state of the bell does not need any energy input (1).

231. Current and magnetism

1 (a) at least two concentric circles on each diagram (2)

  (b) clockwise arrows on cross diagram (1); anti-clockwise arrows on dot diagram (1)

  (c) by increasing the current (1)

2 (a) bar magnet (1)

  (b) Insert an iron core into the solenoid (1).

3 The force acting on a current-carrying wire in a magnetic field depends on the length / l (1) of the wire, the current / I (1) in the wire and the magnetic flux density / B (1).

232. Extended response – Magnetism and electromagnetism

The answer should include some of the following points: (6)

- A long straight conductor could be connected to a cell, an ammeter and a small resistor to prevent overheating in the conductor.
- When the current is switched on the direction of the magnetic field generated around a long straight conductor can be found using the right-hand grip rule.
- The right-hand grip rule points the thumb in the direction of conventional current and the direction of the fingers shows the direction of the magnetic field.
- A card can be cut halfway through and placed at right angles to the long straight conductor. A plotting compass can be used to show the shape and direction of the magnetic field.
- The shape of the magnetic field around the long straight conductor will be circular / concentric circles as the current flows through it.
- The strength of the magnetic field depends on the distance from the conductor.
- The concentric magnetic field lines mean that the field becomes weaker with increasing distance.
- The strength of the magnetic field can be increased by increasing the current.

Physics Equation Sheet

(final velocity)^2 − (initial velocity)^2 = 2 × acceleration × distance	$v^2 - u^2 = 2\,a\,s$
elastic potential energy = 0.5 × spring constant × (extension)^2	$E_e = \frac{1}{2}\,k\,e^2$
change in thermal energy = mass × specific heat capacity × temperature change	$\Delta E = m\,c\,\Delta\theta$
period = $\dfrac{1}{\text{frequency}}$	
thermal energy for a change of state = mass × specific latent heat	$E = m\,L$

The Periodic Table of the Elements

Key

| relative atomic mass |
| **atomic symbol** |
| name |
| atomic (proton) number |

Example:

1 / **H** / hydrogen / 1

1	2											3	4	5	6	7	0
								1 **H** hydrogen 1									4 **He** helium 2
7 **Li** lithium 3	9 **Be** beryllium 4											11 **B** boron 5	12 **C** carbon 6	14 **N** nitrogen 7	16 **O** oxygen 8	19 **F** fluorine 9	20 **Ne** neon 10
23 **Na** sodium 11	24 **Mg** magnesium 12											27 **Al** aluminium 13	28 **Si** silicon 14	31 **P** phosphorus 15	32 **S** sulfur 16	35.5 **Cl** chlorine 17	40 **Ar** argon 18
39 **K** potassium 19	40 **Ca** calcium 20	45 **Sc** scandium 21	48 **Ti** titanium 22	51 **V** vanadium 23	52 **Cr** chromium 24	55 **Mn** manganese 25	56 **Fe** iron 26	59 **Co** cobalt 27	59 **Ni** nickel 28	63.5 **Cu** copper 29	65 **Zn** zinc 30	70 **Ga** gallium 31	73 **Ge** germanium 32	75 **As** arsenic 33	79 **Se** selenium 34	80 **Br** bromine 35	84 **Kr** krypton 36
85 **Rb** rubidium 37	88 **Sr** strontium 38	89 **Y** yttrium 39	91 **Zr** zirconium 40	93 **Nb** niobium 41	96 **Mo** molybdenum 42	[98] **Tc** technetium 43	101 **Ru** ruthenium 44	103 **Rh** rhodium 45	106 **Pd** palladium 46	108 **Ag** silver 47	112 **Cd** cadmium 48	115 **In** indium 49	119 **Sn** tin 50	122 **Sb** antimony 51	128 **Te** tellurium 52	127 **I** iodine 53	131 **Xe** xenon 54
133 **Cs** caesium 55	137 **Ba** barium 56	139 **La*** lanthanum 57	178 **Hf** hafnium 72	181 **Ta** tantalum 73	184 **W** tungsten 74	186 **Re** rhenium 75	190 **Os** osmium 76	192 **Ir** iridium 77	195 **Pt** platinum 78	197 **Au** gold 79	201 **Hg** mercury 80	204 **Tl** thallium 81	207 **Pb** lead 82	209 **Bi** bismuth 83	[209] **Po** polonium 84	[210] **At** astatine 85	[222] **Rn** radon 86
[223] **Fr** francium 87	[226] **Ra** radium 88	[227] **Ac*** actinium 89	[261] **Rf** rutherfordium 104	[262] **Db** dubnium 105	[266] **Sg** seaborgium 106	[264] **Bh** bohrium 107	[277] **Hs** hassium 108	[268] **Mt** meitnerium 109	[271] **Ds** darmstadtium 110	[272] **Rg** roentgenium 111	[285] **Cn** copernicium 112	[286] **Uut** ununtrium 113	[289] **Fl** flerovium 114	[289] **Uup** ununpentium 115	[293] **Lv** livermorium 116	[294] **Uus** ununseptium 117	[294] **Uuo** ununoctium 118

* The Lanthanides (atomic numbers 58 – 71) and the Actinides (atomic numbers 90 – 103) have been omitted.

Relative atomic masses for **Cu** and **Cl** have not been rounded to the nearest whole number.

Published by Pearson Education Limited, 80 Strand, London, WC2R 0RL.

www.pearsonschoolsandfecolleges.co.uk

Text and illustrations © Pearson Education Limited 2018
Typeset, illustrated and produced by Phoenix Photosetting
Cover illustration by Miriam Sturdee

The rights of Nora Henry, Nigel Saunders and Catherine Wilson to be identified as authors of this work
have been asserted by them in accordance with the Copyright, Designs and Patents Act 1988.

First published 2018

21 20 19 18
10 9 8 7 6 5 4 3 2 1

British Library Cataloguing in Publication Data
A catalogue record for this book is available from the British Library

ISBN 978 1 292 13167 2

Printed in Slovakia by Neografia.

Acknowledgements
Content written by Iain Brand, Peter Ellis and Dr Stephen Hoare has been included in this book.

Photos
Science Photo Library Ltd: BioPhoto Associates 1, Steve Gschmeissner 6, 7

Figures
Page 168, Patterns of energy use, graph includes data from BP Statistical Review of World Energy 2012
www.bp.com/statisticalreview; page 220, Highway Code stopping distances: Contains public sector
information licensed under the Open Government Licence v1.0.

All other images © Pearson Education

Note from the publisher
Pearson has robust editorial processes, including answer and fact checks, to ensure the accuracy of the
content in this publication, and every effort is made to ensure this publication is free of errors. We are,
however, only human, and occasionally errors do occur. Pearson is not liable for any misunderstandings
that arise as a result of errors in this publication, but it is our priority to ensure that the content is accurate.
If you spot an error, please do contact us at resourcescorrections@pearson.com so we can make sure it
is corrected.

Printed in Great Britain
by Amazon

48247445R00148